To Márta with love

MULTIVARIATE ANALYSIS
IN VEGETATION RESEARCH

MULTIVARIATE ANALYSIS
IN VEGETATION RESEARCH

László Orlóci

University of Western Ontario

DR. W. JUNK B.V. - PUBLISHERS - THE HAGUE 1975

ISBN 90 6193 178 9

PREFACE

It seems that vegetation ecology has become increasingly dependent on the use of statistical and other mathematical methods in the solution of its problems. Such methods obviously represent an invaluable tool in the hands of the trained ecologist who can clearly understand their intrinsic limitations.

There is growing interest among ecologists in the methods of multivariate analysis including many conventional and not so conventional procedures. This is not in the least surprising, considering that ecological data are normally multidimensional and that the analysis of such kind of data is most profitably accomplished *via* a multivariate method. Such a method of analysis, and data, are set apart from their univariate counterparts by the important fact that they can provide information about variate interactions, or correlations in general, which the univariate methods and data cannot.

The present book addresses multivariate analysis from the viewpoint of the plant ecologist experimenting with new directions of data analysis. It presents materials which have been used in a graduate plant ecology course given for students with some mathematical and statistical training in their background. The book's objectives are two-fold. On the one hand, it should provide an introduction to concepts and procedures that need to be known about the methods before applications. On the other hand, it should also serve as a source for worked examples and useful computer routines. With these dual objectives in mind the contents are offered for class use in courses with an interest in data analysis, and also, to research workers interested in broadening their experience with data analysis.

The contents are presented in a monographic style, arranged in six chapters, subdivided into sections and paragraphs, a Glossary, Indices, and an Appendix. Chapter I discusses steps prior to data collection and analysis. Chapter II represents resemblance functions and Chapter III treats ordinations. Chapter IV is concerned with classifications, Chapter V describes different identification methods, and Chapter VI gives the concluding remarks aimed at helping the reader to choose between the different methods. The Appendix contains computer programs. Each chapter is followed by a list of references.

Because of limitations imposed on the scope by various conditions, omissions must be accepted. The most noted of these are the family of open-model factor analysis which R.B. CATTELL considers in detail in a review article "Factor analysis: an introduction to essentials", *Biometrics* 21 : 190-215, 405-435 (1965), and the procedures of overlapping clustering which N. JARDINE & R. SIBSON describe with great eloquence in their book

"Mathematical Taxonomy", London, Wiley (1971). Graph theory clustering represents another, although not a serious omission, considering that the method of single linkage clustering is dealt with in some detail in Chapter IV. Regarding details of the relevant aspects of graph theory clustering the reader may consult G. ESTABROOK's article "A mathematical model in graph theory for biological classification", *J. theoret. Biol.* 12: 297-310 (1966) and references therein.

To complete this *Preface* I would like to record my thanks to my colleagues THEODORE J. CROVELLO, ROBERT C. JANCEY, ROBERT P. McINTOSH and JAMES B. PHIPPS for helpful suggestions after kindly reading the draft, to Miss CATHERINE PITT for her help with the program listings in the Appendix, and to Miss JOANNE LEMON and Mrs. GAIL RONEY for the typing. I have done much of the preliminary work on this book in the Department of Botany at the University of Hawaii during my sabbatical year. My thanks are due to NOEL P. KEFFORD and DIETER MUELLER-DOMBOIS at U.H. for a pleasant and stimulating environment in their department.

L. ORLÓCI

CONTENTS

I. INTRODUCTION

In this chapter we shall discuss certain ideas and present facts which can help us to set the stage for multivariate analysis. We shall name possible objectives to be pursued, discuss the advantages of formal methods, as compared to the informal techniques which characterize classical vegetation ecology, and consider a number of decisions that must be made about the problem, variables, sampling design, etc., before the collection and analysis of the data may begin. In the discussions we shall make the point repeatedly that the methodological decisions at different stages in a vegetation study are interrelated.

1.1 General Objectives

There are characteristics of the vegetation which readily appear on first sight to the trained observer. For example, a brief field survey may suffice to discover that the composition of the vegetation changes with altitude in a mountainous area, or to verify that species occur in zones with changing elevation on a flood plain.

Properties of this sort exemplify descriptive characteristics readily apparent to the trained observer without any statistical or other mathematical analysis of precise measurements. But when interests turn toward the finer details, the ecologist may have to rely on formal methods of sampling, precise measurements and powerful methods of data analysis to be able to reveal trends and classes of variation in the vegetation. When the ecologist relies on such formal methods of sampling and analysis, the objectives of a vegetation study can be broadened and the details investigated can be refined.

In a vegetation study the objectives tend to be concerned with:
1. Spatial arrangements of individuals or species on the ground or in the vertical profile.
2. Trends and classes of variation in the similarity or dissimilarity relations of species or entire stands.
3. Population processes affecting the spatial or temporal pattern in an area.
4. Vegetation response to environmental influences, and the dynamics of such a response.

These properties represent grossly different methodological problems but with one important common aspect; they are not normally amenable to *exact* determination, they have to be *estimated* via a limited sample.

1.2 Formal Methods

Vegetation ecology is changing very rapidly. The early phytosociological approach, in which the *art* of intuitive classifications on the basis of preferential sampling occupies a central position, is fading into relative obscurity. A *new* approach has emerged which lead in recent years to a massive introduction of the formal methods in vegetation research, including sampling and experimental design, data analysis, and statistical inference. Experience suggests that vegetation ecology benefits greatly from the use of such methods. Firstly, these methods require the user to be precise and explicit in the formulation of the problem foreseeing the implications for the type of data to be collected, sampling design used, and method of data analysis and statistical inference chosen. This is in direct contrast with the informal phytosociological methods in which such considerations have only limited relevance because they operate on the basis of personal preference and without mathematical foundations. Secondly, the formal methods require from the user uniformity and consistency in the implementation of the operational rules and decisions throughout the entire process of data collection, analysis, and inference. In contrast, the informal methods do not use nor can they offer such a uniformity and consistency. Thirdly, the formal methods, because of their uniformity and consistency, naturally lend themselves to computer processing. In this respect they have certain logistic advantages over the informal methods. But beyond the logistic advantages, they have also qualitative advantages due to the fact that they can promote interdisciplinary cooperation between the ecologists, the programmers and systems men, and other groups of specialists from whom a feedback of useful ideas and methodological advances can be expected.

1.3 Steps Prior to Data Collection

Before the collection and analysis of data can begin the ecologist is expected to have explicitly defined the problem and made a number of initial decisions in other connections. We discuss in the following sections the preliminary steps, including:
1. Statement of the problem.
2. Choice of mathematical model.
3. Determination of essential variables.
4. Selection of sampling design.

Only after completing these steps can the implementation of data collection and data analysis begin, followed by hypothesis testing, ecological interpretations, or even further analyses when required. It should be quite clear to the user that steps 1 to 4 are sequentially related. This implies that, for example, without an explicit statement of the problem no intelligent choice of a mathematical mode, variables, sampling design, or method of data analysis can possibly be made. Because of the interdependence of the steps, decisions at each step are expected to limit the user's freedom of choice in the subsequent steps. DALE (1968) and CROVELLO (1970) discuss similar points in connection with general procedures.

1.4 Statement of the Problem

It should be recognized that the success of the analysis depends on how clearly the problem can be defined. In any case, the explicit formulation of the problem should precede data collection, and should preferably involve the statement of simple hypotheses. For example, the statement

H_0 : *Given vegetation types are indistinguishable in terms of soil moisture regime*

is such that it already indicates the possible mathematical mode, variables, sampling design, method of data analysis, etc. Once sufficient data have been obtained, and the analysis performed, H_0 can be objectively tested and accepted or rejected.

Although the specific aspects of a problem may be a matter of local considerations, we can make generalizations about classes of possible problems. In this regard we may be concerned with different properties of vegetation *structure,* or with specific aspects of *function.* It is quite conceivable, for instance, that the solution of a structure oriented problem will require variates, sampling designs, and methods of data analysis which differ radically from what would be considered appropriate when the problem is concerned with function.

Vegetation structure is variously defined as the manner in which species or other components are arranged on the ground or in the vertical profile. In these terms, structure may mean a species structure, biochemical structure, trophic structure, etc. More relevantly to the present discussions, structure may be defined as an abstract property dependent on the resemblance of vegetation stands measured as some objective function of their composition. The principal value of the definition of structure in relation with the concept of resemblance is related to the role which such a definition plays in data analysis. Having defined structure, function may be defined simply as the dynamics in the changing structure for which we may use plant succession as an example.

1.5 The Mathematical Model

Data analysis operates through mathematical models. These models should be visualized not so much in terms of some geometric construct, which may or may not be relevant, but rather as a set of statements in a formal algebraic language. These statements specify the steps that have to be taken to obtain a result. It is convenient to categorize mathematical models such as:
1. Deterministic.
2. Deterministic with a random component.
3. Stochastic.
A deterministic model assumes that population size is small enough to allow all of its elements to be located and measured; the objectives amount to the best possible *approximation* of certain population values. The problem of *estimation*[1] does not arise. When a deterministic model incorporates a random component for sampling or experimental errors, it is variously described as an estimative, statistical, or probabilistic model, implying that the model's objectives are concerned with an estimation of population values. Estimation becomes necessary because not all elements of the population can be located and measured. Lacking a complete enumeration of the elements, the population values cannot be exactly determined, but rather, they have to be estimated on the basis of a limited random sample. The term *stochastic* is meant to indicate probabilistic models of a specific kind. Common to the different stochastic models are *(a)* a random process, *(b)* a probability law which specifies the frequency with which certain events occur, and possibly, *(c)* a memory source which keeps track of the events as they occur.

The application of a mathematical model may make little sense, however, if it is not embedded in a broader procedure characterized by strict internal consistency. It will be useful to consider some examples in this connection:
1. Let us assume that a procedure consists of three major steps:
   a. Sampling.
   b. Data analysis.
   c. Inference.
The ecologist using a procedure of this sort should clearly see that the individual components cannot be considered in isolation. The sampling must provide suitable input for analysis which in turn must produce results that fit the requirements of the chosen model for inference.
2. Let us consider next a procedure incorporating a deterministic model:
   a. Species performance is described within contiguous quadrats which completely cover the survey site.

---

1 The term *estimation* should be clearly distinguished from *approximation*. *Estimation* is a statistical problem, *approximation* is a problem in measurement and computation.

4

b. The quadrats are classified into groups.

c. The groups are mapped on the ground as vegetation types.

Clearly, in this particular case the problem of statistical estimation does not arise. The reason is that the survey site is completely covered by quadrats, all of which are described in terms of species performance, and all descriptions are used, in turn, to produce a vegetation map for the locality.

3. Considering that estimation of certain population values is a common objective in vegetation studies, the following set of statements have general relevance:

a. Determination of species performance within randomly sited quadrats.

b. Computation of sample estimates for mean and variance.

c. Testing the hypothesis of differential performance between species.

The objectives are estimation and hypothesis testing. These are consistent with the procedure because random sampling produces suitable data for computation of the different estimates, which then can provide a suitable basis for testing hypotheses about species differences in the population.

4. An example for a procedure incorporating a stochastic model is like this:

a. Determine birth and death rate in a population. Designate these by symbols μ and ν.

b. Assume that birth or death is a random process, population growth is exponential, and birth and death rate are constant.

c. Use function $N_t = i \exp (\mu\text{-}\nu)t$ to obtain an estimate of population size at time t when population size at time zero is i.

Because of the stochastic properties, $i.e.$ population size in time being under the influence of random events, the change in population size has to be regarded as a random variable which can be predicted only within certain limits of accuracy (see PIELOU, 1969).

In the present book we shall limit the discussions to deterministic models with or without a random component. In this respect we define a broader scope for data analysis than is usual in statistical monographs where the model is always assumed to have a random component. In either case, regardless of the mathematical model, we must find a suitable definition of *population* before any vegetation survey can begin. A definition may suggest, for instance, that the population consists of discrete units represented by stands of vegetation delimited as quadrats. Another definition may stipulate that the population units are plant individuals of the same species. Still another may specify life-form affiliation, physiognomy, etc., as criteria for recognizing populations. The important thing about a suitable definitions is that it allows the user to identify and locate population units without ambiguity.

Thus far our definitions have assumed that the population units are concrete objects. For the purpose of data analysis a population unit may be regarded as an observation (simple or multiple) on one or several characteristics of an object. Counts or measurements of species within quadrats represent an example in which the quantity of species i in quadrat j represents the i,jth population unit X_{ij}. In the case of multiple observations the jth unit is given by $\mathbf{X}_j$ which signifies a p-valued vector, such as the jth column vector in matrix $\mathbf{X}$ below, whose elements are simple observations $X_{1j}, ..., X_{1p}$. The matrix

$$\mathbf{X} = \begin{bmatrix} X_{11} & X_{12} & ... & X_{1j} & ... & X_{1N} \\ X_{21} & X_{22} & & X_{2j} & & X_{2N} \\ . & . & & . & & . \\ X_{h1} & X_{h2} & & X_{hj} & & X_{hN} \\ . & . & & . & & . \\ X_{p1} & X_{p2} & & X_{pj} & & X_{pN} \end{bmatrix}$$

describes a population in terms of N p-valued vectors. A population whose elements can be represented by such vectors is said to be a *p-variate* population. A subset n of the N population units constitutes a *sample*.

1.6 Variables[2]

The ecologist must choose variables which are directly relevant to the problem, and also, which can be handled by the available facilities in the sampling and data analysis. The variables must be meaningful in terms of the formulations in the mathematical model, sensitive to changes in the controlling factors, but at the same time, sufficiently buffered against minor influences that could obscure important trends in their variation. The variables, most commonly used in vegetation surveys, include the following:

Continuous	*Discrete*
Yield	Density
Basal area	Frequency
Cover[3]	Presence
	Cover[4]

While these variables are normally described in terms of actual measurements, counts, or simply as presence scores, sometimes they are subjected to visual estimations based on the use of various arbitrary scales (BECKING, 1957). Certain less often used variables include physiognomy, life-form, phenology (periodicity), leaf morphology, seed dispersal type, etc.

2 The terms *variable* and *variate* are used with the same meaning in this book.
3 Defined as an area or length of line intercept.
4 Determined from point sampling.

6

The ecologist should consider a combination of different criteria in any *a priori* evaluation of the potential relevance of given variables. The order in which these criteria are presented here is not intended to indicate relative importance:

1. *Commensurability.* When two or more variables measure qualitatively comparable properties in identical units they are said to be commensurable. Commensurability is a critical criterion whenever two or more variables are analysed simultaneously. It should be noted in this connection that because qualitative commensarubility implies value judgment by the user, it is not possible to lay down strict rules for selecting variables for simultaneous analysis. When different units of measure are involved the variables may be standardized according to $(X_{ij} - \overline{X}_i)/S_i$, where X_{ij} is the jth measurement on the ith variable with sample mean $\overline{X}_i$ and standard deviation S_i, to establish commensurability. We note that such a standardization removes the scale differences from the observations but it does not render qualitatively different variables more comparable. When a vast size difference exists between the observations, the variables in largest quantity may dominate the analysis. Such differences may be diminished by monotone transformations such as the logarithm, square root, etc., with varying results. As a matter of fact, transformations may alter the data substantially, and may even change the outcome of an analysis.

2. *Additivity.* Commensurable variables are additive if they are also independent. Independence may mean that they have zero covariances, lack mutual information, or do not influence each other's probability of assuming specific states or quantities. Independence may be determined by statistical analysis of actual data, or in some cases, on the basis of reasoning from basic principles. It is a direct consequence of non-commensurability that variables such as density, basal area, or frequency are non-additive. Because of their non-additivity, the use of composite indices of density, basal area, and frequency cannot be recommended.

3. *Dependence on the sampling unit.* Species frequency represents a clear example of a variable that is dependent on the sampling unit. It is absolutely essential, therefore, to specify the number and the size of the sampling units when representing frequency data.

4. *Seasonal variation.* Certain variables may undergo substantial variation related to the development and growth of new organs, or the dying off of old organs or entire plants in seasonal cycles. Species cover and species presence are good examples. Seasonal variation may be a serious problem in long range vegetation surveys.

5. *Relativity.* Most variables can be meaningfully transformed into relative

quantities, as percentages or proportions. But not so frequency, cover (from point estimates), or species presence, which are quite meaningless as relative quantities when compared between samples in which the sizes and number of sampling units are different.

6. *Distribution properties.* In many methods of data analysis the probability distribution of a variable is assumed and the success with the method is dependent on how closely the assumed distribution approximates the true distribution in the sampled population.

The more commonly encountered distributions in ecological work include the *normal, binomial, Poisson, Poisson-Poisson,* and *Poisson-logarithmic.* The *normal or Gaussian* distribution often represents a reasonable approximation for the probability distribution of continuous variables such as length, area, volume, or weight. The normal distribution may be used also as the limiting case for the distribution of discrete variables such as counts and frequency. It, therefore, is logical to expect that the normal distribution is one with which the ecologist may be faced in many vegetation surveys. The normal distribution has two parameters, the mean μ and the variance σ^2. In terms of these parameters the normal *probability density* (co-ordinate) function can be written as,

$$f(X) = B \exp \left[- \frac{(X - \mu)^2}{2\sigma^2} \right] , \quad -\infty < X < \infty \tag{1.1}$$

which measures the height of the normal curve at point X. In this formula B represents a scale factor which we set to equal $1/\sigma\sqrt{2\pi}$. The cumulative *distribution* or area function of the normal distribution,

$$F(X) = B \int_{-\infty}^{X} \exp \left[- \frac{(y - \mu)^2}{2\sigma^2} \right] dy \tag{1.2}$$

measures the area under the normal curve to the left of point X. When B is defined as $1/\sigma\sqrt{2\pi}$, $F(X)$ is characterized by the following properties:

$F(X) = 0$ if $X = -\infty$

$F(X) = 1$ if $X = \infty$

$F(X_1) \leqslant F(X_2)$ if $X_1 \leqslant X_2$

Formulae (1.1) and (1.2) describe the univariate case where X represents a single random variable associated with observations $X_1, ..., X_N$. In the multivariate case of the normal distribution X is defined as a p-dimensional random variable

$$(X_1, ..., X_p)$$

whose elements are unidimensional random variables, e.g. yield of each of p-species in a community. The ith such variable is associated with the observational vector

$$\mathbf{X}_i = (X_{i1} ... X_{iN})$$

with probability density function $f(\mathbf{X}_i)$ and distribution function $F(\mathbf{X}_i)$. The joint density of p independent normal variables (those whose covariances are zero) is a function of their means $\mu_1, ..., \mu_p$ and variances $\sigma_1^2, ..., \sigma_p^2$,

8

$$f(X_{1j}, ..., X_{pj}) = B \exp\left[-\tfrac{1}{2} \sum_i \frac{(X_{ij} - \mu_i)^2}{\sigma_i^2} \right], i = 1, ..., p \qquad (1.3)$$

where quantity B accords with

$$B = \frac{1}{\sigma_1 ... \sigma_p (2\pi)^{p/2}}$$

Formula (1.3) gives the probability density at a point $X_j = (X_{1j} ... X_{pj})$ whose ith co-ordinate X_{ij} is an observed value on variable i of individual j. For any p correlated normal variables with population mean vector

$$\mu = (\mu_1 ... \mu_p)$$

an observational vector

$$X_j = (X_{1j} ... X_{pj})$$

and population covariance matrix

$$\Sigma = \begin{bmatrix} \sigma_{11}^2 & ... & \sigma_{1p}^2 \\ . & ... & . \\ \sigma_{p1}^2 & ... & \sigma_{pp}^2 \end{bmatrix}$$

the p-variate density function can be written as

$$f(X_j) = \frac{1}{|\Sigma|^{1/2} (2\pi)^{p/2}} \exp\left[-\tfrac{1}{2}(X_j - \mu)' \Sigma^{-1} (X_j - \mu) \right] \qquad (1.4)$$

where Σ^{-1} implies the inverse of Σ and $|\Sigma|$ the determinant. The distribution function is given by the integral

$$F(X) = \int_{-\infty}^{\infty} ... \int_{-\infty}^{\infty} f(X) \, dX_1 ... dX_p = 1 \qquad (1.5)$$

In the case of a random sample of n individuals the population parameters μ_i, σ_i, Σ are replaced by their sample estimates $\bar{X}_i$, S_i and S. It is often questioned whether a multivariate normal distribution can represent an appropriate assumption for vegetation data under actual survey conditions. For p random variables, which reflect the influence of many factors acting on the variables in a completely random manner, the *central limit theorem* suggests that their joint distribution tends toward multivariate normality. This observation should in a way encourage a freer hand in the use of multivariate statistical methods under a relatively broad range of circumstances.

The *binomial* distribution is often used as a reference distribution for discrete variables on which the observations can be associated basically with two possible outcomes. As an example we should consider species frequency, determined by inspection of n random sampling units within quadrats, counting the units occupied by a particular species. The resulting distribution has a single parameter p at any given value of n. A term in this distribution,

$$P(k) = b_n(k) = \frac{n!}{k! \, (n - k)!} \, p^k \, q^{n-k} \qquad (1.6)$$

9

(representing a general term in the binomial expansion $(p + q)^n$) gives the probability of finding k occupied sampling units in n random trials when the probability of finding one occupied unit in a single trial is p and the failure $q = 1 - p$. The absolute mean of the binomial distribution is np and its variance is npq. Because of the limiting property, the normal distribution with parameters np and npq may replace the binomial distribution when the number of random trials n is reasonably large and p is not an extreme value.

Similar considerations apply to data which we obtain on the basis of counting individual plants within sampling units. In this case the usual assumption is that the unknown probability distribution is *Poisson* with

$$P(k) = \frac{e^{-\lambda}\lambda^k}{k!} \tag{1.7}$$

representing a general term. In this $P(k)$ gives the probability of finding k individuals in a random sampling unit when the mean number of individuals per sampling unit is λ. It must of course be assumed that the occurrence of an individual in a unit is the consequence of a perfectly random process. In the case of Poisson variables the normal distribution with mean λ and also variance λ is likely to give a good approximation for the actual distribution. This, of course, does not hold true if λ is small, in which case the Poisson distribution is very assymetric. The symmetry of a Poisson distribution can be improved by transformation after which it may resemble more closely the normal distribution. Transformations may also help to break up the relationship between the mean and variance. Similar considerations apply when p is not an extreme value in the binomial distribution; here too symmetry can be improved and the relationship of the mean and variance can be broken up by certain transformations.

Under most survey conditions in natural vegetation the simple Poisson distribution cannot adequately represent count data. PIELOU (1969) considers alternatives to represent the distribution of counts in aggregated populations. Of these the *Poisson-Poisson* is an appropriate distribution to use under those rarely met circumstances when the number of aggregates per sampling unit is a Poisson variable, and the number of individuals per aggregate is a Poisson variable also. When the number of aggregates per sampling unit is known to be a Poisson variable, but the number of individuals per aggregate is logarithmic, a *Poisson-logarithmic* distribution is indicated.

1.7 Sampling Considerations

The choice of a sampling method must take into account the problem, the variables, the mathematical model, and the intended method of data analysis. Furthermore, it should also reflect economic and other practical considerations. When the goal is estimation of population parameters, or statistical inference in general, *random* sampling designs are indicated. Such sampling designs give every individual of the population an equal chance to get into the sample. This in turn assures that the sample is optimally representative. Some specific objectives, such as vegetation mapping for instance, may call for *systematic* sampling in which the sampling units are chosen at regular intervals. Such a sampling is less costly than random sampling of comparable intensity, and also, it provides a more even coverage of the area with sampling units. Vegetation surveys often use *preferential* sampling. In this method stands of vegetation are chosen because they are considered typical, or plant specimens are selected for measurement because they appear representative.

Among the commonly used sampling designs in vegetation surveys *simple random sampling* has special significance. However, because it requires an ordered presentation of all population units, a random sample cannot be drawn if each unit cannot be located and labelled in the population. When the population units are concrete objects, such as for instance individual plants of a species, or cells in a two dimensional grid laid over the survey site, a random sample is drawn on the basis of random numbers. Some sampling methods allow a sample to be constructed from individuals occurring nearest to random sampling points. However, such a sample will almost certainly be non-representative of the respective population. PIELOU (1969) analysed this problem in connection with plant populations and has shown that an individual's chance of being nearest neighbour to a random point is higher in the low density patches of vegetation than in the high density patches. Because of this the individuals in the low density patches will be over-represented in the sample, and the sample will be biased.

Apart from requiring the tedious task of creating an ordered presentation of all population units prior to sampling, simple random sampling suffers also from other weaknesses including a potentially high sampling variance, and in the case of quadrat sampling, notorious underrepresentation of some parts of the survey area. These problems can be diminished based on the use of high sampling intensity.

When simple random sampling is unsatisfactory certain restrictions may be imposed on the randomization. In this connection GREIG-SMITH (1964) suggests *restricted random sampling* in which compartments are recognized in the vegetation, and each compartment is sampled at random with sampling intensities proportional to compartment size. The essential thing about restricting randomization is that it allows a stratification of the population on the basis of information available about the units prior to the sampling. Stratification reduces heterogeneity, separates compartments for which separate results are required, provides for more even sampling, and increases the precision of the sample estimates within the compartments (SAMPFORD, 1962). If the compartment samples are not pooled but treated separately as if each compartment represented a different population, the random samples, being representative of the compartments from which they are taken, will be well suited for analysis by any statistical method aimed at comparing compartments. Some complications may, however, arise if we decide to pool the compartment samples. The reason is that the pooled sample cannot be regarded as a representative sample of the broader population which is stratified into compartments (SAMPFORD, 1962). In spite of this, however, the compartment samples can still be used to compute estimates for such population parameters as the true weighted mean, the true sampling variance of the weighted means, etc., across the compartments.

Considering the vast heterogenity which normally exists within extensive areas of vegetation, compartmentalization is a logical first step in most vegetation surveys. The criteria for delimiting compartments may, however, vary depending on the local circumstances. The criteria may include, for instance, the dominant species, differential species, past stand history (fire, cultivation, etc.), or some environmental conditions having to do with soils, topography, climates, etc. Whatever criteria are used, it must be kept in mind that the compartments cannot be validly compared on the basis of the criteria by which they are delimited. The reason is that such a comparison would involve a circularity of argument. An example of such an inadmissible argument is the use of climatic compartments to *prove* the existence of natural zones in vegetation, knowing that climatologists like to draw climatic boundaries between groups of stations to coincide with apparent boundaries between vegetation zones. On this basis alone it would be quite risky for the ecologist to use as evidence for the distinctness of vegetation zones their coincidence with mapped climatic boundaries. Sampling designs using compartments are not without problems in vegetation surveys. This is related to the need to locate boundaries on the ground before the sampling can begin. It is important, therefore, to have such criteria for compartment recognition that the boundaries can be marked out without too much difficulty.

In *systematic sampling* of finite populations the units may be numbered to create a complete frame for selecting a sample. After numbering all population units the sampling may start with a random unit, after which other units are taken at fixed intervals from the first. A systematic sample which starts with a random unit is said to be *randomly sited*. Random siting has several advantages:
1. It provides accurate estimates for the population mean and, if repeated several times, also for the sampling variance of the mean.
.2. It reduces the sampling costs.
3. It allows an even coverage of the area with sampling units.
These advantages, when combined with stratification in the sampling, superbly qualify the randomly sited systematic sample as a choice of method when the objective is mapping or general inventory of plant communities.

Preferential sampling is the commonest method which has traditionally been used in vegetation surveys. As a matter of fact, many of the prevailing concepts about the basic aspects of vegetation have their origins in surveys that were based on this method of sampling. In this, 'typical' stands of vegetation are chosen and sampled in 'preferred' sampling sites. Because a sample of this sort is by definition non-representative, the conclusions drawn may not reliably reflect the conditions in the sampled vegetation. Should the ecologist still decide to base a vegetation survey on preferential sampling, the data will not be suited for statistical analysis.

Rather than sample, we may choose to *comp...*
In this type of survey we locate and measure all...
units of the population are measured, nothing n...
jectives reduce to a precise determination of pop...
extent complete enumeration is a logical part of...

The selection of an appropriate sampling unit m...
difficulties. The choice is made especially difficult kno...
size of the sampling units can have a strong influence on t...
survey. An account by GREIG-SMITH (1964) amplifies on t...
gests some solutions. It will be satisfactory here if we consider c...
principles:

1. The sampling units must be clearly distinguishable.
2. Inclusion and exclusion rules for plants in the sampling units must be established and must be followed uniformly and consistently throughout the sampling.
3. Preferably, the sampling units should be uniform in size and shape, or nearly so.
4. The sampling unit of rectangular shape may be preferred which can minimize edge-effect and simplify the matter of establishing its boundaries on the ground.

The shape and size problems may be avoided by using plotless methods of sampling. These methods, however, are limited in their usefulness because they can handle only certain kinds of variables. Regarding the arrangement of sampling units, they may be placed at random or systematically, along transects or within a rectangular grid. Line or belt transects are indicated when the surveyor can recognize natural trends of changes in the vegetation and environment. Most often, however, the sampling units are arranged in a rectangular grid.

The choice of sampling design will no doubt be influenced by economic considerations. Attemps at economy may lead to simplifications involving the use of low intensity sampling, preference for sampling designs other than the random, elimination of species from the survey that appear unimportant, and collection of less costly data. Simplifications of this sort are perfectly legitimate, and they are usually effective in reducing sampling costs, but the subsequent loss of information may also be quite substantial. Economy through reduction of sampling intensity, meaning the use of fewer quadrats in a vegetation survey, is an unwise choice if some other ways are open to the ecologist to reduce the costs. For instance we may choose to reduce the number of species. This is a logical choice because the species are usually correlated and the omission of some species may not result in a significant loss of information.

Some ecologists believe that it is best to base a vegetation study on the

...umber of species. The reasoning behind their belief involves ...when large numbers of species are used, the probability of ...e that is really important can be greatly diminished. While this may ..., and under some circumstances the handling of large numbers of spe- ...s may be a workable proposition, under many other circumstances inclusion of large numbers of species may lead to serious difficulties on the account of sampling effort and subsequent data analysis. It is not unusual that in the interest of a more economical survey and data analysis one is forced to delete some of the available species. Once it is decided that some of the species must go, then logically, the problem reduces to finding suitable criteria on the basis of which species can be selected for omission. To find a solution we may proceed on the assumption that relative importance is a local matter, and if we know the local circumstances we can determine species importance experimentally based on a limited *pilot sample.*

Many commonly used methods of data analysis manipulate covariances. By specifying the covariance we automatically commit the determination of species importance to some procedure which incorporates manipulations of the covariance itself, or some covariance related quantity. After statement of this general point let us consider a procedure, following OR LÓCI (1973), that can derive an ordering of species that reflect their relative importance. Let N be the number of quadrats in the pilot sample, and let p represent the number of species in a subsample out of a total P available species. Let $\mathbf{D}_p$ represent an $N \times N$ Euclidean distance matrix (see section 2.4 for definitions) with elements relating the N quadrats in pairs. The distances in $\mathbf{D}_p$ are possibly burdened with a certain amount of distortion due to the fact that they utilize only p species of the available P species. The undistorted distances in matrix $\mathbf{D}_P$, computed from the P species, and the distorted distances in $\mathbf{D}_p$ can be related in some stress function $\sigma(p; N,P)$ at fixed P and N and varying p. This function measures the distortion in the sample distance structure due to deletion of $P-p$ species when computing the distances in $\mathbf{D}_p$. Given the decision that only p species, or less, will be considered in the survey, the determination of the best p-species sample in the course of a limited pilot survey by one method represents a problem in combinatorials:

1. Compute a value of the function $\sigma(p; N,P)$ for each distinct combination of P species in groups of p species. Note that there are $P!/(p!(P-p)!)$ such combinations.

2. The best p-species combination will minimize $\sigma(p; N,P)$.

If p is not specified, two more steps may have to be performed:

3. Repeat finding the best p-species samples at different values of p, and construct a stress curve (Fig. 1-1) showing the minimum values of $\sigma(p; N,P)$ at $p = 1, ..., P-1$.

4. Inspect the stress curve and choose a species sample from that region of

the curve which lies in the vicinity of point A where the curve appears rapidly flattening off. This point may have to be determined subjectively.

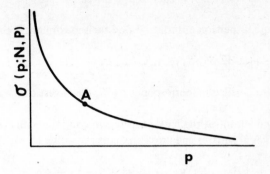

Fig. 1-1. Stress $\sigma(p;N,P)$ in sample structure as a function of species number p.

Even if p is given *a priori*, a method based on the use of combinatorials may prove to be a computational impossibility because of the extremely high number of combinations to be computed at even relatively small values of P. A computationally simpler method has been described (ORLÓCI, 1973), a summary of which is given below:

1. Assume that only p out of a total of P common species are allowed in the analysis.
2. Designate the pilot sample of N quadrats and P common species by **X** and an observation by X_{hj}. The subscripts identify the hth species in the jth quadrat.
3. Determine for each species its *independent* share of the total sum of squares and rank the species accordingly.
4. Use the first p highest ranking species in the subsequent survey.

If we assume that the data to be collected will be analyzed in some covariance related analysis, it will make sense to rank the species by a sum of squares criterion. To determine the independent components of the sum of squares specific to each species proceed as follows:

1. Center the data within species (rows of **X**) to obtain matrix **A**. The centering is specified by

$$A_{hj} = (X_{hj} - \bar{X}_h)/Q_h \qquad (1.8)$$

where $\bar{X}_h$ and Q_h represent respectively the mean and a factor of standardization (or other type of adjustment) in species h. Let us define Q_h as 1 at this point.

2. Compute the cross products **S** according to $\mathbf{S} = \mathbf{AA}'$ with elements relating

15

species. A characteristic element in **S** accords with the formula

$$S_{hi} = \sum_j A_{hj} A_{ij}, \quad j = 1, ..., N \tag{1.9}$$

3. Compute dispersion criteria and find their maximum, such as

$$SS = \max \left[\sum_h S_{h1}^2 / S_{11}, ..., \sum_h S_{hP}^2 / S_{PP} \right], \quad h = 1, ..., P \tag{1.10}$$

The species, labelled m, corresponds to SS, the largest of the P sums, and has *rank 1*.

4. Having determined the rank of species m continue with computing the residual sum of squares and cross products according to

$$S_{hi} := S_{hi} - Y_{hm} Y_{im} \text{ for any } h, i = 1, ..., P \tag{1.11}$$

This expression reads: the entry in the hi cell in matrix **S** is replaced by its own value minus the product of two co-ordinates,

$$Y_{hm} = S_{hm} / \sqrt{S_{mm}} \text{ and } Y_{im} = S_{im} / \sqrt{S_{mm}} \tag{1.12}$$

5. Compute a new value for SS from the elements of the residual **S**, declare *rank 2* on the species which corresponds to the new maximum SS, and then continue with step 4 repeating the steps over and over again until all species are ranked.

The ranking just described orders species according to their independent share of the total sum of squares. The partitioning of sum of squares is orthogonal. The ratio $SS / \sum_h S_{hh}$, $h = 1, ..., P$, is a measure for relative importance. It should be stressed that this procedure will produce 'importance values' for species which will represent a meaningful input for further consideration only in those analyses in which S_{hi} itself is a valid parameter. For the best p-species sample we take the first p species whose ranks are highest. When the value of p is not specified, one should use a strategically chosen *minimum* rank below which no species will be further considered. Ideally the minimum rank should be such that the species below it will contribute no significant amounts of sum of squares to the total in the sample. But we do not have such a test of significance. The best we can do is to rely on an approximate procedure. We may follow these steps:

1. Omit the last k species whose relative importance is zero.
2. Compute the stress values $\sigma(p; N, P)$ at fixed N and P and varying p such that $p = P-k, P-k-1, P-k-2, ..., 1$.
3. Inspect the stress curve (*e.g.* Fig. 1.1) and select the cut off point *(A)* at a value of p where the curve appears rapidly leveling off.

Considering the foregoing ranking method, the following example illustrates the computations. The data are given in Table 1-1. The computer program is

Table 1-1. Sample data. Counts of individuals within quadrats

Species						Quadrat				
	1	*2*	*3*	*4*	*5*	*6*	*7*	*8*	*9*	*10*
X_1	45	2	9	26	3	5	2	90	31	16
X_2	18	92	32	48	73	80	95	13	92	78
X_3	3	40	5	83	68	27	2	17	1	23
X_4	10	61	11	3	32	2	39	2	8	6
X_5	9	53	99	21	49	81	72	6	90	62

listed under RANK in the Appendix. After assuming that standardization is not needed, we proceed as follows[5]:

1. Center data according to formula (1.8) with Q set equal to one to obtain

$$
A = \begin{bmatrix}
22.1 & -20.9 & -13.9 & 3.1 & -19.9 & -17.9 & -20.9 & 67.1 & 8.1 & -6.9 \\
-44.1 & 29.9 & -30.1 & -14.1 & 10.9 & 17.9 & 32.9 & -49.1 & 29.9 & 15.9 \\
-23.9 & 13.1 & -21.9 & 56.1 & 41.1 & 0.1 & -24.9 & -9.9 & -25.9 & -3.9 \\
-7.4 & 43.6 & -6.4 & -14.4 & 14.6 & -15.4 & 21.6 & -15.4 & -9.4 & -11.4 \\
-45.2 & -1.2 & 44.8 & -33.2 & -5.2 & 26.8 & 17.8 & -48.2 & 35.8 & 7.8
\end{bmatrix}
$$

2. Compute the S matrix according to formula (1.9). For example,

$$
S_{12} = \sum_j A_{1j} A_{2j} = (22.1)(-44.1) + (-20.9)(29.9) + ... + (8.1)(29.9)
$$

$$
+ (-6.9)(15.9) = -5611.90
$$

The complete S matrix is given by

$$
S = \begin{bmatrix}
6896.9 & -5611.9 & -1470.1 & -2527.6 & -5445.8 \\
-5611.9 & 9022.9 & 594.1 & 2913.6 & 5646.8 \\
-1470.1 & 594.1 & 7462.9 & 581.4 & -2913.8 \\
-2527.6 & 2913.6 & 581.4 & 3576.4 & 686.2 \\
-5445.8 & 5646.8 & -2913.8 & 686.2 & 9881.6
\end{bmatrix}
$$

3. Determine the sum of squares next according to formula (1.10). For the first species,

5 All numerical results are given within computer rounding errors.

$$\sum_h S^2_{h1}/S_{11} = (6896.9^2 + (-5611.9)^2 + (-1470.1)^2 + (-2527.6)^2$$

$$+ (-5445.8)^2) / 6896.9 = 17002.9$$

After computing values for all species the criterion sum of squares becomes

$$SS = \max (17002.9, 17027.2, 8982.74, 7962.58, 17016.5) = 17027.2$$

This identifies *rank 1* for species 2.
4. Now derive co-ordinates according to formula (1.12). For instance, for species 3 and 4 on vector $m = 2$ these become

$$Y_{32} = S_{32} / \sqrt{S_{22}} = 594.1 / \sqrt{9022.9} = 6.25441$$
$$Y_{42} = S_{42} / \sqrt{S_{22}} = 2913.6 / \sqrt{9022.9} = 30.6730$$

(We use six significant digits in the long-hand results so that we can reproduce the computer figures in the residual S matrix.)
5. Compute the elements in the first residual of S. For example, according to formula (1.11)

$$S_{34} := S_{34} - Y_{32} Y_{42}$$
$$= 581.4 - (6.25441)(30.6730)$$
$$= 389.558$$

Similar calculations yield the entire matrix of residuals,

$$\begin{bmatrix} 3406.51 & 0.00000 & -1100.59 & -715.452 & -1933.71 \\ 0.00000 & 0.00000 & 0.00000 & 0.00000 & 0.00000 \\ -1100.59 & 0.00000 & 7423.78 & 389.558 & -3285.61 \\ -715.452 & 0.00000 & 389.558 & 2635.56 & -1137.22 \\ -1933.71 & 0.00000 & -3285.61 & -1137.22 & 6347.66 \end{bmatrix}$$

6. Now compute the criterion

$$SS = \max (5010.03, 0.00000, 9061.53, 3378.06, 8841.13)$$
$$= 9061.53$$

This identifies species 3 as the second highest ranking species.
7. Compute the elements in the second residual of S. This is done similarly as in the case of the first residual to obtain

18

$$\begin{bmatrix} 3243.35 & 0.00000 & 0.00000 & -657.699 & -2420.80 \\ 0.00000 & 0.00000 & 0.00000 & 0.00000 & 0.00000 \\ 0.00000 & 0.00000 & 0.00000 & 0.00000 & 0.00000 \\ -657.699 & 0.00000 & 0.00000 & 2615.12 & -964.808 \\ -2420.80 & 0.00000 & 0.00000 & -964.808 & 4893.53 \end{bmatrix}$$

8. From these derive

$$SS = \max (5183.58, 0.00000, 0.00000, 3136.48, 6281.31)$$
$$= 6281.31$$

This indicates *rank 3* for species 5.

9.   The third residual of **S** becomes

$$\begin{bmatrix} 2045.79 & 0.00000 & 0.00000 & -1134.98 & 0.00000 \\ 0.00000 & 0.00000 & 0.00000 & 0.00000 & 0.00000 \\ 0.00000 & 0.00000 & 0.00000 & 0.00000 & 0.00000 \\ -1134.98 & 0.00000 & 0.00000 & 2424.90 & 0.00000 \\ 0.00000 & 0.00000 & 0.00000 & 0.00000 & 0.00000 \end{bmatrix}$$

10. Find the next sum of squares criterion,

$$SS = \max (2675.47, 0.00000, 0.00000, 2956.14, 0.00000)$$
$$= 2956.14$$

which identifies *rank 4* for species 4.

11. The last residual has a single non-zero element $S_{11} = 1514.55$ representing the specific sum of squares for species 1.

We now summarize the results:

Species	Rank	Specific sum of squares	Specific sum of squares as a proportion
1	5	1514.55	0.041
2	1	17027.20	0.462
3	2	9061.53	0.246
4	4	2956.14	0.080
5	3	6281.31	0.171
	Total	36840.73	1.000

19

The sum of the specific sum of squares is equal to the sum of diagonal elements in the original S matrix. This indicates that our method partitions the sum of squares additively into components.

Suppose that we want to perform some classification on the data, and we intend to use the distance function

$$d(j,k) = \left[\sum_h (X_{hj} - X_{hk})^2 \right]^{1/2} , \quad h = 1, ..., P \qquad (1.13)$$

or some related quantity such as the sum of squares as the classification criterion to arrange the quadrats into discrete groups. Also suppose that we wish to determine the distortion that would result from reducing the number of species in the analysis from 5 to 4, 3, 2, and finally to 1. Given $N = 10$, $P = 5$, and $p = 1, 2, 3, 4, 5$, we define a stress function

$$\sigma(p; 10, 5) = 1 - \rho^2 (\mathbf{D}_p ; \mathbf{D}_P)$$

where $\rho^2 (\mathbf{D}_p ; \mathbf{D}_P)$ is the square of the simple correlation coefficient, used as a mathematical index rather than a statistic, which relates the elements in matrix $\mathbf{D}_P$ defined according to formula (1.13) on the basis of 5 species, and the elements in $\mathbf{D}_p$; defined similarly as $\mathbf{D}_P$ but based on p species. When we perform the computations (see program STRESS in the Appendix) we obtain the following values for stress:

p	Species in reduced sample	$\rho(\mathbf{D}_p ; \mathbf{D}_P)$	$\sigma(p; 10, 5)$ %
1	2	0.729	46.9
2	2, 3	0.728	47.0
3	2, 3, 5	0.886	21.5
4	2, 3, 5, 4	0.920	15.4
5	2, 3, 5, 4, 1	1.000	0.0

In realistic samples of data the curve plotted from the stress values could be examined to decide how many of the P species would be worth further consideration. It is interesting to note that in this example when the two highest ranking species are used, stress slightly increases. This can happen; but the general trend is a reduction in stress with increased number of species.

In planning extensive sample surveys problems always arise regarding the kind of data to be collected. For example when contemplating count data it is logical to ask if it is worth the effort to count all individuals within a sampling unit or only up to a predetermined maximum number. With k as the maximum, the surveyor will continue counting individuals within a sampling unit until one of two things happens: either k is reached and the counting stops, or all individuals are counted before reaching the allowed limit k. The question, which can be answered in the course of a pilot survey, can be put this way: how much information would be lost by not counting individuals beyond the maximum number k? The matter of finding an appropriate answer to this question has considerable importance in view of the possibility of very high numbers of individuals per sampling unit, the counting of which may require a sampling effort far out of proportion with the gain in information. We assume in the following example that we have in hands counts of all individuals in quadrats of a pilot sample, that the quadrats (sampling units) derive by random sampling, that the method of analysis to which the data will be subjected eventually is known, and that the species list is reasonably complete. Let us suppose that the objective is a classification of quadrats based on a method in which formula (1.13), or a related function, is a basis for decisions. Let there be p species and N quadrats in the pilot sample. Let D represent the distance matrix computed from the data of all counts, and D_k the distance matrix computed from truncated counts neither of which exceeds k. The anticipated loss of information by truncating the counts is proportional to the distortion in D_k relative to D. This can be measured in terms of the stress function (ORLÓCI & MUKKATTU, 1973),

$$\sigma(D_k; D) = 1 - \rho^2(D_k; D)$$

where $\rho^2(D_k; D)$ is the squared correlation coefficient, used here as a mathematical index rather than a statistic. The correlation coefficient relates the elements in D_k to the elements in D. The stress values at different values of k in the table below, computed in program STRESC in the Appendix, correspond to the data in Table 1-1, which we hereby assume to represent plant counts in given quadrats:

Value of k	$\rho(D_k; D)$	$\sigma(D_k; D)$	Sampling effort %
10	0.278	92.3	4.3
20	0.489	76.1	8.3
30	0.640	59.0	13.6
40	0.768	41.0	23.1
50	0.858	26.4	30.8
60	0.913	16.6	33.7
70	0.955	8.8	44.1
80	0.983	3.4	60.7
90	0.997	0.6	79.4

We assume that the sampling effort is directly proportional to the number of individuals counted. We can see from the table that stress and sampling effort have an inverse non-linear relationship. In this particular example, for instance, counting up to $k = 50$ means an expenditure of about 31% of the total sampling effort and yet only a 26% distortion. A roughly 100% increase of sampling effort from 31% to about 61% would produce an almost 8-fold reduction in stress.

Presence/absence data represent a special case, equivalent to counting only 1. In the case of a sample like the one in Table 1-1, in which no absences are registered and in which all variation is associated with the changing quantity of the species, the presence scores would yield totally uninformative data. Very often, however, samples incorporate absences which introduce zeros into the data. In such a case, quantitative data can be partitioned into one component specific to species presence and another representing residuals. Such a partitioning is outlined below following WILLIAMS & DALE (1962):

1. Represent species i by vector $(0, X_i)$ in which zeros indicate absences and the X_i represent quantities. Let M_{Xi} be the mean of the non-zero values. For example, in the observational vector

$$(0, X_i) = (0 \ 1 \ 0 \ 8 \ 3 \ 7)$$

the mean M_{Xi} is equal to 19/4. The vector $(0, X_i)$ has as many elements as there are quadrats in the sample.

2. Now partition $(0, X_i)$ into two independent components,

$$(0, M_{Xi}) = (0 \ 19/4 \ 0 \ 19/4 \ 19/4 \ 19/4)$$

for presence, and

$$(0, X_i - M_{Xi}) = (0 \ 1\text{-}19/4 \ 0 \ 8\text{-}19/4 \ 3\text{-}19/4 \ 7\text{-}19/4)$$

for the residual. The vector product,

$$(0, M_{Xi}) (0, X_i - M_{Xi})' = 0$$

indicates that the partition is orthogonal.

When we decide to use presence data in a vegetational analysis we must anticipate an amount of information loss. This loss is proportional to the residual component's contribution to variability in the data. Let us assume that the objective is a classification of quadrats based on formula (1.13). Under these circumstances the loss of information is proportional to the stress or distortion in the distance configuration $\mathbf{D}_{PR}$ based on the presence component of data relative to the distance configuration **D** computed from the unpartitioned data. The function

$$\sigma(\mathbf{D}_{PR}; \mathbf{D}) = 1 - \rho^2(\mathbf{D}_{PR}; \mathbf{D})$$

quantifies stress as the one-complement of the squared correlation which relates the elements in $\mathbf{D}_{PR}$ to the corresponding elements in **D**.

A stress analysis of this sort is applicable also to measurement data. In one case it may be meaningful to consider the relative merits of sets of data of different complexity with regard to sampling effort and information content. Tree height *(H)*, basal area *(B)*, and volume *(V)* represent data that are often collected in surveys of forest communities. In order to determine volume we need both basal area and height — both of them very time consuming for measurement. Now if we want to economize in the survey we may decide to use either height or basal area, but not both. The question is then which of the two would retain more of the total variation associated with volume. A comparison of two stress values may provide a basis for decision:

$$\sigma(\mathbf{D}_B; \mathbf{D}_V) = 1 - \rho^2(\mathbf{D}_B; \mathbf{D}_V)$$
$$\sigma(\mathbf{D}_H; \mathbf{D}_V) = 1 - \rho^2(\mathbf{D}_H; \mathbf{D}_V)$$

We may choose basal area if $\sigma(\mathbf{D}_B; \mathbf{D}_V)$ is smallest. It is assumed that we have data from a pilot survey for basal area, height, and volume. The $\mathbf{D}_B$, $\mathbf{D}_H$, and $\mathbf{D}_V$ are distance matrices defined depending on the objectives of the subsequent analysis to be performed on the data. Function ρ is defined as before.

We shall now turn to a systematic description of resemblance functions of which formula (1.13) represents an example.

1.8 References

BECKING, R.W. 1957. The Zürich-Montpellier School of Phytosociology. *Bot. Rev.* 7: 411-488.

CROVELLO, T.J. 1970. Analysis of character variation in ecology and systematics. *In*: R.F. JOHNSTON (ed.), *Annual Review of Ecology and Systematics,* pp. 55-98. Palo Alto, Annual Reviews Inc.

DALE, M.B. 1968. On property structure, numerical taxonomy and data handling. *In*: V.H. HEYWOOD (ed.), *Modern Methods in Plant Taxonomy*, pp. 185-197. London, Academic Press.

GREIG-SMITH, P. 1964. *Quantitative Plant Ecology.* 2nd ed. London, Butterworth.

ORLÓCI, L. 1973. Ranking characters by a dispersion criterion. *Nature* 244: 371-373.

ORLÓCI, L. & M.M. MUKKATTU. 1973. The effect of species number and type of data on the resemblance structure of a phytosociological collection. *J. Ecol.* 61: 37-46.

PIELOU, E.C. 1969. *An Introduction to Mathematical Ecology.* New York, Wiley-Interscience.

SAMPFORD, M.R. 1962. *An Introduction to Sampling Theory.* Edinburgh, Oliver and Boyd.

WILLIAMS, W.T. & M.B. DALE. 1962. Partition correlation matrices for heterogeneous quantitative data. *Nature* 196: 602.

II. RESEMBLANCE FUNCTIONS

In this chapter we discuss the concepts of resemblance and give explicit definitions. We describe and evaluate different resemblance functions and illustrate their computations through numerical examples for species and quadrats. It will be seen that these functions are essential in multivariate analysis because they generate input for the different methods.

2.1 General Aspects

The term *resemblance* is used here in the colloquial sense. We note that resemblance is a measurable property of objects, either as a likeness or dissimilarity, in terms of different functions based on the characteristics which the objects possess. The objects may represent individual species, entire stands of vegetation, or some entities other than these.

There are several general aspects to be considered before we turn to a detailed discussion of resemblance structure and resemblance functions:
1. The conceptual picture which we form about ecological objects, their role, or their significance, is dependent on our perception of their similarities. This picture about the objects cannot be more precise than the accuracy with which we can determine similarities. Consistency and objectivity are prime requirements in this connection.
2. The formal methods of data analysis often assume that the resemblance of given objects is measured without personal bias. This makes the use of objective functions inevitable.
3. Because there are many functions to choose from, the choice between them raises problems. Firstly, there may be restrictions on mathematical admissibility. These require the user to understand the mathematical properties of the resemblance function, and also, the relevant properties of the method of analysis to which the resemblance values may be subjected. Secondly, a resemblance function may do more than what the user want it to do in ways of a standardization or other adjustments that may be definitely to the detriment of the objectives. Thirdly, the different functions are not equally simple for computations. Because of this, the user will select the simplest function if not objected on other grounds.

2.2 Resemblance Structure

To the ecologist, resemblance structure often means some kind of a covariance structure which most of us can readily see in samples of vegetation data. Recognition of such a resemblance structure comes naturally to the person whose training is traditionally strong in Euclidean geometry. However, a covariance structure is not the only kind that can be associated with vegetation data. Functions other than the covariance may reveal structures which are radically different.

In specific terms we can define resemblance structure as a set of resemblance values measured between objects in a given sample according to some objective function. It directly follows from this definition that no single kind of structure may be singularly characteristic for a given sample. In other words, the same sample may be associated with different resemblance structures depending on the resemblance function.

2.3 Sample Space

Let us consider the data in Table 2-1. These data represent our sample on

Table 2-1. Species abundance estimates

| Species | Quadrat | | | | | Total | Mean |
	1	2	3	4	5		
X_1	2	5	2	1	0	10	2.0
X_2	0	1	4	3	1	9	1.8
X_3	3	4	1	0	0	8	1.6

which an analysis is to be performed. We shall use symbol p to designate the number of species ($p = 3$) and symbol n to signify the number of quadrats ($n = 5$ in the present example). We should note that in more realistic samples there may be many more species and a greater number of quadrats than p or n in the present sample.

The raw data in Table 2-1 can be presented in matrix form such as

$$X = \begin{bmatrix} X_{11} & X_{12} & X_{13} & X_{14} & X_{15} \\ X_{21} & X_{22} & X_{23} & X_{24} & X_{25} \\ X_{31} & X_{32} & X_{33} & X_{34} & X_{35} \end{bmatrix} = \begin{bmatrix} 2 & 5 & 2 & 1 & 0 \\ 0 & 1 & 4 & 3 & 1 \\ 3 & 4 & 1 & 0 & 0 \end{bmatrix}$$

Each row in **X** describes a species and each column holds values which signify performance in one quadrat. A row of **X** may be called as a *species vector* and a column a *quadrat* vector. These terms may be interchanged with terms such as *row vector* or *column vector*.

It may be convenient to conceive n quadrats as a multitude of n points in space. The relative placements of the points in such a space is in proportion to differences in species composition in the quadrats. The points and the resemblance function $f(j, k)$, which measures the spatial placement of the points, constitutes a *sample space*. The function $f(j, k)$ may represent a distance or it can be a measure of similarity. In either case $f(j, k)$ is said to be a *spatial parameter*. Because $f(j, k)$ associates a number with each pair (j, k) of objects it is quite appropriately referred to as a *pair-function*.

There are several important consequences of the foregoing definition of sample space:

1. The sample space and resemblance structure exist independently from the actual sampling location of the objects or their ground distance.
2. The resemblance structure and the raw data are only indirectly related according to transformations specified in the resemblance function.
3. The information, revealed by a technique of data analysis, is the information which is realized in the sample resemblance structure, which is not necessarily the information contained in the raw data.
4. When the raw data are given, and a resemblance function specified, the sample space is completely defined.

2.4 Metrics and Metric-Related Functions

A. Constraints on a metric

Resemblance functions must obey certain simple restrictions. We examine these restrictions under the assumption that the function $f(j, k)$ is a measure of distance. We further stipulate that $f(j, k)$ is a particular type of distance known as a *metric*. We also note that ecologists have used 'distance' functions that are not of the category of metrics, and that when we define j, k as two quadrats, $f(j, k)$ is an abstract measure, depending on species composition, and not a 'ground' distance.

Functions which ecologists have used to measure distance are conveniently categorized on the basis of the extent to which they satisfy certain conditions known as the metric space axioms. We shall examine these on the assumption that a distance is measured between vegetation quadrats:

Axiom 1. If $A = B$ then $d(A, B) = 0$

Axiom 2. If $A \neq B$ then $d(A, B) > 0$

Axiom 3. $d(A, B) = d(B, A)$

Axiom 4. $d(A, B) \leqslant d(A, C) + d(B, C)$

Axiom 1 states that quadrats of identical composition ($A = B$) are indistinguishable. *Axiom 2* makes explicit that the distance must be positive, and other than zero, when A and B are non-identicals. *Axiom 3* states the symmetry property, implying that the order in which the quadrants are compared must not influence the resulting distance. *Axiom 4* is known as the triangle inequality axiom, according to which the distance between two quadrats A, B cannot be greater than the sum of their individual distances from a third quadrat C.

The extent to which the function $f(j, k)$ shares properties in common with the metric $d(A, B)$ is the criterion in our system for categorization. On this basis we can make an arbitrary distinction between *metric, semimetric* and *non-metric* categories. These categories are quite relevant to us considering that distances from all of these categories have been used by ecologists in vegetation studies. The user must, however, realize that distances from the different categories are not equally suited for the definition of resemblance under specified conditions of application.

A distance function which satisfies all four of the metric space axioms is said to be a metric. (We note that the term *metric* may be used either as an adjective or as a noun.) Some resemblance functions are metric related in the sense that they can be derived directly from a metric. We shall consider later on in this chapter important metric related functions, such as the covariance, after a detailed consideration of metrics.

B. The Euclidean distance, variants of formulae, and related cross product forms

The most familiar expression of Euclidean distance is given by

$$e(j, k) = \left[\sum_h (X_{hj} - X_{hk})^2 \right]^{1/2}, \quad h = 1, ..., p \tag{2.1}$$

In this expression the symbol p indicates the number of species in the sample, and X_{hj} or X_{hk} signifies the quantity or state of species h in quadrat j or k. Formula (2.1) defines a distance between two quadrats as a simple sum of p squared differences. The computational steps are illustrated below based on the data in Table 2-1:

Species	Quadrat 1	2	Deviation	Squared deviation
X_1	2	5	−3	9
X_2	0	1	−1	1
X_3	3	4	−1	1
			Sum:	11

27

We take the square root of the sum of squared differences to obtain $e(1,2) =$ 3.317.

Distances measured on the basis of formula (2.1) have several peculiarities which may or may not be desired:
1. No fixed upper bound.
2. Reliance on absolute species quantity.
3. Dependence on species correlations.

The first of these is rather important because it can render the distance values incomparable. We would normally prefer a relative measure on the basis of which we can decide whether a distance value is small or large. The size of $e(j, k)$ depends on the magnitude of the actual difference in species quantities between the quadrats. Because of the reliance on such differences an anomalous situation can arise: *two quadrats which have no species in common may appear more similar than two other quadrats whose species lists are identical.* Three quadrats with data vectors

$$\mathbf{X}_A = \begin{bmatrix} 0 \\ 1 \\ 1 \end{bmatrix} \qquad \mathbf{X}_B = \begin{bmatrix} 1 \\ 0 \\ 0 \end{bmatrix} \qquad \mathbf{X}_C = \begin{bmatrix} 0 \\ 4 \\ 4 \end{bmatrix}$$

represent an example for such an anomalous situation. In terms of formula (2.1) quadrat A is more similar to B $(e(A, B) = 1.732)$ with which it shares none of the species than to C $(e(A, C) = 4.243)$ with which it shares an identical species list. The Euclidean distance with such properties is not particularly useful in measuring quadrat resemblances. The problem can nevertheless be overcome by computation of relative distances in the following manner:
1. Normalize the quadrat vectors. This is done by setting their lengths equal to unity. If for instance the vector which describes a quadrat is (2 0 3) with the sum of squared elements equal to 13 the normalized vector is obtained according to $(2/\sqrt{13} \quad 0 \quad 3/\sqrt{13})$. When the elements in the normalized vector are squared and summed the sum should be unity if no mistakes were made in the computation.
2. Compute a Euclidean distance based on normalized quadrat vectors. The distance so computed is called a *chord distance* (ORLÓCI, 1967) indicating that the length of the chord connecting two points on the surface of a sphere of unit radius has been measured. The chord distance can be obtained directly based on the formula

$$c(j, k) = \left[2(1 - q_{jk} / \sqrt{q_{jj} q_{kk}} \right]^{1/2} \tag{2.2}$$

where

$$q_{jk} = \sum_h X_{hj} X_{hk} \; , \quad q_{jj} = \sum_h X_{hj}^2 \text{ and } q_{kk} = \sum_h X_{hk}^2 \; , \quad h = 1, ..., p$$

The distance in formula (2.2) is characterized by the conditions,

a. $0 \leqslant c(j, k) \leqslant \sqrt{2}$

b. $c(j, k) = 0$ if $X_{hj}/X_{ij} = X_{hk}/X_{ik}$ for any h or i

c. $c(j, k) = \sqrt{2}$ if $X_{hj} = 0$ implies $X_{hk} > 0$ and $X_{hk} = 0$ implies $X_{hj} > 0$.

These indicate that for the chord distance to be zero the two quadrats need not have the same species in equal quantity; it is sufficient if the species quantities are in the same proportion. When the species quantities are proportional the normalized quadrat vectors will turn out to be the same. For the normalized data vectors of quadrats A, B, C,

$$\mathbf{X}_A{}^* = \begin{bmatrix} 0 \\ 0.707 \\ 0.707 \end{bmatrix} \qquad \mathbf{X}_B{}^* = \begin{bmatrix} 1 \\ 0 \\ 0 \end{bmatrix} \qquad \mathbf{X}_C{}^* = \begin{bmatrix} 0 \\ 0.707 \\ 0.707 \end{bmatrix}$$

the quadrat distances are $c(A, B) = c(B, C) = \sqrt{2}$ and $c(A, C) = 0$. The order established in the case of the $e(j, k)$ distances is completely reversed here; A and C are declared 'identical' and both completely different from B. A further example in the table below utilizes the data in Table 2-1:

Species	Quadrat 1	Quadrat 2	$X_{h1}X_{h2}$	X_{h1}^2	X_{h2}^2
X_1	2	5	10	4	25
X_2	0	1	0	0	1
X_3	3	4	12	9	16
			$q_{12} = 22$	$q_{11} = 13$	$q_{22} = 42$

From these we obtain $c(1,2) = (2(1 - 22/\sqrt{(13)(42)}))^{1/2} = 0.342$. The program EUCD in the Appendix gives options to compute Euclidean distance based on formula (2.1) or (2.2).

The influence of species correlations on the distance measure leads to reasoning along two rather distinct lines:

1. Species correlations are the carriers of information about trends in the sample. Linear species correlations associate with linear trends and non-linear correlations indicate curved trends in the sense of points being placed in a curved line, surface, or some solid of certain complexity. Should we decide to remove the influence of species correlations from a multivariate sample, we would impose a spherical shape on the point configuration with a simultaneous obliteration of existing trends. It is clear then that when the objectives of an analysis call for trend seeking we shall prefer those distance functions which reflect the influence of species correlations. Formula (2.1) and also formula (2.2) are examples in this connection.

29

2. The influence of species correlations on the distance measure may be thoroughly undesired in the case of analyses in which an individual's class affiliation is identified based on a direct comparison of distances. To clarify this point let us assume that an external quadrat j is compared to quadrat k of vegetation type A and to quadrat m of vegetation type B. The distance $e(j, k)$ or $e(j, m)$ is under the influence of correlations S_A in type A or S_B in type B. Distance $e(j, k)$ can logically be compared to $e(j, m)$ only if the two vegetation types are characterized by an identical pattern of species correlations in terms of $S_A = S_B$. Otherwise their comparison lacks a common basis. To remove the effect of species correlations from the distance measure and in this way to provide a common ground for comparison, we may use oblique co-ordinate axes with their obliqueness proportional to species correlations, following the method of GENGERELLI (1963), rely on the use of the MAHALANOBIS (1936) generalized distance, or utilize other suitable measures.

An expression for Euclidean distance can be formulated for the case of oblique axes on the basis of Fig. 2-1. In this figure $\cos w_{hi} = S_{hi}$ represents

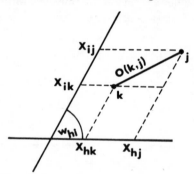

Fig. 2-1. Diagramatic representation of an oblique reference system.

a simple product moment correlation coefficient (used here as a direction cosine rather than a statistic); j and k indicate quadrats with data vectors (X_{hj}, X_{ij}) and (X_{hk}, X_{ik}). The correlation coefficient is defined according to

$$S_{hi} = \sum_j (X_{hj} - \bar{X}_h)(X_{ij} - \bar{X}_i) \Big/ \left[\sum_j (X_{hj} - \bar{X}_h)^2 \sum_j (X_{ij} - \bar{X}_i)^2 \right]^{1/2}$$

with summations taken from $j = 1$ to n. Symbols $\bar{X}_h$, $\bar{X}_i$ represent species means. The formula for the squared Euclidean distance of j and k based on oblique co-ordinates then is given by

$$o^2(j, k) = (X_{hj} - X_{hk})^2 + (X_{ij} - X_{ik})^2 - 2(X_{hj} - X_{hk})(X_{ij} - X_{ik})$$
$$\cos(180° - w_{hi})$$

For any number of species p with correlations S_{hi}, h, $i = 1, ..., p$, the distance formula becomes

$$o(j, k) = \left[\sum_h (X_{hj} - X_{hk})^2 + 2 \sum_h \sum_i (X_{hj} - X_{hk})(X_{ij} - X_{ik}) S_{hi} \right]^{1/2} \quad (2.3)$$

with summations taken from $h = 1$ to p in the first sum, or $h = 1$ to $p-1$ and $i = h+1$ to p in the second. The first sum represents the squared Euclidean distance of formula (2.1). Added to this sum is a correction term for species correlations. With such a correction we inject new information into the definition of distance. This information is external to the objects (j, k) between which the distance is measured, dependent on the entire sample in which the correlations are computed. The following numerical example illustrates the calculation:

1. Select two quadrat vectors,

$$X_1 = \begin{bmatrix} 2 \\ 0 \\ 3 \end{bmatrix} \quad \text{and} \quad X_2 = \begin{bmatrix} 5 \\ 1 \\ 4 \end{bmatrix}$$

These represent the first and second quadrat in Table 2-1.

2. Compute correlation coefficients for species. These are given as the elements in

$$S = \begin{bmatrix} S_{11} & S_{12} & S_{13} \\ S_{21} & S_{22} & S_{23} \\ S_{31} & S_{32} & S_{33} \end{bmatrix} = \begin{bmatrix} 1.000 & -0.163 & 0.883 \\ -0.163 & 1.000 & -0.536 \\ 0.883 & -0.536 & 1.000 \end{bmatrix}$$

3. Compute

$$\begin{aligned} o(1, 2) = (&(2-5)^2 + (0-1)^2 + (3-4)^2 + 2(2-5)(0-1)(-0.163) \\ &+ (2-5)(3-4)(0.883) + (0-1)(3-4)(-0.536)))^{1/2} \\ = \;&3.775 \end{aligned}$$

Program OBLIK of the Appendix can be used for the computations after program CORRS has generated a file for species correlations.

The generalized distance of quadrats j and k is computed by

$$m(j, k) = ((X_j - X_k)' S^{-1} (X_j - X_k))^{1/2} \quad (2.4)$$

In this X_j and X_k represent quadrat vectors and S^{-1} symbolizes the inverse of the species covariance matrix. When the species are uncorrelated, and their variances are equal to unity, formula (2.4) reduces to formula (2.1). The com-

31

putational steps are illustrated on data from Table 2-1:

1. Determine

$$(X_1 - X_2) = \begin{bmatrix} -3 \\ -1 \\ -1 \end{bmatrix}$$

for quadrats *1* and *2*.

2. Compute covariances S_{hi} according to the formula

$$S_{hi} = \sum_j (X_{hj} - \bar{X}_h)(X_{ij} - \bar{X}_i)/(n - 1), j = 1, ..., n,$$

where X_h is the mean of species h and $\bar{X}_i$ is the mean of species i. The sample values are given as the elements in

$$S = \begin{bmatrix} S_{11} & S_{12} & S_{13} \\ S_{21} & S_{22} & S_{23} \\ S_{31} & S_{32} & S_{33} \end{bmatrix} = \begin{bmatrix} 3.5 & -0.5 & 3.0 \\ -0.5 & 2.7 & -1.6 \\ 3.0 & -1.6 & 3.3 \end{bmatrix}$$

3. Invert **S** to obtain S^{-1}. This is easiest to accomplish on a computer. When, however, the covariance matrix is of order three, as in the present example, longhand computations are not really inhibiting. The first step in finding the inverse of **S** is to find the cofactors associated with **S**. We recall from matrix algebra that the cofactor A_{hi} of S_{hi} is $(-1)^{h+i}$ times the determinant of the submatrix obtained by deleting the *h*th row and *i*th column from **S**. For example the cofactor A_{23} of S_{23} is defined by

$$A_{23} = (-1)^{2+3} \begin{vmatrix} 3.5 & -0.5 \\ 3.0 & -1.6 \end{vmatrix} = (-1)^5 ((3.5)(-1.6) - (-0.5)(3.0))$$

$$= 4.1$$

The cofactors of the remaining elements are similarly computed to obtain the entire matrix,

$$A = \begin{bmatrix} 6.35 & -3.15 & -7.30 \\ -3.15 & 2.55 & 4.10 \\ -7.30 & 4.10 & 9.20 \end{bmatrix}$$

It is noted that because the upper and lower halves of **S** are mirror images of each other it is sufficient to calculate the off diagonal elements in one half of **A**. In the next step we compute the determinant of **S**,

32

$$\det S = \begin{vmatrix} 3.5 & -0.5 & 3.0 \\ -0.5 & 2.7 & -1.6 \\ 3.0 & -1.6 & 3.3 \end{vmatrix} = (3.5)(2.7)(3.3) + (-0.5)(-1.6)(3.0)$$

$$+ (3.0)(-0.5)(-1.6) - (3.0)(2.7)(3.0) - (3.5)(-1.6)(-1.6)$$

$$- (-0.5)(-0.5)(3.3) = 1.9$$

We now proceed to finding the inverse by dividing each element in **A** by det**S**,

$$S^{-1} = \begin{bmatrix} 3.342 & -1.658 & -3.842 \\ -1.658 & 1.342 & 2.158 \\ -3.842 & 2.158 & 4.842 \end{bmatrix}$$

4. From the foregoing results the generalized distance can be computed according to

$$m^2(1,2) = (-3 \;\; -1 \;\; -1) \begin{bmatrix} 3.342 & -1.658 & -3.842 \\ -1.658 & 1.342 & 2.158 \\ -3.842 & 2.158 & 4.842 \end{bmatrix} \begin{bmatrix} -3 \\ -1 \\ -1 \end{bmatrix} = 7.578$$

or $m(1,2) = 2.753$. The application of $m^2(j, k)$ is considered further in connection with identification problems in Chapter V. The computer program for generalized distance is given under GEND in the Appendix.

Vegetation data are often presented in binary (1,0) form indicating species presence or absence in quadrats. Such data can convey information about the number of species common to different quadrats and the frequency with which the different species occur in the entire sample. We can compute resemblance values for quadrats, or determine the intensity of association between species, from presence/absence data in a 2 × 2 table. An example is given below:

		Quadrat j		Total
		1	0	
Quadrat k	1	a	b	a + b
	0	c	d	c + d
Total		a + c	b + d	a + b + c + d = p

In this table symbol a represents the number of common species in the two quadrats, b indicates the number of species which occur in quadrat k but not

33

in quadrat j, c signifies the number of species occurring in quadrat j but not in k, and d represents the number of species absent from both quadrats. In terms of these symbols a distance of two quadrats may be defined according to

$$\sqrt{((b+c)/p)} = \sqrt{(1 - (a+d)/p)} \qquad (2.5)$$

where $(a+d)/p$ is SOKAL's matching coefficient (SOKAL & MICHENER, 1958). It is noted that division by p, the number of species in the entire sample, in the Euclidean distance $\sqrt{((b+c)/p)}$ may not be a particularly effective operation because apart from scaling down the distances by a factor p nothing much will happen. A more substantial and possibly undesirable effect results when p is defined as the number of species in the two quadrats $(a+b+c)$, because such a definition, implicit for instance in GOWER's (1971) general coefficient, may alter the scale of measure variably depending on the quadrats compared. This property and its consequences on the measurement of resemblance are discussed later in the text.

When formula (2.5) is used, the distance will retain the properties which we considered in connection with formula (2.1). A relative form of $\sqrt{(b+c)}$ may be derived by a method other than dividing $(b+c)$ by p. Firstly, we note that the cosine separation of two vectors of binary elements is incorporated in the formula

$$(b+c) = (a+b) + (a+c) - 2\sqrt{((a+b)(a+c))} \cos \alpha_{jk}$$

After simple rearrangement of terms we obtain the cosine separation

$$\cos \alpha_{jk} = a/\sqrt{((a+b)(a+c))}$$

This formula represents the OCHIAI (1957) coefficient. From this we obtain

$$c(j, k) = \sqrt{2(1 - \cos \alpha_{jk})}$$

This represents the familiar chord distance.

We can use presence scores to define a Euclidean distance in the form of

$$d(j, k) = (2(1 - \sqrt{\chi_{jk}^2/p}))^{1/2} \qquad (2.6)$$

in which χ_{jk}^2/p represents the so called mean square contingency function associated with a 2×2 table. It is noted that because $\sqrt{\chi_{jk}^2/p}$ is the direction cosine of two vectors of binary elements, $d(j, k)$ of formula (2.6) represents a chord distance. A related formula

$$\max \chi^2 - \sqrt{\chi_{jk}^2} = \max \chi^2 \, (1 - \sqrt{\chi_{jk}^2} / \max \chi^2) \qquad (2.7)$$

34

where max signifies a sample maximum of χ^2, has been used by BEALS (1965). This obviously defines a multiple of the squared Euclidean distance. Formula (2.6) is nevertheless preferred because it defines a relative distance on an unchanging scale whereas formula (2.7) does not.

Directly derivable from Euclidean distance are certain pair functions known as *scalar (inner) products of vectors* which we compute normally as a sum of cross products of co-ordinates. The term *scalar product* signifies the product of the lengths of two vectors and the cosine of their subtending angle. The OCHIAI coefficient is an example for the scalar product of two binary vectors normalized to unit lengths. The vectors have common origin in the zero point of the co-ordinate axes. Because all such vectors point in the positive direction, the values of the OCHIAI coefficient fall within 0 and 1 inclusive. The product moment *correlation coefficient* is another example for scalar products of normalized vectors; but in this case the common origin is in the centroid of the system defined by the mean values of the co-ordinates. With origins in the centroid, the vectors may point in any direction; this naturally explains why the value of the correlation coefficient should fall between -1 to $+1$ inclusive. The *covariance* can be interpreted as a scalar product of nonnormalized vectors with the origin in the centroid. But in the case of the covariance, because the vectors are not normalized, the values, positive or negative, do not have a fixed upper bound.

The scalar products play an important role in several methods of data analysis as we shall see in Chapter III in connection with certain ordinations. The forms which are most often encountered include the following:

$$S_{hi} = \sum_{j} A_{hj} A_{ij}, \ j = 1, ..., n \tag{2.8}$$

for any two species h and i, and

$$q_{jk} = \sum_{h} A_{hj} A_{hk}, \ h = 1, ..., p \tag{2.9}$$

for any two quadrats j and k. When A_{hj} is defined as

$$A_{hj} = (X_{hj} - \bar{X}_h) / \sqrt{(n-1)}$$

where $\bar{X}_h$ is the sample mean of species h, S_{hi} will represent the covariance of species h and i. When A_{hj} is defined according to

$$A_{hj} = (X_{hj} - \bar{X}_h) / \left[\sum_{e} (X_{eh} - \bar{X}_h)^2 \right]^{1/2}, \ e = 1, ..., n$$

S_{hi} will represent the product moment correlation coefficient. The quantity q_{jk} of formula (2.9) is sometimes referred to as the Q-expression for the covariance or correlation of quadrats. The Q-expression has special importance as a dual measure replacing formula (2.1) in some methods of ordination which can more conveniently handle scalar products than distances. Scalar products can be computed in program CORRS given in the Appendix.

A further point of importance is the relationship of the Euclidean distance computed from the A_{hj} type data according to

$$d(j, k) = \left[\sum_h (A_{hj} - A_{hk})^2 \right]^{1/2} , \quad h = 1, ..., p \tag{2.10}$$

and the scalar products determined on the basis of formula (2.9). This relationship is of the form

$$d^2(j, k) = q_{jj} + q_{kk} - 2q_{jk} \tag{2.11}$$

or in the reverse

$$q_{jk} = -0.5 (d^2(j, k) - \overline{d_j^2} - \overline{d_k^2} + \overline{d^2}) \tag{2.12}$$

where $\overline{d_j^2}$, $\overline{d_k^2}$ and $\overline{d^2}$ are mean squared quadrat distances computed according to

$$\overline{d_j^2} = \sum_k d^2(j, k)/n, \, k = 1, ..., n$$

$$\overline{d_k^2} = \sum_j d^2(j, k)/n, \, j = 1, ..., n$$

$$\overline{d^2} = \sum_j \sum_k d^2(j, k)/n^2, \, j, k = 1, ..., n$$

We shall build on these relationships when we develop an algorithm for component analysis in Chapter III.

C. Absolute value function

This is another formulation for distance defined as a sum of absolute species differences,

$$a(j, k) = \sum_h |X_{hj} - X_{hk}|, \, h = 1, ..., p \tag{2.13}$$

This distance, like the Euclidean distance of formula (2.1), is affected by species correlations. It lacks any fixed upper bound, and it suffers from the reliance on absolute species differences between quadrats. Because of these, it can give rise to the anomalous situation in which two quadrats with no species in common may appear more similar than two other quadrats which contain an identical set of species. It may seem then that there is little to be gained by the use of formula (2.13) as compared to formula (2.1).

The absolute value function can be made relative (WHITTAKER, 1952),

$$w(j, k) = \sum_h |X_{hj}/Q_j - X_{hk}/Q_k|, \, h = 1, ..., p \tag{2.14}$$

where

$$Q_j = \sum_h X_{hj} \text{ and } Q_k = \sum_h X_{hk} \; ;$$

these are the sums of species quantities in the two quadrats. The values of this relative form lie between 0 and 2 inclusive. Zero indicates that the two quadrats have the species in similar proportions, *i.e.* $X_{hj}/X_{ij} = X_{hk}/X_{ik}$ for any species h or i. When the two quadrats have no species in common $w(j, k)$ is equal to 2. In these respects formula (2.14) is similar to formula (2.2). SOKAL & SNEATH (1963, 1973) consider the lack of squaring of terms in the formulae an advantage because in this way the differences between the entities compared are not exaggerated. More importantly, as we shall see later in this chapter, formula (2.14) tends to linearize trends in the data, but in sharp contrast to formula (2.2) it is not Euclidean. Consequently, it has narrower established utility in conventional data analysis.

To illustrate the computation of the relative form of the absolute value function, including the first two quadrats of Table 2-1, we give the example below:

$$Q_1 = 2 + 0 + 3 = 5$$
$$Q_2 = 5 + 1 + 4 = 10$$
$$w(1, 2) = |2/5 - 5/10| + |0 - 1/10| + |3/5 - 4/10| = 0.4$$

The distance based on formula (2.13), in which values have not been made relative, is somewhat simpler to compute because it needs no adjustments in the quadrat vectors. For this, we have

$$a(1, 2) = |2 - 5| + |0 - 1| + |3 - 4| = 5.$$

A certain kind of double adjustment, where the conversion is from X_{hj} to $X_{hj}/\sqrt{Q_h Q_j}$, where the Qs represent respectively the hth species total and the jth quadrat total in the sample, has been described by WILLIAMS (1952). Such an adjustment, as we shall see in Chapter III, has a profound effect on the results of certain ordinations.

D. Geodesic metric

The space in which this metric is a spatial parameter is the surface of an n-dimensional hypersphere. The geodesic metric measures the shorter arc between points. When we write for the geodesic metric,

$$g(j, k) = \arccos \sum_h X_{hj} X_{hk} / \left[\sum_h X_{hj}^2 \sum X_{hk}^2 \right]^{1/2} , \, h = 1, ..., p \qquad (2.15)$$

the hypersphere has unit radius. The geodesic metric can be derived from the chord distance

$$g(j, k) = \arccos (1 - c^2(j, k)/2) \qquad (2.16)$$

The values of $g(j, k)$ in our case extend from 0 (when $c(j, k)$ is zero) to $\pi/2$ (when $c(j, k)$ equals $\sqrt{2}$). We can thus see that the geodesic metric is similar in many respects to the chord distance but it is not Euclidean.

E. Rajski's metric

Before we can define this metric it will be necessary to consider some general aspects about frequency distributions, entropy, and information. Any set of observed values or symbols $X_h = (X_{h1} ... X_{hn})$ can be condensed into a frequency distribution $F_h = (f_{h1} ... f_{hs_h})$ by simply setting up s_h frequency classes and counting the number of observations falling into each. When the data is categorical, representing counts or frequencies, X_h itself may be considered as a frequency distribution so that F_h is equivalent to X_h.

The distribution F_h is an observed distribution. There may be a second distribution F_h^0 such that both distributions have identical totals $f_{h.} = f_{h.}^0 = n$, and are identically ordered in the sense that for each element in F_h there is a corresponding element in F_h^0. Any element in F_h or F_h^0 can be expressed as a proportion,

$$p_{hj} = f_{hj}/f_{h.} \text{ or } p_{hj}^0 = f_{hj}^0/f_{h.}$$

such that

$$\sum_j p_{hj} = \sum_j p_{hj}^0 = 1.$$

When the distribution F_h describes the hth species in the sample, the element f_{hj} will indicate the frequency with which the observed values or symbols occur in the jth class. Consider for example the data in Table 2-2. In this table

Table 2-2. Species quantities in quadrats estimated on an arbitrary scale.
Data after PIETSCH & MULLER-STOLL (1968)

Species	Quadrat
	1 2 3 4 5 6 7 8 9 10 11 12 13 14 15 16 17 18 19 20 21 22 23 24 25
X_1	1 1 + + 1 + + + . r + + 1 + 1 4 1 4 3 2 1 1 3 1 3
X_2	3 4 3 3 1 3 + 4 r 2 + + + 1 + 1 + . . 1 1 2 . 1 +

X_1 – *Eleocharis ovata*
X_2 – *Carex bohemica*

the entries include numerals, mixed with one letter of the alphabet, a period
and a +. A period indicates absence, *r* and + signify species of very low or low
quantitative representation; the numerals *1, 2, 3, 4* are abundance estimates
for the species which occur in greater quantity. With discrete symbols it is
logical to define ., *r*, +, *1, 2, 3, 4* as the class symbols, and then to obtain the
values for the elements in F_1, F_2 by counting occurrences of the class symbols in the data. These counts are given in Table 2-3.

Table 2-3. Distribution of class symbols for species in Table 2-2

Species as frequency distribution	Class symbol							Total
	.	*r*	+	*1*	*2*	*3*	*4*	
F_1	1	1	8	9	1	3	2	25
F_2	3	1	7	6	2	4	2	25

In this example F_1, F_2 both are 7-valued ($s_1 = s_2 = 7$) and their totals are the
same $f_1. = f_2. = 25$. Furthermore, the elements are identically ordered in both
distributions according to the 7 common class symbols. The relative frequencies are obtained based on division by 25. These have been computed and are
given in Table 2-4.

Table 2-4. Relative frequencies of class symbols for species in Table 2-2

Species as frequency distribution	Class symbol							Total
	.	*r*	+	*1*	*2*	*3*	*4*	
P_1	0.04	0.04	0.32	0.36	0.04	0.12	0.08	1
P_2	0.12	0.04	0.28	0.24	0.08	0.16	0.08	1

Let us assume that the class frequencies in a distribution $\mathbf{F}_h^0 = (f_{h1}^0 \ldots f_{hs_h}^0)$ have different observed weights, specified by the elements in $\mathbf{P}_h = (p_{h1} \ldots p_{hs_h})$. If no such weights are given the distributions $\mathbf{F}_h$, $\mathbf{F}_h^0$ are taken to be identical. The entropy, or average information, in $\mathbf{F}_h^0$ relative to $\mathbf{F}_h$ is defined as the sum

$$H(\mathbf{P}_h^0) = -\sum_j p_{hj} \ln p_{hj}^0, \quad j = 1, \ldots, s_h \qquad (2.17)$$

where 'ln' indicates the natural logarithm. The minimum value of $H(\mathbf{P}_h^0)$ corresponds to the condition $\mathbf{P}_h = \mathbf{P}_h^0$,

$$\min H(\mathbf{P}_h^0) = H(\mathbf{P}_h) = -\sum_j p_{hj} \ln p_{hj}, \quad j = 1, \ldots, s_h \qquad (2.18)$$

This is SHANNON's (1948) entropy function, also known as *entropy of order one* (RÉNYI, 1961), distinguished from entropies of other higher order,

$$H(\mathbf{P}_h)^k = -\sum_j p_{hj} \ln^k p_{hj}, \quad j = 1, \ldots, s_h$$

for $k > 1$.

The entropy $H(\mathbf{P}_h)$ has a number of properties that are useful to know before attempting to apply any of the formulae to vegetation data:
1. Continuity for values of p in the interval $0 < p < 1$.
2. Symmetry in the sense that the order in which the p_{hj} are considered has no influence.
3. Maximum value at $p_{h1} = p_{h2} = \ldots = p_{hs_h} = 1/s_h$.
4. Additivity in the sense of $H(\mathbf{P}_h \mathbf{P}_i) = H(\mathbf{P}_h) + H(\mathbf{P}_i)$ where $\mathbf{P}_h \mathbf{P}_i$ indicates the direct product of two sets of independent frequencies.
5. Consistency and approximate normality when $\mathbf{X}_h$, from which $\mathbf{P}_h$ is derived, represents a random sample from a normal population (BASHARIN, 1959).
6. Improved normality with increased sample size.

Considering the data in Table 2-2 we can compute $H(\mathbf{P}_h)$ of formula (2.18) according to the equivalent formula,

$$H(\mathbf{P}_h) = \frac{1}{f_{h.}} \left[f_{h.} \ln f_{h.} - \sum_j f_{hj} \ln f_{hj} \right] \qquad (2.19)$$

with corresponding numerical values,

$$H(\mathbf{P}_1) = \frac{1}{25}(25 \ln 25 - (3 \ln 1 + 8 \ln 8 + 9 \ln 9 + 3 \ln 3 + 2 \ln 2))$$
$$= 1.5752$$

$$H(\mathbf{P}_2) = \frac{1}{25}(25 \ln 25 - (3 \ln 3 + 1 \ln 1 + 7 \ln 7 + 6 \ln 6 + 4 \ln 2$$
$$+ 4 \ln 4)) = 1.7795$$

In this example we used data which consist of discrete symbols. It was natural to identify the different symbols as class symbols when we constructed the frequency distributions. A similar procedure could be followed in the case of continuous data, but with modification; the frequency classes would have to be defined as non-overlapping intervals. When the data are categorical; the original observations can be regarded as frequencies and used directly in formula (2.19).

Relative frequencies and the average information are sometimess less convenient for handling than their $f_{h.}$ multiple,

$$I(\mathbf{F}_h) = f_{h.} \; H(\mathbf{P}_h) = -\sum_j f_{hj} \ln f_{hj}/f_{h.}$$

$$= f_{h.} \; \ln f_{h.} - \sum_j f_{hj} \ln f_{hj}, \quad j = 1, ..., s_h \tag{2.20}$$

The corresponding numerical values for the two species in Table 2-2 are given by

$$I(\mathbf{F}_1) = 25 \; H(\mathbf{P}_1) = 39.379$$
$$I(\mathbf{F}_2) = 25 \; H(\mathbf{P}_2) = 44.486$$

When a population distribution $\mathbf{P}_h^0$ is replaced by the observed sample distribution $\mathbf{P}_h$ the information generated can be measured as a divergence,

$$H(\mathbf{P}_h ; \mathbf{P}_h^0) = H(\mathbf{P}_h^0) - H(\mathbf{P}_h) = \sum_j p_{hj} \ln p_{hj}/p_{hj}^0, \quad j = 1, ..., s_h \tag{2.21}$$

Formula (2.21) is known as *information of order one* (RÉNYI, 1961), and its multiple

$$2I(\mathbf{F}_h ; \mathbf{F}_h^0) = 2 \sum_j f_{hj} \ln f_{hj}/f_{hj}^0, \quad j = 1, ..., s_h \tag{2.22}$$

is the *minimum discrimination information statistic* (KULLBACK, 1959). It should be noted that formula (2.21) or (2.22) represents a one-way or *I*-divergence, $\mathbf{P}_h^0 \rightarrow \mathbf{P}_h$ or $\mathbf{F}_h^0 \rightarrow \mathbf{F}_h$, which is not the same as $\mathbf{P}_h^0 \leftarrow \mathbf{P}_h$ or $\mathbf{F}_h^0 \leftarrow \mathbf{F}_h$ where the comparison is reversed. A two-way divergence $\mathbf{P}_h \rightleftharpoons \mathbf{P}_h^0$ or $\mathbf{F}_h \rightleftharpoons \mathbf{F}_h^0$ is known as a *J*-divergence. The *J*-divergence is a symmetric divergence, with respect to $\mathbf{F}_h$ and $\mathbf{F}_i$, given by

$$J(\mathbf{F}_h ; \mathbf{F}_i) = \sum_j (f_{hj} - f_{ij}) \ln f_{hj}/f_{ij}, \quad j = 1, ..., s_h \tag{2.23}$$

In this the order in which $\mathbf{F}_h$ and $\mathbf{F}_i$ are compared is immaterial and $s_h = s_i$.

We shall consider further *I*-divergences in the sequel. As far as their characterization is concerned it will be sufficient to state that they are not influenced by zero elements in $\mathbf{F}^0$ and $\mathbf{F}$; and the order in which the f/f^0 terms are

41

taken has no influence as long as f and f^0 are not interchanged. (In a J-divergence f_h and f_i can be interchanged.) The I-divergence of formula (2.22) and the J-divergence of formula (2.23) both have sampling distributions comparable to the χ^2 distribution with $s_h - 1$ degrees of freedom under the null hypothesis that $\mathbf{F}_h$ represents a random sample from a population completely specified by $\mathbf{F}_h^0$, or that $\mathbf{F}_h$ and $\mathbf{F}_i$ are random samples from the same population.

KULLBACK'S (1959) results provide a basis for our derivation of a sampling distribution for $2I(\mathbf{F};\mathbf{F}^0)$. Consider the relation,

$$1 - e/f \leqslant \ln f/e \leqslant f/e - 1$$

which holds true when $f/e > 0$, with equality when $f = e$. Use as a first approximation to $\ln f/e$ the average of the two limits, $i.e.$

$$\ln f/e \approx ((f/e - 1) + (1 - e/f))/2$$
$$= (f/e - e/f)/2$$
$$= (f^2 - e^2)/2fe$$

or $2f \ln f/e \approx (f^2 - e^2)/e$. After observing that

$$\sum_i (e_i^2 - f_i e_i)/e_i = 0, \quad i = 1, ..., s$$

because $\Sigma f_i = \Sigma e_i$, derive the chi square approximation as the quantity

$$2I(\mathbf{F};\mathbf{E}) = 2\sum_i f_i \ln f_i/e_i$$
$$\approx \sum_i (f_i^2 - e_i^2)/e_i + \Sigma(2e_i^2 - 2f_i e_i)/e_i$$
$$= \sum_i ((f_i^2 - e_i^2) + (2e_i^2 - 2f_i e_i))/e_i$$
$$= \sum_i (f_i^2 - 2f_i e_i + e_i^2)/e_i$$
$$= \Sigma(f_i - e_i)^2/e_i, \quad i = 1, ..., s$$

— which is the familiar expression for chi square. The approximation improves as the ratio f/e approaches unity.

Under specified circumstances the quantity $\Sigma(f_i - e_i)^2/e_i$, and $2I(\mathbf{F};\mathbf{E})$ too, can be referred to the hypothetical chi square distribution with $s - 1$ degrees of freedom. This should not obscure the fact that under most practical situations we use the hypothetical chi square distribution only as an approximation with these quantities, knowing that their true sampling distribution is likely to be different. Obviously then if we are to use the chi square distribution as a reference distribution for $2I(\mathbf{F};\mathbf{E})$ we may have a potentially weak, double approximation on hand — an approximation of the quantity

$$\sum_i (f_i - e_i)^2/e_i$$

by the quantity

$$2\sum_i f_i \ln f_i/e_i,$$

and another, of the true sampling distribution of $\Sigma(f_i - e_i)^2/e_i$ under the prevailing local conditions by the hypothetical chi square distribution.

Any two distributions F_h and F_i such as the two species in Table 2-3 and the relationship between them can be represented in an $s_h \times s_i$ table (Table 2-5). In such a table the individual frequency distributions appear as the prin-

Table 2-5. Tabular representation of frequency distributions and the relationship between them

		Class value or class symbol in F_i				Total in F_h
		1	2	...	s_i	
Class value or class symbol in F_h	1	$f_{h1,i1}$	$f_{h1,i2}$	...	f_{h1,is_i}	f_{h1}
	2	$f_{h2,i1}$	$f_{h2,i2}$	...	f_{h2,is_i}	f_{h2}
	.	.	.	...	.	.
	s_h	$f_{hs_h,i1}$	$f_{hs_h,i2}$	...	f_{hs_h,is_i}	f_{hs_h}
Total in	F_i	f_{i1}	f_{i2}	...	f_{is_i}	$f_{h.} = f_{i.} = f_{h.,i.}$

cipal marginal distributions, and an element $f_{hj,\ ik}$ in the body of the table indicates the joint frequency of the jth class value (or class symbol) in F_h and the kth class value (or class symbol) in F_i. In other words, $f_{hj,\ ik}$ indicates the frequency of the joint observation in which one element can be identified with the jth class in F_h and another with the kth class in F_i. We can define the following information quantities for Table 2-5:

1. Information in the marginal distributions

$$I(F_h) = f_{h.}\ \ln f_{h.} - \sum_j f_{hj} \ln f_{hj}, \ j = 1, ..., s_h$$

$$I(F_i) = f_{i.}\ \ln f_{i.} - \sum_j f_{ij} \ln f_{ij}, \ j = 1, ..., s_i$$

2. Joint information

$$I(F_h, F_i) = f_{h.,i.}\ \ln f_{h.,i.} - \sum_j \sum_k f_{hj,ik} \ln f_{hj,ik} \ ,$$
$$j = 1, ..., s_h; k = 1, ..., s_i \qquad (2.24)$$

3. Mutual information

$$I(F_h; F_i) = I(F_h) + I(F_i) - I(F_h, F_i)$$
$$= \sum_j \sum_k f_{hj,ik} \ln\ f_{hj,ik} f_{h.,i.}/(f_{hj}f_{ik}) \ ,$$
$$j = 1, ..., s_h; k = 1, ..., s_i \qquad (2.25)$$

$I(\mathbf{F}_h; \mathbf{F}_i)$ represents an *I*-divergence. The other terms $I(\mathbf{F}_h)$, $I(\mathbf{F}_i)$ or $I(\mathbf{F}_h, \mathbf{F}_i)$ represent multiples of entropy of order one.

From these information quantitites we obtain the equivocation information,

$$E(\mathbf{F}_h; \mathbf{F}_i) = I(\mathbf{F}_h, \mathbf{F}_i) - I(\mathbf{F}_h; \mathbf{F}_i)$$

$$= - \sum_j \sum_k f_{hj,ik} \ln \ (f_{hj,ik}/f_{hj})(f_{hj,ik}/f_{ik}) \ ,$$

$$j = 1, ..., s_h; \ k = 1, ..., s_i \tag{2.26}$$

where $f_{hj,ik}/f_{hj}$ and $f_{hj,ik}/f_{ik}$ are conditional probabilities. When $\mathbf{F}_h$ and $\mathbf{F}_i$ represent two species, $f_{hj,ik}/f_{hj}$ specifies the probability for species i to have state k when the state of species h is known to be j. Similarly, $f_{hj,ik}/f_{ik}$ gives the probability for species h to have state j when the state of species i is known to be k. A definition of RAJSKI's metric $d(\mathbf{F}_h; \mathbf{F}_i)$ follows directly from the foregoing quantities:

$$d(\mathbf{F}_h; \mathbf{F}_i) = \frac{E(\mathbf{F}_h; \mathbf{F}_i)}{I(\mathbf{F}_h, \mathbf{F}_i)} = 1 - \frac{I(\mathbf{F}_h; \mathbf{F}_i)}{I(\mathbf{F}_h, \mathbf{F}_i)} \tag{2.27}$$

RAJKI's metric is a relative measure of the two-way divergence of F_h, F_i with 0 and 1 as limit values. From this metric a similarity measure can be derived according to

$$r(\mathbf{F}_h; \mathbf{F}_i) = \sqrt{(1 - d^2(\mathbf{F}_h; \mathbf{F}_i))} \tag{2.28}$$

This is known as the *coherence coefficient*. Its limits are one and zero.

Let us now turn to an example. We shall compute $d(\mathbf{F}_1; \mathbf{F}_2)$ and $r(\mathbf{F}_1; \mathbf{F}_2)$ for the two species in Table 2-2. We find the joint frequencies in Table 2-6. In

Table 2-6. Joint frequencies for two species in Table 2-2

		Class symbol in $\mathbf{F}_2$						Total in $\mathbf{F}_1$
		.	r	+	1	2	3	4	
	.		1						1
	r					1			1
Class	+			3	1		3	1	8
symbol	1			3	3	1	1	1	9
in $\mathbf{F}_1$	2				1				1
	3	2		1					3
	4	1			1				2
Total in $\mathbf{F}_2$		3	1	7	6	2	4	2	25

44

connection with this table we note that, for instance, the joint frequency of the third class symbol *(+)* in F_1 and the sixth class symbol *(3)* in F_2 is $f_{13,26} = 3$. But this is not the same as $f_{16,23}$ which happens to be 1. Clearly, the sequence in which the class symbols occur, whether *(+,3)* or *(3,+)* in the example, must be carefully checked when counting their joint frequencies. We note that the cells in the body of the table that correspond to unrealized combinations are left blank, and the corresponding terms in the formula are arbitrarily set to zero. The information quantities have the following numerical values:

$$
\begin{aligned}
I(\mathbf{F}_1) \quad &= 39.379 \\
I(\mathbf{F}_2) \quad &= 44.486 \\
I(\mathbf{F}_1, \mathbf{F}_2) \quad &= 25 \ln 25 - 4(3 \ln 3) - 2 \ln 2 = 65.902 \\
I(\mathbf{F}_1 ; \mathbf{F}_2) \quad &= 39.379 + 44.486 - 65.902 = 17.963 \\
E(\mathbf{F}_1 ; \mathbf{F}_2) \quad &= 65.902 - 17.963 = 47.939 \\
d(\mathbf{F}_1 ; \mathbf{F}_2) \quad &= 47.939/65.902 = 0.727 \\
r(\mathbf{F}_1 ; \mathbf{F}_2) \quad &= \sqrt{(1 - 0.727^2)} = 0.686
\end{aligned}
$$

Program INFC in the Appendix computes the different information terms from input data of the kind which were used in the example. We can see that the information quantities so far considered are especially well suited to analyse vegetational data which consists of arbitrary symbols designating abundance estimates for species. We shall consider the case of count and frequency data later in connection with different information type divergences.

2.5 Semimetrics and Other Scrambled Forms

When a distance function fails on the triangle inequality axiom, without failing on the others, it is said to be a *semimetric*. We begin with the well known distance measure of BRAY & CURTIS (1957) to illustrate the loss of metric properties in a function due to scrambling by a variable scale. We can write this measure as

$$
b(j, k) = 1 - 2 \sum_h \min (X_{hj}, X_{hk})/Q_{jk} = \sum_h |X_{hj} - X_{hk}|/Q_{jk},
$$
$$
h = 1, ..., p \tag{2.29}
$$

where min signifies the smallest of the pair X_{hj}, X_{hk} and $Q_{jk} = \sum_h (X_{hj} + X_{hk})$, $h = 1, ..., p$. It can be seen that this measure is related to the absolute value function; the difference lies in the division by Q_{jk} which represents the sum of all species quantities in the two quadrats. When this sum is constant for all quadrat pairs formula (2.29) will uniformly represent a scaled down absolute value function *without* loss of any metric properties. However, when Q_{jk} is not a constant for the sample, varying from one quadrat pair to the next, formula (2.29) will measure on a *new* scale with each new value of Q_{jk} and will no longer qualify as a metric. A changing scale of measure will disqualify this or any other function from being a consistent definition of distance, and thus, an acceptable measure in data analysis.

Semimetrics have been used in ordinations where they do not fit because they do not produce distances from which Euclidean triangles can be formed. Consider

$$Y_k = d(j, k) \cos \alpha_{km} = (d^2(j, k) + d^2(j, m) - d^2(k,m))/2d(j,m) \qquad (2.30)$$

which BEALS (1960) has used to define co-ordinates for quadrats in an ordination. In this formula symbol Y_k represents the co-ordinate of quadrat k on the first ordination axis through quadrats j and m which represent ordination poles. The distances in the formula are squared quadrat distances. The cosine relation naturally requires that the function generating the quadrat distances be capable of forming ordinary Euclidean triangles. If it cannot then Y_k will not be uniquely defined.

When we carry out the computations and find that $Y_k/d(j, k)$ exceeds unity or is less than -1 we know that the cosine relation does not hold, *i.e.* the distances fail to produce Euclidean triangles. This would be an indication that the distance measure is a semimetric or not a metric at all. This situation can arise when $b(j, k)$ is substituted for $d(j, k)$ in formula (2.30). Let us consider in this connection an example involving three quadrats given by their data vectors,

$$\mathbf{x}_j = \begin{bmatrix} 2 \\ 5 \\ 2 \\ 5 \\ 3 \end{bmatrix} \qquad \mathbf{X}_k = \begin{bmatrix} 3 \\ 5 \\ 2 \\ 4 \\ 3 \end{bmatrix} \qquad \mathbf{X}_m = \begin{bmatrix} 9 \\ 1 \\ 1 \\ 1 \\ 1 \end{bmatrix}$$

The totals are respectively $Q_j = Q_k = 17$ and $Q_m = 13$. The distance of quadrats j and k is

$$b(j, k) = (|2-3| + |5-5| + |2-2| + |5-4| + |3-3|)/34$$
$$= 0.05882$$

The distance of quadrats j,m and k,m are $b(j,m) = 0.6$ and $b(k,m) = 0.53333$. We note the inequality

$$b(j, m) > b(j, k) + b(j, m)$$

in direct reverse of the inequality stipulated by the fourth metric space axiom. This indicates that in this particular example the BRAY & CURTIS distance function has failed in operations in which it has been put to use by its proponents. When, in spite of this, we force an ordination based on this function, coupled with formula (2.30),we end up with a co-ordinate

$$Y_k = (0,05882^2 + 0.6^2 - 0.53333^2)/((2)(0.6)) = 0.06585$$

greater than $b(j, k)$ itself.

One only wonders how did the proponents resolve the problem with $b(j, k)$ in their manipulations of Euclidean triangles in the BRAY & CURTIS ordination, knowing from what we have seen so far that $b(j,k)$ does not always yield distances from which Euclidean triangles can be produced. We therefore suggest that $b(j, k)$ be used with extreme caution as a measure of distance in ordinations, restricting it to such samples where the quantity Q_{jk} remains a constant for all quadrat pairs.

BEALS' (1960) ecological measure, which can be written as

$$v(j, k) = \max L - L = b(j, k) + e \tag{2.31}$$

where $\max L$ is the maximum value of $L = 2 \sum_h \min(X_{hj}, X_{hk})/Q_{jk}$, and $e = \max L - 1$, exemplifies further scrambling in the absolute value function. It can be seen that in formula (2.31) a distance $b(j, k)$ is decremented by a constant e. Whenever e is not a zero value, $i.e.$ $\max L < 1$, formula (2.31) can fail on all except the third metric space axiom. Because of these reasons formula (2.31) is even $less$ suited than formula (2.29) for use in analyses which manipulate Euclidean triangles.

This is not to say, of course, that formulae (2.29) and (2.31) will not have validity as ecological measures because they are not metric functions. What really makes these functions universally undesired is a changing scale which they may incorporate because of the division by Q_{jk}. Due to this property, it is suggested that the ecologist avoid using formulae (2.29) or (2.31) when Q_{jk} is not a constant quantity for all quadrat pairs in the same sample. No hardship should follow such an action, considering that the roles for which these functions were intended in the first place, $i.e.$ to provide relative distance measures in a Euclidean ordination, can be performed better by other reliable functions of which formula (2.2) represents an example. This represents a metric, has a consistent scale of measure, and never will fail to form Euclidean triangles. We shall consider the implications of a changing scale in the resemblance function further in a section later in this chapter.

2.6 A Probabilistic Similarity Index

The resemblance measures which we considered so far define the likeness of objects as a composite of individual bits of resemblance values, each contributed by a different variable. In such a definition the resemblance of a given pair of objects is completely independent from the resemblance of any other pair in the sample. GOODALL (1964, 1966) suggests an index which takes into account comparisons between all pairs of objects when determining the resemblance of any given pair.

When the data describes species quantity within quadrats a probability index for quadrats can be calculated based on the steps in the following procedure (see also program PINDEX in the Appendix):

1. Define δ_{jkh} as the dissimilarity of quadrats j and k with respect to species h. When the number of quadrats is n the number of δ_{jkh} values is $n(n-1)/2$ for any species h.
2. Rank the δ values according to size within species h.
3. Define the dissimilarity of quadrats j, k with respect to species h as the proportion $p_{jkh} = P(\delta \leqslant \delta_{jkh})$. This is the proportion of δ values that are smaller or equal to δ_{jkh} within species h; the higher the proportion the more dissimilar j and k with respect to h. It is important to realize that when p_{jkh} implies maximum similarity δ_{jkh} may be a quantity other than zero.
4. Compute p_{jkh} for each of the available r species, and combine the proportions as the product $\pi_{jk} = \Pi p_{jkh}$, $h = 1, ..., r$. It is obvious that the p_{jkh} values are not zero. We must assume that the p_{jkh} are independent, which we interpret as a lack of correlation between the species, to justify combining the p_{jkh} in a simple product. If linear correlations exist their effect can be removed from the similarity index if the species are replaced by sets of component scores (see Chapter III) which are uncorrelated.
5. Define an index of similarity in one of two possible ways: *(a)* Order the individual π_{jk} values, of which there are $n(n-1)/2$ in total, and determine the proportion $P(\pi \geqslant \pi_{jk})$; use this proportion as a measure of similarity $S(j, k)$. *(b)* Alternatively, compute the quantity,

$$\chi^2_{jk} = -2 \sum_h \ln p_{jkh} = -2 \ln \pi_{jk}, \quad h = 1, ..., r$$

This has the χ^2 distribution at $2r$ degrees of freedom on the assumption that the p_{jkh} values represent independent probabilities. A similarity index can be derived as $S(j, k) = 1 - P(\chi^2 \geq \chi^2_{jk})$, i.e. the one complement of the probability that a random value χ^2 can exceed the observed value χ^2_{jk}. It may be noted that a small value of χ^2_{jk} associates with a large probability, and low similarity. The reasoning should be clear from the following logical sequence: large $p_{jkh} \to$ low similarity of quadrats j and k with respect to species $h \to$ small contribution to $\chi^2_{jk} \to$ large probability of an equal or greater $\chi^2 \to$ low similarity of j, k.

Let us now consider an example for the index based on the use of quadrats 1 and 2 in Table 1-1. We define a distance function according to $\delta_{jkh} = |X_{hj} - X_{hk}|$. There are $10(10-1)/2 = 45$ such differences to be computed within each species. For example, for quadrats 1 and 2 the first difference is given by $\delta_{121} = |45-2| = 43$. The entire vector of δ_{jkl} values is $\delta_1 = (43\ 36\ 19\ 42\ 40\ 43\ 45\ 14\ 29\ 7\ 24\ 1\ 3\ 0\ 88\ 29\ 14\ 17\ 6\ 4\ 7\ 81\ 22\ 7\ 23\ 21\ 24\ 64\ 5\ 10\ 2\ 1\ 87\ 28\ 13\ 3\ 85\ 26\ 11\ 88\ 29\ 14\ 59\ 74\ 15)$. The number of δ_{jkl} values not exceeding $\delta_{121} = 43$ is 36. This gives $p_{121} = 36/45 = 0.8$. The remaining 4 species are similarly treated. The proportions are $p_{122} = 0.911, p_{123} = 0.622, p_{124} = 0.889, p_{125} = 0.622$ (within computer rounding errors). The computed proportions may be combined in $\chi^2_{jk} = -2 \ln ((0.8)(0.911)(0.622)(0.889)(0.622)) = 2.766$. This quantity is compared to the values in the χ^2 table at $2r = 10$ degrees of freedom. From the table we have $P(\chi^2 \geq 2.766) \approx 0.986$ and $S(1,2) = 1 - 0.986 = 0.014$ or 1.4%. This indicates a very low similarity between the two quadrats. The alternative method for determining $S(1,2)$ involves ordering the combined probabilities π of which $\pi_{12} = 0.251$. There are 45 such values of which 43 are smaller than 0.251. Thus $P(\pi \geq 0.251) = S(1,2) \approx 0.04$ or about 4%. This, similarly to χ^2, puts a very low value on the similarity of the two quadrats.

This index combines r individual probabilities. Its precision will therefore depend on the degree to which the probabilities are independent. But apart from the difficulty arising from the need to assume that the probabilities are independent a probabilistic index can be a useful measure of quadrat resemblance. Its principal advantage resides in the flexibility of handling different types of data as GOODALL himself has shown in different publications. The index has the further advantage of being made relative on a zero to one scale which under independence of probabilities is itself a linear probabilistic scale. The definition of resemblance by this index, however, is local to the sample in which the quadrats occur. In other words, the same two quadrats may appear differently similar in terms of such an index when embedded in different samples.

2.7 Further Measures of Information Divergence

In this section we shall discuss different information theory functions which, similarly to RAJSKI's metric, can measure the divergence of frequency distributions. We shall begin with a categorization of frequency distributions according to their totals and the ordering of elements.

1. The first category includes distributions whose totals are identical and the elements are identically ordered. An identical ordering implies that for every element in one of the distributions there is a corresponding element in every other. The distributions F_1 and F_2 in Table 2-3 are examples of this category.

2. Distributions of the second category are most frequent in vegetation data; they are characterized by an identical ordering of elements, but different totals. The rows in Table 1-1 represent examples in this connection.

3. The elements of distributions in the third category are unordered and their totals are also different. Such distributions could arise if we subdivided Table 1-1 into two groups, for instance, A from quadrat 1 to 4 and B from 5 to 10. After subdivision, the species vector X_{1A} in group A and its counterpart X_{1B} in group B represent a problem in comparisons requiring considerations of their totals rather than their elements.

The information functions that may serve as measures of divergence in these categories are basically I- or J-divergences. When a standard F^0 is specified formula (2.22) is the relevant expression; but when no standard is given formula (2.23) is appropriate. $I(F_h; F_i)$ of formula (2.25) represents an example for an I-divergence with observed frequencies $F = (f_{hj, ik})$ and expectations $F^0 = (f_{hj}f_{ik}/f_{h.,i.})$ where the elements of distribution F and F^0 are identically ordered and their totals are also identical. We shall consider the application of the I-divergence information to distributions whose elements are identically ordered but their totals are different.

Let $F_1 = (f_{11} \ldots f_{p1})$ and $F_2 = (f_{12} \ldots f_{p2})$ represent two quadrats described on the basis of the frequencies of p species. The frequencies are such that $\sum_h f_{h1} \neq \sum_h f_{h2}$, $h = 1, \ldots, p$; for every element f_{h1} in F_1 there is a corresponding element f_{h2} in F_2. The criterion which identically orders the frequency in F_1 and F_2 is the common set of species which they completely share. In this particular case we can write an I-divergence as

$$I(F_1; F_2) = \sum_h I(F_h; F_h^0) = \sum_h \sum_j f_{hj} \ln 2f_{hj}/(f_{h1} + f_{h2}),$$
$$h = 1, \ldots, p; \quad j = 1, 2 \tag{2.32}$$

where p is the number of species. In this formula the hth observed frequency distribution is given by $F_h = (f_{h1} \ f_{h2})$ and the standard by the distribution $F_h^0 = ((f_{h1} + f_{h2})/2 \ (f_{h1} + f_{h2})/2)$. When we define F_1 and F_2 to represent quadrats 1 and 2 in Table 1-1, we have

$$F_1 = (45 \ 18 \ 3 \ 10 \ 9) \text{ and } F_2 = (2 \ 92 \ 40 \ 61 \ 53)$$

From these we can derive $\mathbf{F}_h$ or $\mathbf{F}_h^0$ for any species. For instance, for the fourth species, we have

$$\mathbf{F}_4 = [10 \ 61] \quad \text{and} \quad \mathbf{F}_4^0 = \begin{bmatrix} \dfrac{71}{2} & \dfrac{71}{2} \end{bmatrix}$$

The I-divergence of the two quadrats can be computed according to

$$
\begin{aligned}
I(\mathbf{F}_1 ; \mathbf{F}_2) = I(\text{quadrat 1; quadrat 2}) &= \sum_h I(\mathbf{F}_h ; \mathbf{F}_h^0) = 45 \ln 45/ \\
&((45+2)/2) + 2 \ln 2/((45+2)/2) + 18 \ln 18/((18+92)/2) \\
&+ 92 \ln 92/((18+92)/2) + 3 \ln 3/((3+40)/2) \\
&+ 40 \ln 40/((3+40)/2) + 10 \ln 10/((10+61)/2) \\
&+ 61 \ln 61/((10+61)/2) + 9 \ln 9/((9+53)/2) \\
&+ 53 \ln 53/((9+53)/2) = 108.102
\end{aligned}
$$

In this example we can use the data from Table 1-1 directly in the formula for I-divergence because the data represent counts of individuals. Species frequencies could be similarly used; but not so measurements for which a different I-divergence may have to be defined (see KULLBACK, 1959).

Formula (2.32) involves a summation of information quantities $I(\mathbf{F}_h ; \mathbf{F}_h^0)$, $h = 1, ..., p$, each of which is specific to one species. Strictly speaking, such a summation may be objectionable if the species are not independent, *i.e.* if they have mutual information, which can bias the measured divergence in the sense that $I(\mathbf{F}_1 ; \mathbf{F}_2)$ will indicate an I-divergence for the two quadrats greater than their actual divergence. To eliminate the influence of mutual information of species on the measure of divergence we may regard $\mathbf{F}_1$ and $\mathbf{F}_2$ as columns in a $p \times 2$ contingency table and compute an information quantity for them in terms of

$$
I(\text{species; quadrats}) = \sum_h \sum_j f_{hj} \ln f_{hj} f_{..}/(f_h. f_{.j}) ,
$$
$$
h = 1, ..., p; \ j = 1, 2 \tag{2.33}
$$

This relates two criteria of classification; the first is the species affiliation of an observation and the second is its quadrat of occurrence. The frequency symbols in formula (2.33) are defined as follows:

f_{hj} = quantity of species h in qudrat j

$$f_{..} = \sum_h \sum_j f_{hj}, \quad f_h. = \sum_j f_{hj}, \quad f_{.j} = \sum_h f_{hj}$$

Formula (2.33) can be used as a measure of divergence between $\mathbf{F}_1$ and $\mathbf{F}_2$ without the need for assuming that the p species are independent. We

51

can compare formula (2.33) and (2.32) to discover that their difference is

$$\Delta(1;2) = I(\mathbf{F}_1;\mathbf{F}_2) - I(species;\ quadrats)$$

$$= \sum_h \sum_j f_{hj}\ (\ln 2\ f_{hj}/f_h. - \ln f_{hj} f_{..}/(f_h.f_{.j}))$$

$$= \sum_j f_{.j} \ln 2 f_{.j}/f_{..}\ ,\ j = 1,\ 2 \tag{2.34}$$

Because $\sum_j f_{.j} \ln 2 f_{.j}/f_{..}$ is always a positive quantity, or zero, $I(\mathbf{F}_1;\mathbf{F}_2)$ is always larger than $I(species;\ quadrats)$ when they are not equal.

Formulae (2.32), (2.33) and (2.34) each represent a different I-divergence information. We have already considered an example for the computation of formula (2.32). We can use the same data to illustrate the computations in the case of formulae (2.33) and (2.34). A $p \times 2$ table is constructed first:

Species	Quadrat		Total
	1	2	
X_1	45	2	47
X_2	18	92	110
X_3	3	40	43
X_4	10	61	71
X_5	9	53	62
Total	85	248	333

Then we compute for formula (2.33),

$$I(species;\ quadrats) = \sum_h \sum_j f_{hj} \ln f_{hj} + f_{..}\ \ln f_{..} - \sum_h f_h.\ \ln f_h.$$

$$- \sum_j f_{.j} \ln f_{.j} = 45 \ln 45 + 2 \ln 2 + 18 \ln 18 + 92 \ln 92$$

$$+ 3 \ln 3 + 40 \ln 40 + 10 \ln 10 + 61 \ln 61 + 9 \ln 9$$

$$+ 53 \ln 53 + 333 \ln 333 - 47 \ln 47 - 110 \ln 110$$

$$- 43 \ln 43 - 71 \ln 71 - 62 \ln 62 - 85 \ln 85 - 248 \ln 248$$

$$= 66.440.$$

This is a substantially smaller quantity than what we computed for $I(\mathbf{F}_1;\mathbf{F}_2)$ based on formula (2.32). The difference according to formula (2.34) is

$$\Delta(1,\ 2) = I(\mathbf{F}_1;\mathbf{F}_2) - I(species;\ quadrats)$$

$$= 108.102 - 66.440$$

$$= 41.662$$

which measures a divergence based on the distribution totals. Note that formula (2.33) represents a less restrictive measure of divergence than formula (2.32) because whereas a zero value of $I(species; quadrats)$ of formula (2.33) may imply only a proportionality of species quantities in the quadrats, such as $f_{h1}/f_{h2} = f_{i1}/f_{i2}$ a zero value of the $I(\mathbf{F}_1; \mathbf{F}_2)$ of formula (2.32) always implies an identity such as $f_{h1} = f_{h2}$ regardless of species.

An I-divergence may be computed not only between individual distributions but also among groups of distributions. The table below indicates the form in which the data may be presented:

Species	Quadrats in group A			Group total A	Quadrats in group B			Group total B	Total A + B
	1	2	...	n_A	1	2	...	n_B	
X_1	f_{A11} f_{A12}		f_{A1n_A}	$f_{A1.}$	f_{B11} f_{B12}		f_{B1n_B}	$f_{B1.}$	$f_{.1,}$
X_2	f_{A21} f_{A22}		f_{A2n_A}	$f_{A2.}$	f_{B21} f_{B22}		f_{B2n_B}	$f_{B2.}$	$f_{.2.}$
.	. .		.	.	. .		.	.	.
X_p	f_{Ap1} f_{Ap2}		f_{Apn_A}	$f_{Ap.}$	f_{Bp1} f_{Bp2}		f_{Bpn_B}	$f_{Bp.}$	$f_{.p.}$
Total	$f_{A.1}$ $f_{A.2}$		$f_{A.n_A}$	$f_{A..}$	$f_{B.1}$ $f_{B.2}$		$f_{B.n_B}$	$f_{B..}$	$f_{...}$

The I-divergence of A and B based on formula (2.32) can be written as

$$I(A; B) = \sum_k \sum_h \sum_j f_{khj} \ln (n_A + n_B) f_{khj}/f_{.h.} - \sum_h \sum_j f_{Ahj} \ln n_A f_{Ahj}/f_{Ah.}$$
$$- \sum_h \sum_j f_{Bhj} \ln n_B f_{Bhj}/f_{Bh.}$$
$$= \sum_h \sum_k f_{kh.} \ln (f_{kh.}/n_k)/(f_{.h.}/(n_A + n_B)),$$
$$k = A, B; \quad h = 1, ..., p; \quad j = 1, ..., n_A \text{ or } n_B \tag{2.35}$$

As in formula (2.32), in formula (2.35) also, we assume that the species are independent.

A less restrictive measure can be obtained based on formula (2.33), in terms of

$$I(A; B) = I(species; quadrats)_{A+B} - I(species; quadrats)_A$$
$$- I(species; quadrats)_B = \sum_h \sum_k f_{kh.} \ln (f_{kh.}\, f_{...}/(f_{k..}\, f_{.h.}),$$
$$h = 1, ..., p; \quad k = A, B \tag{2.36}$$

In this case species independence need not be assumed. The least informative measure takes the form

$$\Delta(A; B) = \sum_k f_{k..} \ \ln (f_{k..}/f_{...}) \ (n_A + n_B)/n_k \ , \ \ k = A, B \quad (2.37)$$

in which the weighted group means are compared.

Let the first four quadrats of Table 1-1 be included in group A, and let the last six be assigned to group B. The group totals are given by

Species	Total A	Total B	Total A + B
X_1	82	147	229
X_2	190	431	621
X_3	131	138	269
X_4	85	89	174
X_5	182	360	542
Total	670	1165	1835

Computing formula (2.35) we have

$$\begin{aligned}
I(A; B) = \ & 82 \ln (82/4)/(229/10)) + 190 \ln ((190/4)/(621/10)) \\
& + 131 \ln ((131/4)/(269/10)) + 85 \ln ((85/4)/(174/10)) \\
& + 182 \ln ((182/4)/(542/10)) + 147 \ln ((147/6)/(229/10)) \\
& + 431 \ln ((431/6)/(621/10)) + 138 \ln ((138/6)/(269/10)) \\
& + 89 \ln ((89/6)/(174/10)) + 360 \ln ((360/6)/(542/10)) \\
= \ & 24.386.
\end{aligned}$$

We compute formula (2.36) in the expanded form,

$$\begin{aligned}
I(A; B) = \ & \sum_k \sum_h f_{kh.} \ \ln f_{kh.} + f_{...} \ \ln f_{...} - \sum_k f_{k..} \ \ln f_{k..} - \sum_h f_{.h.} \ \ln f_{.h.} \\
= \ & 82 \ln 82 + 190 \ln 190 + 131 \ln 131 + 85 \ln 85 + 182 \ln 182 \\
& + 147 \ln 147 + 431 \ln 431 + 138 \ln 138 + 89 \ln 89 + 360 \ln 360 \\
& + 1835 \ln 1835 - 670 \ln 670 - 1165 \ln 1165 - 229 \ln 229 \\
& - 621 \ln 621 - 269 \ln 269 - 174 \ln 174 - 542 \ln 542 \\
= \ & 19.685.
\end{aligned}$$

From these we have for formula (2.37)

$$\Delta(A; B) = 24.386 - 19.685 = 4.701$$

All divergence quantities can be used probabilistically, based on the relationship between $2I$ and χ^2 at specified degrees of freedom, under specified circumstances:

Formula	Degrees of freedom	Null hypothesis tested based on 2I
(2.32)	p	Distributions F_1 and F_2 which represent two quadrats are random samples from the same multi-species population. Species are assumed independent
(2.33)	$p-1$	An observation's species affiliation is unpredictable from its quadrat of occurrence in the population of which the two quadrats represent a random sample
(2.34)	1	The parent populations from which F_1 and F_2 are taken at random have identical totals
(2.35)	p	The parent populations from which groups A and B are taken at random have specified total frequencies $(f._1 \ldots f._p)$. Species are assumed independent
(2.36)	$p-1$	An observations species affiliation is unpredictable from its group of occurrence in the populations from which the two groups represent random samples
(2.37)	1	The parent population from which groups A and B are random samples have identical totals

Under the null hypothesis $2I$ is distributed approximately as a χ^2 variable at the specified degrees of freedom. The approximation improves with increased number of observations.

When the elements in the observed frequency distributions are not ordered by a single criterion, they cannot be paired up in any meaningful way between distributions; but still an I-divergence can be computed based on the distribution totals in a manner exemplified by formulae (2.34) and (2.37). These formulae actually represent comparisons between distribution means weighted by the number of observations.

2.8 Important Inequalities

A. Information

It is obvious from the discussions that the information content in the union group $A + B$ cannot be less than the sum of the information contents in the subgroups. This property is stated in the inequality

$$I_{A+B} \geqslant I_A + I_B$$

B. *Sum of Squares*

A similar inequality can be stated for the sum of squares

$$Q_{A+B} \geqslant Q_A + Q_B$$

i.e. the sum of squares in the union group $A + B$ cannot be less than the sum of the sum of the squares in the subgroups. This inequality, similarly to the information inequality, plays an important role in classifications requiring comparisons between groups. Some classifications use the difference

$$I_{A+B} - I_A - I_B \quad \text{or} \quad Q_{A+B} - Q_A - Q_B$$

as a decision criterion for fusions or subdivisions. We shall deal with them in Chapter IV.

2.9 Transformations Implicit in Resemblance Functions

Resemblance functions often incorporate transformations or other adjustments which have the same effect as if the raw data were manipulated first and then a similarity or a dissimilarity value computed from the manipulated data. The transformations may be so substantial that when implemented the data may retain little resemblance to the original observations. A brief account will clarify the above points:

1. The *Euclidean distance* based on formula (2.1) incorporates no implicit adjustments of any sort. The resemblance structure which it imposes on the quadrats is the same as the resemblance structure imposed on the quadrats by the raw data as rectangular co-ordinates. The points in Fig.2-2a illustrate a similar situation based on the data given in Table 2-7.

Table 2-7. Quadrats from a simulated two-species community. Entries in the table indicate species abundance in the quadrats

Species	Quadrat									
	1	4	3	5	10	2	6	9	7	8
X_1	0.6	5.0	4.0	4.0	0	1.6	1.6	0.1	0.6	0.3
X_2	0.1	1.6	0.6	4.0	0.3	0.3	5.0	0.6	4.0	1.6

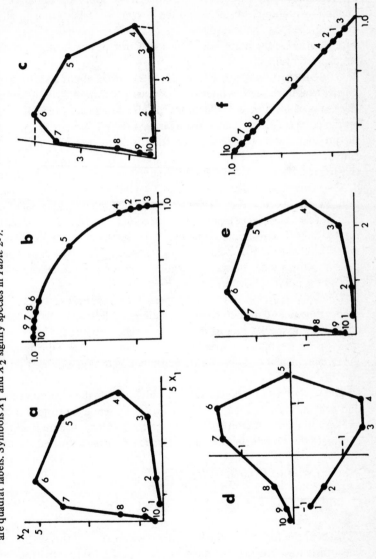

Fig. 2-2. The effect of transformations implicit in resemblance functions on the joint distribution of species. *Legend to figures:* (a) no transformation; (b) normalization within quadrat vectors; (c) oblique axes; (d) standardization within the components; (e) standardization within species; (f) transformation to unit sum within quadrats. Numbers inside diagrams are quadrat labels. Symbols X_1 and X_2 signify species in *Table 2-7.*

57

2. The *chord length* (formula 2.2)) is different in this respect because it incorporates normalization of the quadrat vectors. Because this has the effect of setting the length of each quadrat vector to unity, the net result is one of projecting the sample points onto the surface of some sphere (circle in two dimensions) of unit radius. The results of such a normalization are illustrated in Fig. 2-2b. It can be seen that it drastically alters the structure of the point configuration as the horseshoe-shaped sequence of points unfolds into a circular arrangement.

3. GENGERELLI's *distance* (formula (2.3)) brings about an infolding of the species axes until their obliqueness becomes proportional to the sample species correlations. Fig. 2-2c illustrates the effect of such an infolding of axes on the points. The angle enclosed by axes X_1, X_2 is arc cos S_{12} where S_{12} is the product moment correlation coefficient. In the example $S_{12} = 0.1841$ and arc cos $S_{12} = 79°23'$ approximately. Note that GENGERELLI's distance, if it has an effect, may exaggerate the curvature in the point configuration.

4. The *generalized distance* (formula (2.4)) incorporates a double transformation. Firstly, the axes X_1, X_2 are rigidly rotated to an orthogonal position Y_1, Y_2 (zero covariance). Secondly, the co-ordinates are standardized on the rotated axes. The rotation has no effect on the shape of the point configuration. The change in Fig. 2-2d, as compared to Fig. 2-2a, is a consequence of the standardization. The standardization does not seem to reduce the curvature of the point configuration.

5. When S_{hi} or q_{ik} are computed, representing expressions for the simple product moment correlation or its Q-equivalent defined by formulae (2.8) and (2.9), the species vectors are centered and normalized. The effect of these on the resemblance structure is seen from Fig. 2-2e. Obviously, here the strong original curvature in the point configuration is at least retained or possibly intensified.

6. The WHITTAKER transformation which adjusts the quadrat vectors to unit sum in formula (2.14) has the most drastic tendency toward increasing *linearity* in the point configuration (Fig. 2-2f). It may be convenient to incorporate this transformation in the Euclidean distance formula to obtain

$$u(j, k) = \left[\sum_h (X_{hj}/Q_j - X_{hk}/Q_k)^2 \right]^{1/2} \tag{2.38}$$

where

$$Q_j = \sum_h X_{hj} \text{ and } Q_k = \sum_h X_{hk}, \ h = 1, ..., p.$$

7. Whereas the functions which we already examined in this section measure linear distances, the *geodesic metric* of formula (2.16) is noted for nonlinearity. It resembles the chord distance of formula (2.2) in so far as it incorporates a similar polar projection of points onto a sphere or a circle. However, the geodesic metric differs from the chord distance in that it measures

58

the distance of points along the shorter arc rather than in the direction of the chord. In this way it can transform a very complex non-linearity in the point configuration into a simpler spherical non-linearity.

8. The foregoing resemblance functions are consistent in their transformations in the sense that they retain the same scale within the same sample. Formulae (2.29) and (2.31) *do not always* have this property and can change their scale depending on the objects compared. The lack of a uniform scale of measure can lead to a very peculiar situation under which formula (2.29) and (2.31) cannot uniquely describe a given point configuration. This means that as their scale keeps changing the points keep migrating through braod regions of the sample space. The actual migration of the point representing quadrat *1* in Table 2-7 under the influence of a changing scale in formula (2.29) due to the changing quantity Q_{1k} is traced by the scatter of positions in Fig. 2-3.

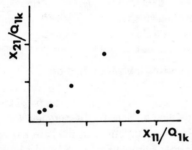

Fig. 2-3.   Migration of a point, representing quadrat *1* in *Table 2-7* in sample
space, under the influence of a changing scale in formula (2.29).
Point positions indicate comparisons with second, third, fourth,
etc., quadrats.

Each time Q_{1k} changes its value quadrat *1* also changes its position to occupy a different point in the diagram. For example, when quadrat *1* is compared to quadrat *2* for which $Q_{12} = Q_1 + Q_2 = 0.7 + 1.9 = 2.6$, quadrat *1* will be represented by a point whose co-ordinates are

$$Y_1 = X_{11}/Q_{12} = 0.6/2.6 = 0.231$$

$$Y_2 = X_{21}/Q_{12} = 0.1/2.6 = 0.039$$

These values accord with the transformations in formula (2.29). When, however, the comparison is with quadrat *3* the point representing quadrat *1* migrates to a new position marked by the new co-ordinates

$$Y_1 = X_{11}/Q_{13} = 0.6/5.3 = 0.113$$

$$Y_2 = X_{21}/Q_{13} = 0.1/5.3 = 0.019$$

The varying Y_1, Y_2 values as co-ordinates thus trace the positions of quadrat I in Fig. 2-3 in response to the changing sum Q_{Ik}. Functions that cause such a migration of points in sample space are throughly undesirable in data analysis. Here we refer to the discussion in section 2.5.

9. We may convert the *probabilistic index* of section 2.6 into a quadrat distance $\sqrt{2(1 - S_{jk})}$; but the resemblance structure which this distance imposes on the quadrats may bear little resemblance to the covariance structure which appears from the raw data. The reason is quite simply that this particular index uses the data only to derive probabilities which then impose a completely new structure on the sample. Similar considerations apply also to RAJSKI's *metric* in which the data is condensed into frequency distributions. These distributions redescribe the objects in a form suitable for computation of a metric information divergence. The other *information divergences* may also include such a condensation of the data into frequency distributions, with the case of categorical data representing an obvious exception, and impose on the sample a structure which can be radically different from the covariance.

2.10 Further Remarks on Resemblance Functions

The preceding treatment of resemblance functions provides a convenient framework of reference within which the ecologist can consider, categorize and evaluate still other resemblance functions which have not been discussed in this monograph. In this connection we refer to articles by ČEŠKA (1968), ORLÓCI (1972) and GOODALL (1973) which treat resemblance functions and discuss also certain ecological applications.

For the ecologist computation of a resemblance value may not represent a goal in itself. Often such values provide input in different analyses such as classification, ordination, etc. It is reasonable then to require the resemblance functions, to be admissible in ecological work, to satisfy several criteria such as:

1. Meaningfulness in mathematical as well as ecological terms.
2. Uniform scale of measure.
3. Desired probabilistic properties.
4. Reasonable computational load.

In any method of data analysis the resemblance function must be mathematically meaningful. But by meeting the conditions of mathematical meaningfulness, the function may not necessarily be desired in ecological terms. Formula (2.1) is an eclatant example in this connection; while it represents a mathematically meaningful formulation, it has only limited usefulness in ecological applications because it does not measure on a relative scale. The lack of such a scale can lead to anomalous situations which we have discussed in section 2.4.

When it comes to choosing a resemblance function for analysis the mathematical properties may remove certain functions from consideration. The changing scale, which we discussed in connection with formulae (2.29) and (2.31), weighs heavily in our decisions. Once a function is identified as one having a variable scale dependent on the objects being compared, it may be completely pointless even to consider ecological meaningfulness or other aspects related to applications. The scale of measure whether absolute or relative, linear or non-linear, is another important internal property. Classifications of the same set of qaudrats, for example when based on formula (2.1) in which the scale is absolute, may produce drastically different clusters than another classification which is based on formula (2.2) in which the scale is relative.

In ecology resemblance functions more often than not are subjected to non-statistical uses. This is particularly so in classifications whose goal is cluster recognition. Quite often, however, classificatory analyses try to find the class which represents a most likely parent population for a particular individual. This is clearly a statistical problem requiring the probabilistic use of resemblance functions. There is though one big problem with the statistical uses of resemblance functions: we rarely know exactly the types of sampling distributions with which they should be associated. The generalized distance is an example for the opposite with known sampling distirbution under random sampling in a multivariate normal population. But functions which do not qualify as probabilistic measures because of the circumstances of sampling and data collection may still be used as efficient mathematical descriptors of the vegetation. Such a deterministic use of resemblance functions is most common in ecological practice.

The need for heavy computations may rule out the use of some resemblance functions. RAJSKI's metric and the generalized distance are two examples of computationally difficult functions. They are not normally contemplated for longhand calculations, and in larger samples they cannot even be attempted if a suitable computer is unavailable.

It is hardly possible to lay down strict guidelines for the selection of resemblance functions. The foregoing discussions should nevertheless prove helpful in the search for the right kind of resemblance function. It may be added that the ecologist should select resemblance functions of known properties and try to *avoid* those not sufficiently described or understood. Functions of known probability distributions should be preferred provided that they have an appropriate scale of measure and that the computations are not inhibiting.

Keeping in mind the foregoing points about resemblance functions we turn in the next chapter to a discussion of ordinations and their uses in vegetation studies.

2.11 References

BASHARIN, G.P. 1959. On a statistical estimate for the entropy of a sequence of independent random variables. *Theory Prob. Applic.* 4: 333-336.

BEALS, E.W. 1960. Forest bird communities in the Apostle Islands of Wisconsin. *The Wilson Bulletin* 72: 156-181.

BEALS, E.W. 1965. Ordination of some corticolous cryptogamic communities in south-central Wisconsin. *Oikos* 16: 1-8.

BRAY, J.R. & J.T. CURTIS. 1957. An ordination of the upland forest communities of southern Wisconsin. *Ecol. Monogr.* 27: 325-349.

ČEŠKA, A. 1968. Application of association coefficients for estimating the mean similarity between sets of vegetational relevés. *Folia geobot. phytotax. Praha* 3: 57-64.

GENGERELLI, J.A. 1963. A method for detecting subgroups in a population and specifying their membership. *J. Psychology* 55: 457-468.

GOODALL, D.W. 1964. A probabilistic similarity index. *Nature* 203: 1098.

GOODALL, D.W. 1966. A new similarity index based on probability. *Biometrics* 22: 882-907.

GOODALL, D.W. 1973. Sample similarity and species correlation. *In*: R.H. WHITTAKER (ed.), *Handbook of Vegetation Science*, Vol. V, pp. 105-156. The Hague, W. Junk.

GOWER, J. 1971. A general coefficient of similarity and some of its properties. *Biometrics* 27: 857-871.

KULLBACK, S. 1959. *Information Theory and Statistics.* New York, Wiley, Chapman and Hall.

MAHALANOBIS, P.C. 1936. On the generalized distance in statistics. *Proc. Nat. Inst. Sci. India* 2: 49-55.

OCHIAI, A. 1957. Zoogeographic studies on the soleoid fishes found in Japan and its neighbouring regions. *Bull. Jap. Soc. Sci. Fish.* 22: 526-530.

ORLÓCI, L. 1967. An agglomerative method for classification of plant communities. *J, Ecol.* 55: 193-205.

ORLÓCI, L. 1972. On objective functions of phytosociological resemblance. *Am. Midl. Nat.* 88: 28-55.

PIETSCH, W. & W.R. MULLER-STOLL. 1968. Die Zwergbinsen-Gesellschaft der nackten Teichboden im ostlichen Mitteleuropa, Eleocharito – Caricetum bohemicae. *Mitt. Flor. – soz. Arbeitsgem. N.F.* 13: 14-47.

RÉNYI, A. 1961. On measures of entropy and information. *In:* J. NEYMAN (ed.), *Proceedings of the 4th Berkeley Symposium on Mathematical Statistics and Porbability,* Vol. 1, pp. 547-561. Berkeley – Los Angeles, Univ. Calif. Press.

SHANNON, C.E. 1948. A methemathical theory of communication. *Bell System Tech. J.* 27: 379-423, 623-656.

SOKAL, R.R. & C.D. MICHENER. 1958. A statistical method for evaluating systematic relationships. *Univ. Kansas Sci. Bull.* 38: 1409-1438.

SNEATH, P.H.A. & R.R. SOKAL. 1973. *Numerical Taxonomy.* San Francisco, Freeman.

SOKAL, R.R. & P.H.A. SNEATH. 1963. *Principles of Numerical Taxonomy.* San Francisco, Freeman.

WHITTAKER, R.H. 1952. A study of summer foliage insect communities in the Great Smoky Mountains. *Ecol. Monogr.* 22: 1-44.

WILLIAMS, E.J. 1952. Use of scores for the analysis of association in contingency tables. *Biometrika*, 39: 274-289.

III. ORDINATIONS

Once we impose on the sample a certain resemblance structure by a suitably chosen resemblance function, our further choice of method may be ordination. In this chapter we consider the different objectives that call for ordination, describe different methods and outline the conditions of their application. We shall see that ordinations, contrary to popular belief, represent no 'general preference' methods for data analysis, but rather, they are techniques specifically designed to serve certain narrow objectives.

3.1 Ordination Objectives

Ordination methods have been put to many uses in vegetation studies to achieve different goals. Among these:
1. Summarization.
2. Multidimensional scaling.
3. Trend seeking.
4. Reciprocal ordering.
Summatization means reduction of dimensionality in the data for the purpose of convenient handling and interpretations. Summarization is regarded efficient when the reduction is as great as possible without loss of information. To elaborate on this point further let us consider a sample of 20 quadrats described on the basis of 100 species. When we visualize the quadrats as a cluster of 20 points in a space of 100 dimensions it is not too difficult to realize that such a representation must be inherently redundant because it requires 100 dimensions to represent a point cluster whose intrinsic dimensionality cannot be more than 19. Summarization should remove the redundant dimensions and produce a parsimonious representation of the points in a space of dimensions equal to the number of intrinsic dimensions in the cluster. When a summarization succeeds in reducing the sample's dimensionality to the number of intrinsic dimensions it is said to be efficient. *Multidomensional scaling* extracts from the data *new* co-ordinates for individuals from a matrix of similarity values or distances. Although multidimensional scaling as a method may be implicit in any ordination, as an objective it is really limited to those rare circumstances where co-ordinate data do not exist initially. *Trend seeking* is concerned with the discovery and simple representation of trends in vegetational variation and their correlation with environmental variables. In *reciprocal ordering* the direct objective is to arrange stands into a definite order based on species scores, indicating optima on an environmental gradient or co-ordinates extracted from a particular species scalar product matrix. Either of these objectives calls for suitable methods, the choice of which will greatly depend on the data structure.

3.2 Data Structures

Fig. 3-1 illustrates two basic types of data structure. In the *linear case* (a) the

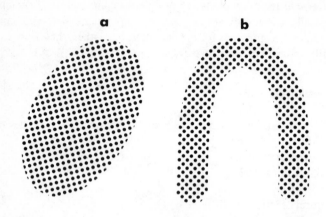

Fig. 3-1. Linear and non-linear point clusters.

points fill out an ellipse, and in the *non-linear* case (b) they fall into a curved area. In higher dimensions the points would fill out a hyper-volume, or fall on the surface of some manifold which could turn and twist through space in any regular or irregular fashion.

It is reasonable to suspect on the basis of Fig. 3-1 that there may be a connection between the shape of the point cluster and the relationship of some variables as axes. We can postulate that linear clusters associate with linear correlations of the variables, and non-linear clusters with correlations that have in addition a non-linear component. To complicate matters, a non-linear correlation can have a linear component, or a linear and non-linear cluster may both have the same underlying linear correlation structure, in spite of their differences in point arrangement.

In certain ordinations, which rely on the analysis of linear correlations, one may regard two clusters of points as identical if their linear correlation structures are identical, even if they happen to differ in other important respects. This does not mean that such kind of ordinations cannot be used to represent non-linear point clusters. They actually can, which will be shown, but such representations are likely to prove inefficient because the ordination axes do not respond to non-linear correlations.

To be regarded as efficient, an ordination must represent a given data structure in the fewest possible dimensions. In the linear case, efficiency is achieved by making the axes linearly independent. In the non-linear case the interpretation of efficiency is somewhat more complicated because it may mean different things depending on the existing non-linearity. For instance, if there is a single continuous cluster of points, which may turn and twist through space essentially in a single dimension, efficiency could mean that the ordination axis turns and twists exactly the same way. In other words, an efficient ordination finds the best fitting path through the cluster and represents it by a suitable curved axis. When, however, the points fall on the surface of a manifold, efficiency would have to be defined differently. It may mean finding a simple curved surface, or a suitable set of curved axes, on which the cluster of points can be most efficiently unfolded or flattened.

3.3 Summarization

When all sample points fall into a single linear cluster, and if the objective is to summarize such a structure on axes, thereby reducing it to some simpler form better suited for handling and analysis, *component analysis* is indicated. Component analysis is an efficient summarizer because it extracts components, which, unlike the species, are uncorrelated and thus free from the redundancies attributable to linear correlations. Because the components are not redundant fewer are needed for instance to completely redescribe a set of quadrats than the number of species on which the original descriptions are based.

It appears that the method of component analysis is a direct outgrowth of HOTELLING's (1933) work with correlation matrices. However, the modern applications are rarely associated with the correlation matrix, but rather with the covariance, or equivalently, with the Euclidean distance. Because the covariance and the correlation are efficient descriptors only of linear data structures, component analysis will be an efficient summarizer when the data structure is linear. A separate aspect of linearity is obvious in the basic model of component analysis

$$Y_{ij} = \sum_h b_{hi} X_{hj} = b_{1i} X_{1j} + ... + b_{pi} X_{pj} \tag{3.1}$$

This specifies linear transformations of species quantities (or other variates) $X_{1j}, ..., X_{pj}$ which yield the *component score* Y_{ij} for quadrat j. The component score Y_{ij} can be used as a rectangular co-ordinate on the ith component representing an axis. The coefficients $b_{1i}, ..., b_{pi}$, relating the species to the ith component, are called *component coefficients*. As direction cosines they satisfy the condition $\mathbf{b}_i' \mathbf{b}_i = b_{1i}^2 + ... + b_{pi}^2 = 1$. The symbol $\mathbf{b}_i$ represents the ith column vector in matrix $\mathbf{B}$ (given below) and $\mathbf{b}_i'$ is its transpose.

Given a set of raw observations, component analysis extracts component coefficients for the species and component scores for the quadrats. When there are p species in the collection, and t is the number of intrinsic dimensions in the sample, the transformations based on formula (3.1) require $p \times t$ component coefficients,

$$\mathbf{B} = \begin{bmatrix} b_{11} & b_{12} & ... & b_{1t} \\ b_{21} & b_{22} & ... & b_{2t} \\ . & . & ... & . \\ b_{p1} & b_{p2} & ... & b_{pt} \end{bmatrix}$$

We should note that as far as the computations are concerned the column vectors in $\mathbf{B}$ represent the normalized eigenvectors $b_1, ..., b_t$ associated with the eigenvalues $\lambda_1, ..., \lambda_t$ of the covariance (or correlation) matrix $\mathbf{S}$. Keeping in mind that the direct computational objectives include the component coefficients and component scores, we shall turn to an example to illustrate the computational steps while we refer to PCAR in the Appendix as our computer program:

1. The vegetation sample to be analyzed contains two species given as row vectors in the matrix

$$\mathbf{X} = \begin{bmatrix} X_{11} & X_{12} & X_{13} & X_{14} & X_{15} \\ X_{21} & X_{22} & X_{23} & X_{24} & X_{25} \end{bmatrix} = \begin{bmatrix} 2 & 5 & 2 & 1 & 0 \\ 0 & 1 & 4 & 3 & 1 \end{bmatrix}$$

The columns of $\mathbf{X}$ represent quadrats.

2. We may decide at this point to proceed on the basis of the correlation coefficient or the covariance. It is relevant to our choice that if the variables were given in widely different units their linear compounds (formula (3.1)) would not be particularly meaningful. Standardization would be required in a manner implicit in the correlation coefficient. While such a standardization would no doubt be preferred by some ecologists when the variables are measured in different units there may be many other ecologists who would rather implement scaling by the range. Still others could argue that the unit of measure is an intrinsic, logically inseparable property of the variables, and on this ground, express their objections to standardization by any method. When, in the ecologist's opinion, standardization is not required, the use of the covariance is indicated. In the present example we opt for the covariance.

3. The covariance matrix for the two species in $\mathbf{X}$ is given by

$$\mathbf{S} = \begin{bmatrix} S_{11} & S_{12} \\ S_{21} & S_{22} \end{bmatrix} = \begin{bmatrix} 3.5 & -0.5 \\ -0.5 & 2.7 \end{bmatrix}$$

4. When there are only two species in the sample longhand computations are quite feasible. But should the sample be large we would not proceed without having access to a digital computer. One of the longhand methods is based on solving equations. Firstly, we solve the determinantal equation

$$\begin{vmatrix} 3.5 - \lambda & -0.5 \\ -0.5 & 2.7 - \lambda \end{vmatrix} = (3.5 - \lambda)(2.7 - \lambda) - (-0.5)(-0.5)$$

$$= \lambda^2 - 6.2\lambda + 9.2 = 0$$

to obtain two eigenvalues (roots),

$$\lambda_1 = (-b + \sqrt{(b^2 - 4ac)})/2a = (6.2 + \sqrt{(6.2^2 - (4)(9.2))})/2$$
$$= (6.2 + 1.28)/2 = 3.74$$
$$\lambda_2 = (6.2 - 1.28)/2 = 2.46$$

Next, we solve the characteristic equation

$$S\,b_1 = \lambda_1 b_1$$

which can be written in the form of

$$\begin{bmatrix} 3.5 & -0.5 \\ -0.5 & 2.7 \end{bmatrix} \begin{bmatrix} b_{11} \\ b_{21} \end{bmatrix} = \lambda_1 \begin{bmatrix} b_{11} \\ b_{21} \end{bmatrix}$$

This gives rise to two equations,

$$3.5\,b_{11} - 0.5\,b_{21} = 3.74\,b_{11}$$
$$-0.5\,b_{11} + 2.7\,b_{21} = 3.74\,b_{21}$$

which can be reduced to

$$-0.24\,b_{11} - 0.5\,b_{21} = 0$$
$$-0.5\,b_{11} - 1.04\,b_{21} = 0$$

and further to

$$-0.74\,b_{11} - 1.54\,b_{21} = 0$$

Through simple rearrangement of terms we obtain

$$b_{11} = -\frac{1.54}{0.74} b_{21}$$

This relation specifies the size of b_{11} relative to b_{21}. Based on this relationship the normalized eigenvector $\mathbf{b}_1$ corresponding to the largest eigenvalue λ_1 has the solution

$$\mathbf{b}_1 = \begin{bmatrix} b_{11} \\ b_{21} \end{bmatrix} = k_1 \begin{bmatrix} -2.081 \\ 1 \end{bmatrix} = 1/\sqrt{(2.081^2+1)} \begin{bmatrix} -2.081 \\ 1 \end{bmatrix} = \begin{bmatrix} -0.901 \\ 0.433 \end{bmatrix}$$

Note that the condition $\mathbf{b}_1' \mathbf{b}_1 = 1$ is satisfied (within rounding errors).

Having determined the first set of component coefficients associated with λ_1, we proceed to determining the component coefficients associated with λ_2. The characteristic equation to be solved is given by

$$\mathbf{S}\,\mathbf{b}_2 = \lambda_2\,\mathbf{b}_2$$

The solution specifies relative sizes,

$$b_{12} = \frac{0.26}{0.54} b_{22}$$

The eigenvector $\mathbf{b}_2$ then has the solution

$$\mathbf{b}_2 = \begin{bmatrix} b_{12} \\ b_{22} \end{bmatrix} = k_2 \begin{bmatrix} 0.481 \\ 1 \end{bmatrix} = 1/\sqrt{(0.481^2 + 1)} \begin{bmatrix} 0.481 \\ 1 \end{bmatrix} = \begin{bmatrix} 0.433 \\ 0.901 \end{bmatrix}$$

The solution satisfies the condition $\mathbf{b}_2' \mathbf{b}_2 = 1$ (within rounding errors).
5. We summarize the results in a table,

Eigenvalues

$\lambda_1 = 3.74$	$\lambda_2 = 2.46$

Eigenvectors

$\mathbf{b}_1$	$\mathbf{b}_2$
−0.901	0.433
0.433	0.901

Note that the sum of the eigenvalues is 6.2 equal to the sum of species variances $S_{11} + S_{22}$. The efficiency of the components with which they individually account for variation in the sample is $E_1 = 100 \dfrac{3.74}{6.2} = 60.3\%$ and $E_2 = 100 \dfrac{2.46}{6.2} = 39.7\%$.

6. When we compute the component scores we may have to rewrite formula (3.1) in terms of

$$Y_{ij} = \mathbf{A}'_j\mathbf{b}_i = \sum_h b_{hi} A_{hj} = b_{1i} A_{1j} + ... + b_{pi} A_{pj} \qquad (3.2)$$

where $\mathbf{A}'_j$ is a transpose of $\mathbf{A}_j$ whose elements we define depending on the definition of $\mathbf{S}$. When $\mathbf{S}$ is the covariance matrix the elements of $\mathbf{A}$ accord with $A_{hj} = (X_{hj} - \bar{X}_h)/\sqrt{(n-1)}$. With such a definition of $\mathbf{A}$ the solution for Y_{ij} based on formula (3.2) will differ from formula (3.1) only by a factor of $1/\sqrt{(n-1)}$. The translation $X_{hj} - \bar{X}_h$ is not essential, it only shifts the origin of the co-ordinate system. Let us now consider the computations based on formula (3.2):

a. Adjust the data to obtain

$$\mathbf{A} = \begin{bmatrix} A_{11} & A_{12} & A_{13} & A_{14} & A_{15} \\ A_{21} & A_{22} & A_{23} & A_{24} & A_{25} \end{bmatrix} = \begin{bmatrix} 0.0 & 1.5 & 0.0 & -0.5 & -1.0 \\ -0.9 & -0.4 & 1.1 & 0.6 & -0.4 \end{bmatrix}$$

b. Compute the component scores,

$$Y_{11} = (-0.901)(0.0) + (0.433)(-0.9) = -0.390$$

$$Y_{21} = (0.433)(0.0) + (0.901)(-0.9) = -0.811$$

The component scores for other quadrats are similarly computed. The complete set of results is given below:

Component (ordination axis)	Component score (co-ordinate)					Eigenvalue
	1	2	3	4	5	
Y_1	−0.390	−1.525	0.476	0.711	0.728	3.74
Y_2	−0.811	0.289	0.991	0.324	−0.793	2.46

The sum of squared component scores is equal on each component to the associated eigenvalue (within rounding errors in the example). The component scores are rectangular ordination co-ordinates and can be plotted accordingly to form a scatter diagram (Fig. 3-2). Such a diagram shows the joint distribution of the components.

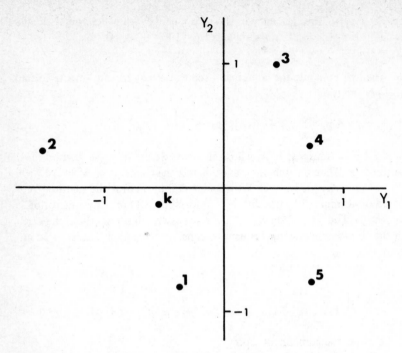

Fig. 3-2. Scatter diagram showing the joint distribution of components.

Further manipulations are likely to be performed on the results in most component analyses. These may include computation of:

1. *Correlation of species h with component i.* We compute this according to the formula

$$r_{hi} = (b_{hi}\sqrt{\lambda_i})/S_{hh}$$

where r_{hi} is the product moment correlation coefficient, b_{hi} a component co-efficient, λ_i an eigenvalue, and S_{hh} the variance of species h. Considering the species in the example we have their correlations with the first and second components,

$$r_{11} = -0.901\sqrt{3.74}/3.5 = -0.931$$

$$r_{21} = 0.433/\sqrt{3.74}/2.7 = 0.510$$

$$r_{12} = 0.433\sqrt{2.46}/3.5 = 0.363$$

$$r_{22} = 0.901\sqrt{2.46}/2.7 = 0.860$$

2. *Placing new quadrats in a scatter diagram.* If the new quadrat is specified by the vector

$$\mathbf{X}_k = \begin{bmatrix} X_{1k} \\ X_{2k} \end{bmatrix} = \begin{bmatrix} 3 \\ 1 \end{bmatrix}$$

for which the A-type data is given by

$$\mathbf{A}_k = \begin{bmatrix} A_{1k} \\ A_{2k} \end{bmatrix} = \begin{bmatrix} \dfrac{3-2}{\sqrt{(5-1)}} \\ \dfrac{1-1.8}{\sqrt{(5-1)}} \end{bmatrix}$$

the ordination co-ordinates are found to be

$$Y_{1k} = (-0.901)(0.5) + (0.433)(-0.4) = -0.624$$

$$Y_{2k} = (0.433)(0.5) + (0.901)(-0.4) = -0.144$$

The co-ordinates Y_{1k} and Y_{2k} determine point k in Fig. 3-2.

2. *Correlation between component i and environmental variable E.* The computation accords with formula

$$r_{Ei} = \sum_j (X_{Ej} - \bar{X}_E) \, Y_{ij} / ((n-1)^2 \, S_E^2 \lambda_i)^{1/2} \, , \; j = 1, ..., n$$

This formula requires n values for variable E, the mean $\bar{X}_E$, the variance S_E^2, n component scores Y_{ij}, and the eigenvalue λ_i.

4. *Canonical correlation analysis.* Based on this we can determine the simultaneous linear correlation of components and a given set of environmental variables.

5. *Mapping.* Environmental or vegetational characteristics may be mapped on scatter diagrams to reveal existing trends.

The algorithm in the foregoing example, which will be designated as the *R-algorithm,* has the specific advantage of providing component coefficients before it yields component scores. The component coefficients can facilitate mapping of new individuals onto the scatter diagram or computing various correlation quantities. When no objectives call for the computation of component coefficients, the component scores may be obtained more simply in other algorithms. In this connection we shall consider two alternatives:

1. *The Q-algorithm.* To develop this algorithm we follow ORLÓCI (1967). We begin with defining the scalar product matrix $\mathbf{S} = \mathbf{A} \mathbf{A}'$. In this $\mathbf{A}$ contains the adjusted or standardized data. We then define the characteristic equation of

71

$\mathbf{A}\mathbf{A}'$ as $\mathbf{A}\mathbf{A}'\mathbf{b}_i = \lambda_i\mathbf{b}_i$ in which $\mathbf{b}_i$ and λ_i represent respectively the ith eigenvector and the ith eigenvalue of $\mathbf{A}\mathbf{A}'$. After pre-multiplying both sides by $\mathbf{A}'$ we obtain $\mathbf{A}'\mathbf{A}(\mathbf{A}'\mathbf{b}_i) = \lambda_i(\mathbf{A}'\mathbf{b}_i)$. Here $\mathbf{A}'\mathbf{A}$ is an $n \times n$ matrix $\mathbf{Q}$ with elements q_{jk} defined according to formula (2.9) and $\mathbf{A}'\mathbf{b}_i$ is the ith eigenvector of $\mathbf{A}'\mathbf{A}$; this contains after adjustments the component scores on the ith component. Because $\mathbf{A}'_j\mathbf{b}_i$ is the same quantity as Y_{ij} in formula (3.2) the component scores obtained from $\mathbf{Q}$ or $\mathbf{S}$ are one and the same. Based on these relations we can compute component scores for quadrats from matrix $\mathbf{Q}$ as follows:

a. Compute a scalar product matrix according to formula (2.9) to obtain an $n \times n$ matrix $\mathbf{Q}$.

b. Determine the non-zero eigenvalues $(\lambda_1 \ldots \lambda_t)$ and associated eigenvectors $(\mathbf{Y}_1 \ldots \mathbf{Y}_t)$ of $\mathbf{Q}$.

c. Adjust the elements in the eigenvectors so that any eigenvector $\mathbf{Y}_i$ will satisfy the condition $\mathbf{Y}'_i\mathbf{Y}_i = Y^2_{1i} + \ldots + Y^2_{ni} = \lambda_i$. The elements $(Y_{1i} \ldots Y_{ni})$ in $\mathbf{Y}_i$ are the component scores for n quadrats on component i.

2. *The D-algorithm.* We can develop this algorithm most simply through a numerical example. For this we have two quadrats j and k with data vectors

$$\mathbf{X}_j = \begin{bmatrix} 3 \\ 4 \end{bmatrix} \text{ and } \mathbf{X}_k = \begin{bmatrix} 8 \\ 4 + \sqrt{11} \end{bmatrix}$$

Matrix $\mathbf{Q}$ is generated based on formula (2.9),

$$\mathbf{Q} = \begin{bmatrix} 9 & -9 \\ -9 & 9 \end{bmatrix}$$

and matrix $\mathbf{D}$ based on formula (2.1)

$$\mathbf{D} = \begin{bmatrix} 0 & 6 \\ 6 & 0 \end{bmatrix}$$

The elements of $\mathbf{Q}$ and $\mathbf{D}$ are related (formula (2.11)),

$$d^2(j, k) = q_{jj} + q_{kk} - 2q_{jk} = 9 + 9 + 18 = 36$$

or in the reverse

$$q_{jk} = -0.5\, d^2(j, k) + (q_{jj} + q_{kk})/2 = -18 + 9 = -9$$

It is reasonable to suspect after observing the relationship of $\mathbf{Q}$ and $\mathbf{D}$ that when subjected to analysis they will yield related component scores. To verify this

72

let us perform on Q and D the following analysis:

a. Compute

$$D^* = \begin{bmatrix} 0 & -18 \\ -18 & 0 \end{bmatrix}$$

with an element defined according to $-0.5 \, d^2 \, (j,k)$.

b. From the determinantal equation of D^*,

$$\begin{vmatrix} 0-\lambda & -18 \\ -18 & 0-\lambda \end{vmatrix} = \lambda^2 - 324 = 0$$

we find $\lambda = 18$.

c. From the determinantal equation of Q

$$\begin{vmatrix} 9-\lambda & -9 \\ -9 & 9-\lambda \end{vmatrix} = \lambda^2 - 18\lambda = 0$$

we have $\lambda_1 = (18 + \sqrt{324})/2 = 18$ and $\lambda_2 = (18 - \sqrt{324})/2 = 0$. Note that in this example D^* has a single non-zero positive eigenvalue, which happens to be identical to the single non-zero positive eigenvalue of Q. The reader can verify on the basis of other examples that irrespective of the order of Q and D^* their non-zero positive eigenvalues are identical.

d. The characteristic equation of D^*, $0b_{11} - 18b_{21} = 18b_{11}$, indicates that $-b_{21} = b_{11}$. Using the constraint $b_1' b_1 = b_{11}^2 + b_{21}^2 = \lambda$ we find

$$b_1 = \begin{bmatrix} b_{11} \\ b_{21} \end{bmatrix} = \begin{bmatrix} 3 \\ -3 \end{bmatrix}$$

The characteristic equation of Q, $9b_{11} - 9b_{21} = 18b_{11}$, reduces to $-9b_{21} = 9b_{11}$ and therefore $-b_{21} = b_{11}$. Under constraint of $b_{11}^2 + b_{21}^2 = \lambda$ we find

$$b_1 = \begin{bmatrix} b_{11} \\ b_{21} \end{bmatrix} = \begin{bmatrix} 3 \\ -3 \end{bmatrix}$$

This is the only non-zero eigenvector of Q. We conclude from these that Q and D^* have not only identical eigenvalues but also identical eigenvectors. The reader can compute other examples to find that regardless of the order of D^* and Q their eigenvectors associated with their non-zero positive eigenvalues are identical.

73

We now summarize the D-algorithm with reference to program PCAD in the Appendix:

a. Compute matrix $\mathbf{D}^*$ with elements $-0.5\, d^2(j, k)$ where $d^2(j, k)$ is a squared Euclidean distance.

b. Extract all non-zero positive eigenvalues $\lambda_1, ..., \lambda_2$ and associated eigenvectors $\mathbf{b}_1, ..., \mathbf{b}_2$ of $\mathbf{D}^*$.

c. Adjust the eigenvectors $\mathbf{b}_1, ..., \mathbf{b}_t$ to conform to the condition $\mathbf{b}_i'\mathbf{b}_i = \lambda_i$ for any i. The elements in the eigenvectors so adjusted can be used as rectangular ordination co-ordinates. The similarity between the D- and Q-algorithm in steps b and c is obvious.

A direct implication of the foregoing results is that when quadrat distances are computed from the same data matrix, from which we could compute S or Q, we can obtain the same sets of component scores for the quadrats. It should however, be noted that whereas the R-algorithm produces component coefficients, these coefficients are not available in the Q- or D-algorithm. The computational load normally is greatest in the R-algorithm.

The statistical potential of estimation and hypothesis testing in component analysis (MORRISON, 1967) has not been fully utilized in vegetation studies. The reason is that it requires the assumption of multivariate normality in the data which the users have not been prepared to accept under most ecological applications. Nevertheless, if the data represent measurements of species quantity the assumption of multivariate normality may not be too unrealistic.

3.4 Multidimensional Scaling

Broadly speaking all ordinations perform multidimensional scaling when they derive co-ordinates for quadrats or other entities. In this sense all ordinations are methods for multidimensional scaling. But there are few examples where such a scaling would predominate the objectives.

In most vegetation studies the data are in co-ordinate form. When, for example, we describe quadrats based on species abundance, the abundance values can serve as co-ordinates. Such co-ordinates can be manipulated in one analysis or another as the need arises. However, the data may not always come in the form of co-ordinates. It is conceivable that under special circumstances *proximities or resemblances* are observed directly. The point to be made here is that if the data takes the form of resemblances we can analyse the data in few techniques without first extracting from the resemblances co-ordinates. The transformation which leads from resemblance matrix to co-ordinates may be described as *multidimensional scaling*. Regarding the choice of method, scaling techniques are preferred which can efficiently represent the observed data structure. Because the type of structure existing in the data is rarely known precisely, or even approximately prior to the analysis, it is often necessary to perform multidimensional scaling by different methods before satisfactory results are obtained.

The different methods of multidimensional scaling, which we describe below, have common assumptions: the data structure is *continuous and linear.* In other words the methods cannot respond to non-linear trends nor can they detect discontinuities in a sample. If we proceed under these assumptions with the analysis of a matrix S of resemblance values to obtain sets of co-ordinates such that the co-ordinate sets must be efficient summarizers of linear variation, S would have to be defined as a covariance matrix, a matrix of correlation coefficients, or distances which may be directly converted into covariances, and we could choose for our method component analysis. But S may represent a similarity matrix of some other kind, in which case our choice could be GOWER's (1966) method. This method, known as *principal axes analysis,* extracts rectangular co-ordinates from a distance matrix D^* with a characteristic element $S_{jk} - 1$ where S_{jk} is a similarity value in S, interpretable as a direction cosine, relating individuals j and k on a zero to one scale. The method of analysis is mathematically similar to the D-algorithm of component analysis, from which it differs by the definition of S_{jk}. Principal axes analysis flattens the sample into Euclidean planes with potential distortions. The distortion can be measured by the stress index $\sigma = 1 - \rho^2$ where ρ is the product moment correlation between the ordination distances and the corresponding elements in D^* or S.

The example to be outlined admittedly depicts a trivial situation in ecology; but it is simple and suitable to make several important points about applications. The data to be used are given in Table 3-1. Such data could originate

Table 3-1. Data from a soil survey

Soil variable	Site					
	1	*2*	*3*	*4*	*5*	*6*
pH	6.9	8.0	7.8	7.3	6.5	8.1
Calcium kg/ha	3200	6900	5700	6000	2800	6800
Potassium kg/ha	29	266	390	182	48	314
Nitrate N kg/ha	6	21	15	12	8	17
Vegetation type	G	M	M	L	G	M

in the course of any soil survey giving no vegetational details other than the names of vegetation types. If anything is to be concluded from data of this sort about the relationship of vegetation types and the environmental variables it is essential to quantify the information residing in the type affiliation of the sites.

When the surveyor identifies vegetation types he imposes upon the sites a certain kind of resemblance structure. This structure is conveniently described in matrix form with zeros and ones as elements, such as in

$$
S = \begin{array}{c|cccccc|c}
 & 1 & 2 & 3 & 4 & 5 & 6 & \\
\hline
 & 1 & 0 & 0 & 0 & 1 & 0 & 1 \\
 & 0 & 1 & 1 & 0 & 0 & 1 & 2 \\
 & 0 & 1 & 1 & 0 & 0 & 1 & 3 \\
 & 0 & 0 & 0 & 1 & 0 & 0 & 4 \\
 & 1 & 0 & 0 & 0 & 1 & 0 & 5 \\
 & 0 & 1 & 1 & 0 & 0 & 1 & 6 \\
\end{array}
$$

and site labels listed along the margins. A *one* in this matrix indicates sites of the same classification, and a *zero* designates sites of different classifications. From matrix S we derive matrix D^* by subtracting 1 from every element, and then proceed to extracting the eigenvalues and eigenvectors of D^*. When the eigenvectors are adjusted to make the sum of squared elements in each equal to the corresponding eigenvalue, the vector elements represent the rectangular ordination co-ordinates. These are given in Table 3-2. The co-ordinates repre-

Table 3-2. Co-ordinates and efficiency values in two methods of multidimensional scaling

Method[1]	Axis	Co-ordinates for site						λ_i	Efficiency[2]
		1	2	3	4	5	6		%
P.A.A.	Y_1	−0.724	0.678	0.678	−0.236	−0.724	0.678	2.483	64
P.V.O.	Y_1	−0.713	0.624	0.624	−0.445	−0.713	0.624	2.381	65
P.A.A.	Y_2	−0.379	−0.158	−0.158	0.960	−0.379	−0.158	1.284	34
P.V.O.	Y_2	0.463	0.000	0.000	−0.926	0.463	0.000	1.286	35

[1] P.A.A. − Principal axis analysis; P.V.O. − Position vectors ordination (described below)
[2] $100\, \lambda_i/Q$ where Q is the sum of all positive eigenvalues of matrix D^*

sent new data that can be put to further analysis.

The co-ordinates quantify the information which resides in the vegetation type affiliation of different sites. When these co-ordinates are correlated with the environmental variables the correlations may reveal, for instance, the value of the vegetation classification as a predictor of environmental conditions. The simple product moment correlation of Y_1 and Y_2 of P.A.A. in Table 3-2 with the four soil variables in Table 3-1 are given in the table below:

| Principal axis | pH | Soil variable | | N |
		Ca	K	
Y_1	0.799	0.587	0.811	0.818
Y_2	-0.588	-0.542	-0.395	-0.315

It can be seen that the correlations are rather high between the derived co-ordinates of sites on the first principal (vegetation) axis and the measured soil chemical properties. These results indicate that the vegetation types, even though a result of subjective determination, are highly indicative of the measured soil conditions. We can summarize the main points in this example as follows:

a. Estimates of resemblance represent the only source of information about the vegetation in the sites.

b. Resemblance values are analysed into rectangular co-ordinates which in turn are subjected to further analysis to reveal correlations between vegetation types and certain soil properties.

These co-ordinates may be extracted under the stipulated conditions of principal axes analysis more simply by other methods. *Position vectors ordination* (ORLÓCI, 1966) is one of them. It can provide close approximation to principal axes analysis under certain circumstances. To illustrate the technique we shall re-analyse matrix **S** of the preceeding section with the same objective in mind to derive rectangular co-ordinates for the sites using program PVO:

1. Compute on the basis of matrix **S** matrix $\mathbf{D}^*$ with elements $d^2(j, k) = 2(1 - S_{jk})$.

2. Derive matrix **Q** from $\mathbf{D}^*$ according to formula (2.12).

3. Complete position vectors ordination on matrix **Q**.

In steps 1 and 2 we obtain matrix $\mathbf{D}^*$,

$$\mathbf{D}^* = \begin{bmatrix} 0 & 2 & 2 & 2 & 0 & 2 \\ 2 & 0 & 0 & 2 & 2 & 0 \\ 2 & 0 & 0 & 2 & 2 & 0 \\ 2 & 2 & 2 & 0 & 2 & 2 \\ 0 & 2 & 2 & 2 & 0 & 2 \\ 2 & 0 & 0 & 2 & 2 & 0 \end{bmatrix}$$

the average of the squared distances per row (column),

$$
\begin{bmatrix} \overline{d_1^2} \\ \overline{d_2^2} \\ \overline{d_3^2} \\ \overline{d_4^2} \\ \overline{d_5^2} \\ \overline{d_6^2} \end{bmatrix} = \begin{bmatrix} 1.333 \\ 1.000 \\ 1.000 \\ 1.667 \\ 1.333 \\ 1.000 \end{bmatrix}
$$

and

$$
Q = \begin{bmatrix}
0.7222 & -0.4444 & -0.4444 & -0.1111 & 0.7222 & -0.4444 \\
-0.4444 & 0.3889 & 0.3889 & -0.2778 & -0.4444 & 0.3889 \\
-0.4444 & 0.3889 & 0.3889 & -0.2778 & -0.4444 & 0.3889 \\
-0.1111 & -0.2778 & -0.2778 & 1.0556 & -0.1111 & -0.2778 \\
0.7222 & -0.4444 & -0.4444 & -0.1111 & 0.7222 & -0.4444 \\
-0.4444 & 0.3889 & 0.3888 & -0.2778 & -0.4444 & 0.3889
\end{bmatrix}
$$

In position vectors ordination, similarly to principal axes analysis, the point configuration defined by S is flattened into Euclidean planes. The sites are defined in terms of position vectors which represent directed lines to the sites (as points) from the sample centroid (center of gravity of all points). The length of the jth position vector is $\sqrt{q_{jj}}$, and the quantity q_{jj} is the jj value in Q. The sum $q_{11} + \ldots + q_{nn}$ represents a measure of total variation in the sample. Position vectors ordination partitions the total variation into components on strategically selected axes. The first axis coincides with the position vector on which the sum of squared projections of all position vectors is maximum. This position vector is identified by the maximum property:

$$
\max \left[\sum_j q_{j1}^2 / q_{11}, \ldots, \sum_j q_{jn}^2 / q_{nn} \right], j = 1, \ldots, n
$$

If the maximum occurs on the mth vector, the first set of co-ordinates are given by:

$$
Y_1 = (q_{m1}/\sqrt{q_{mm}} \ldots q_{mn}/\sqrt{q_{mm}}) = (Y_{11} \ldots Y_{1n})
$$

The second set of co-ordinates cannot be obtained directly from the Q matrix. A residual matrix Q^* must be computed first. We obtain the elements in this matrix according to

$$
q_{jk}^* = q_{jk} - Y_{1j} Y_{1k}
$$

These are subjected to further manipulations to find

$$\max \left[\sum_j q_{j1}^{*2}/q_{11}^{*}, ..., \sum_j q_{jn}^{*2}/q_{nn}^{*} \right], \quad j = 1, ..., n$$

If the maximum occurs on the zth vector, the second set of co-ordinates are given by

$$\mathbf{Y}_2 = (q_{z1}^{*}/\sqrt{q_{zz}^{*}} ... q_{zn}^{*}/\sqrt{q_{zz}^{*}}) = (Y_{21} ... Y_{2n})$$

Any subsequent set of co-ordinates are determined from a subsequent residual of $\mathbf{Q}$ in the same manner. There will be altogether t sets of co-ordinates where t is equal to or slightly more than the number of independent dimensions in the sample. Considering the numerical values we find the $\sum_j q_{jk}^2/q_{kk}$ quantities and their maximum to be

$$\max (2.2821 \quad 2.3810 \quad 2.3810 \quad 1.2983 \quad 2.2821 \quad 2.3810) = 2.3810$$

To obtain for example the first term in this expression we compute

$$\sum_j q_{j1}^2/q_{11} = (0.7222^2 + (-0.4444)^2 + (-0.4444)^2 + (-0.1111)^2$$
$$+ 0.7722^2 + (-0.4444)^2)/0.7222 = 2.2821$$

The remaining quantities are computed similarly. The maximum indicates that we could select vector 2, 3 or 6 with the same outcome in the next step when we derive the co-ordinates $\mathbf{Y}_1$. These co-ordinates are given in Table 3-2. To obtain for example the fourth co-ordinate in $\mathbf{Y}_1$ we compute

$$Y_{14} = q_{24}/\sqrt{q_{22}} = -0.2778/0.6236 = -0.4455$$

The first residual $\mathbf{Q}^*$ consists of elements which are obtained by subtracting from an element of $\mathbf{Q}$ the product of the corresponding co-ordinates in $\mathbf{Y}_1$. For example, the residual of $q_{34} = -0.2778$ is given by

$$q_{34}^{*} = q_{34} - Y_{13}Y_{14} = -0.2778 - (0.6236)(-0.4455) = 0.0000$$

Another element say q_{14}^{*} is similarly computed,

$$q_{14}^{*} = q_{14} - Y_{11}Y_{14} = -0.1111 - (-0.7217)(-0.4455) = -0.4286$$

The entire set of residual elements is given in

$$
\begin{bmatrix}
0.2143 & 0.0000 & 0.0000 & -0.4286 & 0.2143 & 0.0000 \\
0.0000 & 0.0000 & 0.0000 & 0.0000 & 0.0000 & 0.0000 \\
0.0000 & 0.0000 & 0.0000 & 0.0000 & 0.0000 & 0.0000 \\
-0.4286 & 0.0000 & 0.0000 & 0.8572 & -0.4286 & 0.0000 \\
0.2143 & 0.0000 & 0.0000 & -0.4286 & 0.2143 & 0.0000 \\
0.0000 & 0.0000 & 0.0000 & 0.0000 & 0.0000 & 0.0000
\end{bmatrix}
$$

The next vector to be chosen as an ordination axis accords with

$$\max (1.2857 \quad 0.0000 \quad 0.0000 \quad 1.2857 \quad 1.2857 \quad 0.0000) = 1.2857$$

This species either the first, second, or third vector. We can select either of these vectors and obtain the second set of co-rodinates Y_2 (Table 3-2) in a similar manner as before. For example,

$$Y_{24} = q_{14}^*/\sqrt{q_{11}^*} = 0.4286/0.4629 = -0.9259$$

The second residual Q^{**} has no elements other than zero, indicating that the two axes completely describe variation in the sample.

Based on the results in Table 3-2 we can see a close resemblance between principal axes analysis and position vectors ordination. Experience suggests that the two methods tend to produce similar results in general when the number of sample points is reasonably large and when the points fall into a single cluster with reasonably uniform density. However, position vectors ordination is computationally less complex than principal axes analysis which in certain applications may compensate for the somewhat reduced efficiency in providing parsimonious lower dimensional representations.

Principal axes analysis and position vectors ordination are two of many possible methods which can perform multidimensional scaling; but the best known, and probably the least recommendable, of the scaling techniques is an ordination devised by BRAY & CURTIS (1957). Their method relies on ordination poles to determine the direction of the axes on which vegetation quadrats or other objects are ordered. This simple method attracted many users in the past, and even recently, there were some attempts to explain its advantages and to restore it to a role which it once played in vegetation ecology (GAUCH & WHITTAKER, 1972). In its original form, however, the BRAY & CURTIS method offers no real advantages, apart from computational simplicity and personal selection of poles. We shall elaborate on certain aspects of this method, which will show that it is a rather inefficient method for data reduction, and point out possible revisions in the mathematics while, at the same time, retaining the option of personal choice for ordination poles. At the roots of the problem are the resemblance function which often lacks a consistent scale, axes that are potentially oblique and non-intersecting, and a dubious method which produces scatter diagrams without taking into account the potential obliqueness of the ordination axes.

Past revisions (*e.g.* ORLÓCI, 1966; SWAN, DIX & WEHRHAHN, 1969; VAN DER MAAREL, 1969) went perhaps too far in a way by not retaining the option for personal selection of ordination poles which provided a handle on the method to those ecologists who have no need for automated ordinations. When the goal is a unidimensional scaling, the method needs some revisions:

1. Compute quadrat (stand) distances preferably on the basis of formula (2.2) or formula (2.38).
2. Designate two quadrats *A, B* as ordination poles.
3. Determine co-ordinates for the remaining quadrats in graphical manipulations of triangles as suggested by BRAY & CURTIS (1957), or follow BEAL's (1960) procedure in which co-ordinates are determined analytically.

When, however, the objective is a multidimensional ordination, the co-ordinates have to be determined by a method other than originally suggested by BRAY & CURTIS. The methodological problem of correcting for non-perpendicular axes in the scatter diagram construction simply requires projection of the ordination axes, specified by points *AB* and *CD*, orthogonally onto a given plane *M* which lies parallel to both of the axes. In such a projection the axes appear as intersecting oblique lines which, if required, can be rotated to perpendicular positions analytically. We describe below graphical and analytical solutions both for projection and rotation. In the descriptions we shall use symbols Y_1, Y_2 to designate axes. The numerical results will be derived from the distance values

		A	B	C	D	*j*
	A	0	1.20	0.84	0.96	0.93
C =	B		0	1.02	0.63	0.54
	C			0	0.90	0.84
	D				0	0.12

The elements in **C** define the distances between quadrats representing the ordination poles *A, B, C, D* and another quadrat designated by *j*. A realistic sample may of course contain more than just 5 quadrats; but the procedure would remain essentially the same. I recommend formula (2.2) or (2.38) as a definition for distance.

The graphical solution, as well as the analytical solution, assumes that the quadrat distances are Euclidean. The steps are described for Fig. 3-3 below:

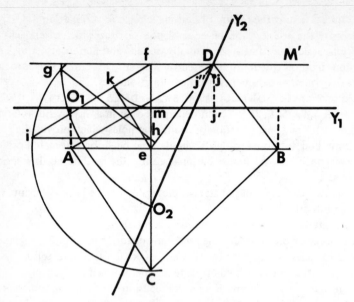

Fig. 3-3. Graphical solution for oblique axes in a modified
BRAY & CURTIS ordination.

1. Draw triangles ABC and ABD using distances from matrix **C**.
2. Draw line M' through point D parallel to line AB. M' is the trace of plane M on plane ABD.
3. Draw line through C perpendicular to M' to meet AB in e, and M' in f.
4. Draw arc with center in D and radius $c(C, D)$, the CD element in matrix **C**, to meet Cf in point O_2. The line Y_2 through D and O_2 is the projection image of axis Y_2 on M. The origin of Y_2 is in O_2.
   At this point we could draw a line through O_2 parallel to AB to obtain the Y_1 axis with origin O_1 in O_2. We could then proceed directly to step 10. However, it is possible to determine the exact projection of Y_1 on plane M by continuing with step 5:
5. Draw arc through C with center in e to meet the arc through O_2 in g.
6. Draw a line through g perpendicular to eD to meet Cf in h. Point h is the projection of quadrat C on plane ABD.
7. Draw hi parallel to AB to meet Cg in i. The length of line hi is the height of point C above plane ABD.
8. Draw ek perpendicular to fi and draw arc through k with center in f to meet Cf in m. Point m is the projection of e in AB on M.
9. Draw Y_1 through m parallel to AB. Line Y_1 is the second ordination axis.
10. Transfer Y_1 and Y_2 to a clear sheet of paper and plot points to represent their joint distribution.

Note that Y_1 and Y_2 are oblique lines; their origins are marked by O_1 and O_2. If so desired each axis may be moved parallel to itself until O_1 and O_2 fall in a common point. (This has not been done in Fig. 3-3).

The co-ordinates of quadrats on Y_1 can be determined graphically by actually drawing triangles, as in the original method, or on the basis of formula

$$Y_{1j} = (c^2(A, j) + c^2(A, B) - c^2(B, j)) \,/\, 2c(A, B) \tag{3.3}$$

For quadrat j we have

$$Y_{1j} = (0.93^2 + 1.2^2 - 0.54^2) \,/\, ((2)(1.2)) = 0.839$$

It is important to remember that the co-ordinates on the Y_2 axis are determined by formula

$$Y_{2j} = (c^2(C, j) + c^2(C, D) - c^2(D, j)) \,/\, 2c(C, D) \tag{3.4}$$

and *not* by BEALS' (1960) second formula which assumes that Y_1 and Y_2 are perpendicular. The Y_{2j} co-ordinate for quadrat j is thus obtained,

$$Y_{2j} = (0.84^2 + 0.9^2 - 0.12^2) \,/\, ((2)(0.9)) = 0.834$$

The point (Y_{1j}, Y_{2j}) is plotted in the scatter diagram according to the following steps:
1. Measure distance Y_{1j} from O_1 on Y_1 and mark the end of this distance by j'.
2; Measure a distance Y_{2j} from O_2 on Y_2 and mark the end of this distance by j''.
3. Draw a line through j' perpendicular to Y_1 and another line through j'' perpendicular to Y_2. These lines meet in j marking the projection of quadrat j as a point in the scatter diagram.

Other quadrats would be placed similarly in the scatter diagram. We note at this point that the outlined procedure can be extended to higher dimensions by analytical means; but then the arithmetic becomes somewhat involved and not presented here. We shall concentrate on the analytical solution of rotation. For this purpose we need to determine first the oblique angle α enclosed by the axes, and then consider the problem of transferring from oblique to rectangular co-ordinates. The oblique angle between the projections of Y_1 and Y_2 in plane M is given by

$$\cos \alpha = \overline{Df} \,/\, c(D, C)$$

where

$$\overline{Df} = |(c^2(A,D) + c^2(A,B) - c^2(D,B))/2c(A,B) - (c^2(A,C) + c^2(A, B)$$
$$- c^2(B,C))/2c(A,B)|$$
$$= |c^2(A,D) + c^2(B,C) - c^2(A,C) - c^2(D,B)| / 2c(A,B)$$

Using the numerical values in matrix **C**, we have

$$\overline{DF} = |0.96^2 + 1.02^2 - 0.84^2 - 0.63^2|/2.4 = 0.8595/2.4 = 0.358125$$

and

$$\cos \alpha = 0.358125/0.9 = 0.397917 \quad \text{and} \quad \alpha = 66°\ 33'\ 07''$$

We transfer from oblique to rectangular co-ordinates according to

$$Y_{2j}^* = Y_{2j} \sin \alpha \pm \Delta_j$$

where Y_{2j} is a co-ordinate based on formula (3.4) and Δ_j is a correction term defined by

$$\Delta_j = ||Y_{1j} - Y_{1C}| - Y_{2j} \cos \alpha |\ \text{tg}\ (90 - \alpha)$$

Note that we define absolute differences in this expression. Also note that Y_{1C} is the co-ordinate of quadrat C (the origin O_2) on the first axis. We declare Δ_j positive if the condition

$$Y_{2j} \sin \alpha > |Y_{1j} - Y_{1C}|\ \text{tg}\ \alpha \qquad (3.5)$$

is satisfied and negative if it is not. When the right and left sides are equal in formula (3.5) $\Delta_j = 0$. Based on the distances in **C** we have the numerical results,

$$Y_{1j} = 0.839$$
$$Y_{1C} = (c^2(A,C) + c^2(A,B) - c^2(B,C))/2c(A,B)$$
$$= (0.84^2 + 1.2^2 - 1.02^2)/2.4 = 1.105/2.4 = 0.461$$
$$Y_{2j} = 0.834$$
$$\cos \alpha = 0.397917$$
$$\text{tg}\ (90 - \alpha) = 0.433734$$

84

$$\Delta_j = \| \, 0.839 - 0.461 \, | - (0.834)(0.397917) | \, 0.433734 = 0.0204$$

$$\sin \alpha = 0.917421$$

$$\mathrm{tg}\,\alpha = 2.305556$$

Because

$$Y_{2j} \sin \alpha = 0.765 < | \, Y_{1j} - Y_{1C} | \, \mathrm{tg}\,\alpha = 0.872$$

we take Δ_j with negative sign and obtain a rectangular co-ordinate for j,

$$Y_{2j}^* = (0.834)(0.917421) - 0.0204 = 0.744$$

The procedure which we just outlined puts the construction of scatter diagrams on firm foundations consistent with the original objectives of the BRAY & CURTIS method. The ordination, however, still remains inefficient as a method for summarization because the axes are likely to be correlated.

We have seen already that in ordinations new co-ordinates are extracted on the basis of transformations either directly from a resemblance matrix or indirectly from the raw co-ordinate data. In the KRUSKAL (1964 a,b) method co-ordinates are derived from either of these sources by the use of a different method. Implicit in this method, similarly to the ordinations considered so far, is the assumption that all points in the sample fall into a single cluster with even density. If it is not so, information will be lost because there is no device given which could discriminate between several clusters should they actually occur in the sample. There are several versions of the KRUSKAL method (KRUSKAL & CARMONE, 1971). They all extract rectangular co-ordinates from the data under the condition that the ordination distances can be derived by monotone transformation from the observed resemblance values. To perform one version one proceeds through the following steps:
1. Specify t the maximum number of ordination axes to be extracted. Each axis will be associated with one set of n co-ordinates for the individuals to be ordinated.
2. Impose on the n individuals a resemblance structure by estimating their pairwise dissimilarities (or similarities). Designate the dissimilarity of individuals j, k by symbol $\delta(j, k)$ and the matrix of all $n \times n$ dissimilarities by Δ.
3. Determine the starting ordination configuration distances. This configuration is obtained by placing n points into a t-dimensional space based on n sets of t arbitrary co-ordinates. Designate the distance of individuals j, k by the symbol $d(j, k)$ and the matrix of all $n \times n$ distances in the ordination configuration by symbol D. At this point an iterative analysis begins.
4. Consider the joint distribution of $\delta(j, k)$ and $d(j, k)$ values as a scatter of

n points in the plane. Fit to the scatter the regression line $\hat{d}(j, k) = f(\delta(j, k))$. The regression performed is a least-squares regression of the ordination distances $d(j, k)$ on the observed resemblance values $\delta(j, k)$. The regression function to be used is chosen by the user. It may be linear or polynomial, normally not higher than degree 4.

5. After determining the regression coefficients, continue by computing a regression approximation for each $d(j, k)$ corresponding to $\delta(j, k)$, and designate the matrix of all $n \times n$ regression approximations by $\hat{\mathbf{D}}$.

6. Compute a value for the stress (distortion) in $\hat{\mathbf{D}}$ relative to $\mathbf{D}$ based on the KRUKSAL & CARMONE (1971) formula,

$$\sigma(\mathbf{D}; \hat{\mathbf{D}}) = \left[\sum_j \sum_k (d(j, k) - \hat{d}(j, k))^2 / \sum_j \sum_k (d(j, k) - \bar{d})^2 \right]^{1/2},$$
$$k > j = 1, ..., n-1$$

where $\bar{d}$ is the mean of the $d(j, k)$ values.

7. After computing stress, all points in the ordination configuration are moved a bit, i.e. their co-ordinates are changed a little, to decrease stress.

8. The procedure starting with a new regression analysis is repeated until finally the value of stress drops below a given threshold limit. The output of the analysis includes t sets of n rectangular co-ordinates which can be plotted jointly in two dimensional scatter diagrams.

KRUSKAL's method may be appealing to the ecologist for several reasons:
1. Extreme flexibility in handling resemblance functions of almost any kind.
2. Reliance on regression analysis the model of which is chosen by the user.
3. Derivation of an ordination configuration which is some pre-selected function of the data.
4. Probable potential in detecting non-linear trends when the regression function is appropriately chosen.

KRUSKAL (1964a) outlines an example which uses 15 points in the plane. The configuration is defined by $15(15 - 1)/2 = 105$ point distances for the elements of Δ. From the known Δ a Δ^* configuration is derived by a monotone distortion of the distances with an added random component. The results of the analysis on Δ^* indicate that the method can recover the Δ configuration with great accuracy. This then suggests that the KRUSKAL method may reveal effectively such structural features in vegetation data which do not readily appear because of random variation in the materials.

3.5 Further on Summarization

There is a great deal of work in progress on non-linear ordinations about which probably a great deal will be published in the future. It may very well happen that when more information comes to light about ordination representations of non-linear data structures our present categorization of some of the methods may have to be revised.

The linear models of ordination may not be suitable for summarizing vegetational data because there may be non-linear trends present to which a linear ordination cannot respond. The recognition of this problem is important, but the ecologist can do little about it because ordinations that can handle the analysis of non-linear data structures are very few in number and rather inefficient. Of the available methods those by SHEPARD & CARROLL (1966) and SNEATH (1965) appear to have broader potential.

The point cluster in Fig. 3-1b represents a trivial example where a non-linear trend can be readily recognized on first inspection. A curve could be fitted to the points with no great difficulty, the points could be projected on the curve, and the projections could be used as ordination co-ordinates. However, in more realistic situations the problem can get greatly complicated if the intrinsic dimensionality of the point cluster exceeds two or three. In such higher dimensions visual inspection will not suffice. We need other methods for representing non-linear point clusters of such higher complexity. One has been suggested by SNEATH (1965). His method seeks out groups of points in a discontinuous sample space, finds the best fitting curve in each, and uses the curves as ordination axes. The input data consists of rectangular co-ordinates.

When the objective of the analysis is to establish a curved co-ordinate system which does for non-linear data structures what component analysis or other linear ordinations do for linear data structures, SHEPARD & CARROLL (1966) suggest continuity analysis. There are two specific assumptions at the basis of their method:

1. The data structure is continuous but the single cluster present may turn and twist through space in any possible manner.
2. It is possible to embed the point cluster within a Euclidean space.

Continuity analysis finds t sets of n rectangular co-ordinates for an s-dimensional ordination configuration such that $t \leqslant s \leqslant n - 1$. The constraints are different from those of other ordinations where individuals are placed closer together if they are more similar. In continuity analysis individuals are placed closer or further to one another in such a manner that their placement maximizes the appearance of continuity in the ordination. SHEPARD & CARROLL suggest the function

$$\kappa = \sum_j \sum_k (\delta^2(j, k)/d^4(j, k)) / \sum_j \sum_k d^2(j, k),$$
$$j = 1, ..., n - 1; \ k = j + 1, ..., n$$

as an inverse measure of continuity, to be minimized in an iterative procedure. In this function $\delta(j, k)$ is an element in Δ, representing a matrix of observed distances between individuals, and $d(j, k)$ is an element in **D** which contains the distances between the points that represent the individuals in the ordination space. Index κ is a generalization of the Neumann index for continuity in higher dimensions. The steps in its derivation are discussed in detail by SHEPARD & CARROLL (1966).

In continuity analysis, just as in other methods of ordination, we can conveniently operate on the basis of the assumption that the observed s-dimensional point configuration with resemblance structure Δ can be replaced by a simpler t-dimensional point configuration with resemblance structure **D** without a substantial loss of information. The t-dimensional configuration is derived in continuity analysis through an iterative procedure. The main steps in the analysis are outlined below on the assumption that the user has already decided what are the maximum dimensions t within which a simpler structure is sought:

1. Define an arbitrary t-dimensional configuration of n points in terms of t sets of n co-ordinates **X**.
2. Compute a Euclidean distance matrix **D** for the n points from the co-ordinates in **X**.
3. Compute κ.
4. Change the co-ordinates a little so that the value of κ is somewhat reduced.
5. Iterate steps 2 to 4 until the value of κ becomes stationary, or almost so.

The matrix **X** at the stationary stage holds the ordination co-ordinates on the basis of which scatter diagrams may be constructed. SHEPARD & CARROLL (1966) give examples in their paper to illustrate their method. These examples suggest that the method can reveal a simple underlying structure in the data if such a structure actually exists. Because redundancy and non-linearity are a rule rather than exception with vegetation data, continuity analysis will probably find interested users among vegetation ecologists.

3.6 Trend Seeking

We may recognize three broadly different approaches for trend seeking. Two of these seek a *direct* representation of trends in species or vegetational variation as a function of certain environmental variables, while the third attempts to predict underlying environmental gradients *indirectly* from trends recognized in a vegetational ordination:

1. *Fitting lines or surfaces by regression analysis.* This may be illustrated by an example in which trends in species response are mapped onto planes in which certain relationships with environmental variables can be clearly observed. Such a map is given as Fig. 3-4, tracing changes in the abundance of

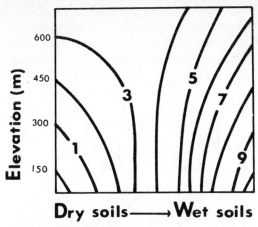

Fig. 3-4. Shown in this diagram are abundance contours for *Blechnum spicant* as a function of elevation and soil-moisture regime. The data originate from sampling in the Coastal Western Hemlock Zone of British Columbia. The contour lines in the diagram represent traces on a quadratic surface whose polynomial expression incorporates an interaction term.

the fern *Blechnum spicant* as a function of elevation above sea level and soil moisture regime.

2. Ordering vegetation stands according to certain environmental criteria. WHITTAKER's (1956) method of direct gradient analysis is one example for such an analysis. In this the distribution of different vegetation types are mapped within a reference system of moisture regime and elevation. From such maps one may infer about trends in vegetation composition with regard to environmental changes.

3. Predicting environmental gradients. In this case the goal is to ordinate sampling units based on vegetational data in such a manner that their order will be maximally predictive of their actual position along a predominant underlying environmental gradient. An approach for such a predictive use of ordination, which WHITTAKER (1967) describes as indirect gradient analysis, can be rationalized in terms of a four-stage procedure:

a. Carry out experiments with different resemblance functions and methods of axis construction on the basis of simulated data with a built-in response to a predominant environmental gradient.

b. Identify the resemblance function and method of axis construction which perform best under the simulated conditions.

c. Use the indicated function and method to analyse an actual vegetation sample.

d. Verify the ecological significance of the ordination by correlation with given environmental variables.

To reflect further on these points let us consider the artificial data in Table 2-7. Each quadrat (column) vector in this table may be represented by a profile which we construct by plotting species abundance in graphs as indicated in Fig. 3-5. Inspection of the profiles, arranged in a certain order, readily

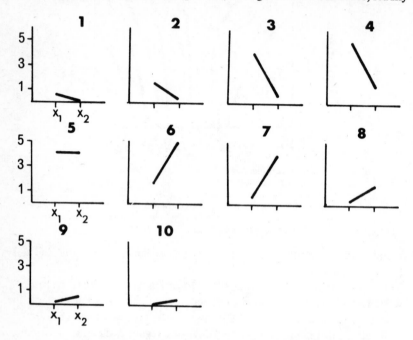

Fig. 3-5. Profiles from quadrat vectors arranged according to labels from *1* to *10* in *Table 2-7.* Vertical scale represents species abundance. X_1 and X_2 signify species.

suggests the existence of a strong unidimensional trend in the data. We subject these profiles to ordinations by different methods and give the results in Fig. 3-6. When plotting profiles as points in Fig. 3-6 according to species (X_1, X_2) as axes, the points fall into a strongly horseshoe-shaped configuration *(G)*. The sequence in which the points occur in *G* is identical to the sequence of the profiles in Fig. 3-5. The horseshoe shape of *G* indicates that the correlation between the species is strongly non-linear. When the same profiles are ordinated by the BRAY & CURTIS (1957) method, based on the use of distance formula (2.1), we obtain axes *X*, *Y* which are superimposed as oblique lines on the original diagram. Component analysis of the profiles, with the same distance function, yields axes Y_1, Y_2 which are also superimposed on Fig. 3-6. We can draw general conclusions from these results which are contrary to the generalizations given by GAUCH & WHITTAKER (1972):

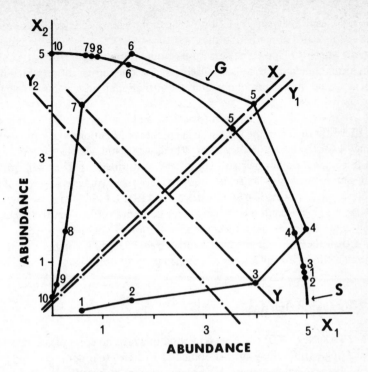

Fig. 3-6. Ordinations by different methods. *Legend to symbols:* Numbers
$1 - 10$ (inside figure) labels for quadrats in *Table 2-7;* X_1, X_2 species
axes; X, Y BRAY & CURTIS axes; $Y_1 Y_2$ component axes; G point
configuration from raw data; S point configuration from normalized
data.

1. The BRAY & CURTIS method and component analysis both reproduce
the original non-linear point configuration G in full dimensions.
2. The BRAY & CURTIS ordination and component analysis are equally un-
successful in providing an efficient summarization of the data structure in
hands, because both methods require two axes to represent an essentially unidimensional trend in the data. Because of this reason, neither of the axes
would be acceptable as a basis for a unidimensional ordering of the quadrats.
3. When normalized quadrat vectors are ordinated, a new ordination configuration *(S)* emerges. This configuration differs from the G configuration with a
substantial reduction in curvature. This is a direct consequence of the normalization which formula (2.2) incorporates. Similar results could be expected
from formulae (2.14) and (2.15) or (2.38). It follows then that the influence
of the distance function on the ordination must be a salient point in any
evaluation of the potential of certain ordinations, and that such an influence
must be clearly separated from the influence of the method of axis construc-

tion. We can safely suggest in this connection that the relative success of the BRAY & CURTIS method in the GAUCH & WHITTAKER (1972) experiment, where it reduced the curvature of the ordination configuration more than component analysis, is a consequence of the normalization which their distance function incorporates, and *not* of their method which extracts the ordination axes.

While we recognize that normalization can linearize some data structures sufficiently to assure the success of such linear ordinations as component analysis or the BRAY & CURTIS method, we should not place too much hope in this respect on normalization or other transformations. They will work in the case of weak non-linearities, but probably they will have little effect under other circumstances. The SHEPARD & CARROLL (1966) method, the SNEATH (1965) method, or some other non-linear ordination technique may help more to achieve an efficient representation of non-linear trends in the data than the ordinations which assume linearity, even if combined with supplementary manipulations of the data prior to ordination.

3.7 Reciprocal Ordering

WHITTAKER (1960) describes a method in which he uses species scores X, indicating optima along an environmental gradient, to order vegetation stands in unidimensional sequences. His ordering criterion accords with the formula

$$Y_j = \sum_i a_{ij} X_i / a_{.j}, \quad i = 1, ..., p \tag{3.6}$$

in which Y_j represents a stand score, i identifies a species, X_i indicates the ith of p species scores, a_{ij} measures the abundance of species i in stand j, and $a_{.j}$ is the sum of the abundance values for all species in stand j. The WHITTAKER method begins with a set of species scores $X_1, X_2, ..., X_p$ and a set of abundance values for s stands:

$$A = \begin{bmatrix} a_{11} & a_{12} & ... & a_{1s} \\ a_{21} & a_{22} & ... & a_{2s} \\ . & . & ... & . \\ a_{p1} & a_{p2} & ... & a_{ps} \end{bmatrix}$$

It is terminated after the first set of stand scores Y are computed. In practical applications A may represent numerical data of any sort. To illustrate the computations we shall consider the species and quadrats in Table 1-1. Let the vector

$$\mathbf{X} = (X_1 \ X_2 \ X_3 \ X_4 \ X_5) = (5 \ \ 4 \ \ 3 \ \ 2 \ \ 1)$$

specify species scores on a soil moisture gradient with 5 indicating wet soils and 1 dry soils. From these we calculate the stand scores according to formula (3.6). We have for quadrat *1*

$$Y_1 = (45(5) + ... + 9(1))/85 = 3.94$$

and for all the quadrats

$$\mathbf{Y} = (3.94 \ \ 2.71 \ \ 1.98 \ \ 3.30 \ \ 2.77 \ \ 2.62 \ \ 2.60 \ \ 4.40 \ \ 2.85 \ \ 2.89)$$

The scores in **Y** define a unique order for the quadrats along the assumed moisture gradient.

Let us proceed from here by assuming that the elements of **A** represent counts of individuals within quadrats. For such categorical data WILLIAMS (1952) has shown that the formula, which maximizes the correlation R between s stand scores and p species scores, is given by

$$Y_j = \sum_i a_{ij} X_i / R a_{.j}, \ \ i = 1, ..., p; \ \ j = 1, ..., s \tag{3.7}$$

where R is a constant derived from

$$a_{..} R^2 = \sum_j \left[\sum_i a_{ij} X_i \right]^2 / a_{.j}, \ \ j = 1, ..., s; \ \ i = 1, ..., p \tag{3.8}$$

and $a_{..} = \sum_i \sum_j a_{ij}$. The quantity R can be regarded as a measure of correlation between species scores and quadrat scores. In terms of these formulae the quadrat scores from the sample data (Table 1-1), for which p = 5 and s = 10, become

$$\mathbf{Y} = (6.82 \ \ 4.70 \ \ 3.43 \ \ 5.72 \ \ 4.80 \ \ 4.54 \ \ 4.50 \ \ 7.61 \ \ 4.93 \ \ 5.01)$$

It is quite obvious that the WILLIAMS formula for stand scores (formula (3.7)) defines a constant multiple of the WHITTAKER formula which we gave as formula (3.6). The constant is $R = 0.578$ which relates the **Y** and **X** scores in terms of formula (3.8).

WILLIAMS (1952) has generalized the procedure for maximizing the correlation of species scores and quadrat scores when the species scores are not *a priori* specified. The application of the generalized procedure to different types of data has been considered by BENZÉCRI (1969), ESCOFIER-CORDIER (1969), HATHEWAY (1971), and more recently, HILL (1973); a related approach has been pursued by DALE & ANDERSON (1973) based on their method of 'inosculate' analysis. These authors emphasize the duality of the analysis, meaning that for every set of stand scores there is a unique set of species scores, and conversely, for every set of species scores there is a unique set of stand scores for which the correspondence is maximized in terms of the correlation

$$\lambda = \sum_i \sum_j a_{ij} X_i Y_j / a_{..}, \quad i = 1, ..., p; \quad j = 1, ..., s \tag{3.9}$$

Because such a maximum property of the correlation is unique to this technique, not found in component analysis or in other ordinations, one may recognize a considerable potential for its application in ecology. To signify the duality of the analysis we shall follow HATHEWAY's (1971) terminology in referring to this method as the RQ-technique. Other designations include 'Analyse Factorielle des Correspondences' by BENZÉCRI (1969), or 'Reciprocal Averaging' by HILL (1973) who describes a simple iterative algorithm and offers it with a computer program. In the present descriptions we shall outline an eigenvalue and vector algorithm with reference to program RQT in the Appendix:

1. Generate a p by s matrix $\mathbf{U}$ from matrix $\mathbf{A}$ according to

$$u_{ij} = a_{ij} / \sqrt{(a_{i.} a_{.j})} - \sqrt{(a_{i.} a_{.j})} / a_{..} \tag{3.10}$$

2. Generate a p by p matrix $\mathbf{S}$ of scalar products, defined by $\mathbf{S} = \mathbf{UU'}$ with a characteristic element

$$S_{hi} = \sum_j u_{hj} u_{ij}, \quad j = 1, ..., s, \text{ for any species pair } h, i \tag{3.11}$$

3. Find the eigenvalues $\lambda_1, ..., \lambda_t$ and associated eigenvectors $\mathbf{X}_1, ..., \mathbf{X}_t$ of matrix $\mathbf{S}$. The elements in the eigenvectors will represent the required species scores.

4. Compute sets of stand scores $\mathbf{Y}_1, ..., \mathbf{Y}_t$. A characteristic element in the hth set is given by

$$Y_{hj} = \sum_i a_{ij} X_{hi} / \sqrt{(\lambda_h)} a_{.j}, \quad i = 1, ..., p \tag{3.12}$$

which represents the score of stand j based on the hth set of species scores.

The square root of the largest eigenvalue λ_1 gives the maximum correlation R of formula (3.8) associated with the scores $\mathbf{X}_1 = (X_{11} ... X_{1p})$ and $\mathbf{Y}_1 = (Y_{11} ... Y_{1s})$. The successive eigenvalues correspond to the second, third, and so forth largest correlation associated with successive sets of **X** and **Y**. The scores for stands or species can be plotted as rectangular co-ordinates to serve as a basis for species or quadrat scatter diagrams. A numerical example,, based on the data in Table 1-1 and program RQT in the Appendix, is given below. Firstly, the scalar product matrix is computed according to formula (3.11). The scalar products are given in

$$
S = \begin{bmatrix}
0.3000 & -0.0685 & -0.0151 & -0.0550 & -0.0799 \\
-0.0685 & 0.0304 & -0.0163 & 0.0116 & 0.0168 \\
-0.0151 & -0.0163 & 0.1293 & -0.0103 & -0.0581 \\
-0.0550 & 0.0116 & -0.0103 & 0.0738 & -0.0112 \\
-0.0799 & 0.0168 & -0.0581 & -0.0112 & 0.0812
\end{bmatrix}
$$

This matrix is subjected to an eigenvalue and vector analysis to obtain estimates for the species scores,

Set h	Species score					Correlation $\sqrt{\lambda_h}$
	1	2	3	4	5	
X_1	0.9151	-0.2185	0.0365	-0.1802	-0.2846	0.5928
X_2	-0.1805	-0.0655	0.8664	0.0602	-0.4571	0.4044

We could extract at least 2 more sets of scores, but they associate with low correlations and thus need not be considered. From the species scores we compute the quadrat scores according to formula (3.12) to obtain the values in the table below,

Set h	Quadrat score					Correlation $\sqrt{\lambda_h}$
	1 6	2 7	3 8	4 9	5 10	
Y_1	0.6548 -0.3057	-0.2917 -0.3725	-0.3107 1.0290	0.0915 -0.1425	-0.2282 -0.1850	0.5928
Y_2	-0.2971 -0.2492	0.0769 -0.4170	-0.6970 -0.0963	0.7467 -0.5726	0.3640 -0.2145	0.4044

Here too, there are at least two more sets of quadrat scores which we did not extract. We note that the scores given can be used as rectangular co-ordinates to construct a scatter diagram for the quadrats. The species and quadrat scores are maximally correlated between X_1 and Y_1 for which the correlation coefficient is 0.5928. The other two sets of scores (X_2, Y_2) have a somewhat lower correlation (0.4044). How should we interpret these correlations? Before we attempt answering this question let us try to picture two extreme situations. In the first extreme, all species within the same quadrat have the same optima, and thus score identically on the same environmental gradient. In the other extreme, within any quadrat the species are completely heterogeneous each with a different score. If we attempt ordering quadrats based on the species scores we would have no difficulty in the first case. The quadrats would fall nicely into order, identical to the species which they incorporate. We would have considerably more difficulty though in ordering quadrats in the second case where the relationship of a quadrat and the species scores within it are not clearly defined. In these terms then, we may regard the one-complement of the squared correlation $1 - \lambda_i$ as an indication of the conceptual difficulty with which the quadrats can be ordered based on the species scores.

It is quite obvious from formula (3.10) that the RQ-technique does not require data centering within species in the same manner required in component analysis. The adjustment of the data in the RQ-technique involves expressing the data elements as departures from their random expectations. Because the RQ-technique draws entirely on vegetational data, any attempt to interpret the species or quadrat scores in environmental terms will necessarily involve certain secondary analyses to establish correlations with the suspected environmental variables. In defining such correlations we may fall back on the simple technique of displaying environmental data on scatter diagrams (GREIG-SMITH, 1964) and deduce from the resulting pattern information about environmental gradients. With a similar purpose in mind we may apply other techniques such as canonical correlation analysis (PIELOU, 1969), or use trend surface analysis (e.g. NEAL & KERSHAW, 1973).

3.8 Sources of Distortion

We may view ordinations as transfer systems in which information flows from raw data to ordination co-ordinates. Naturally, we may expect from such transfer systems certain peculiar properties:
1. Different results by different technique of transfer.
2. Information loss under most circumstances.
3. Optimal performance confined to specific objectives.

The ordination techniques, with differences in their handling of the data, are expected to produce different results. Their differences, however, need not lead to radically different ecological interpretations. On the contrary, ordinations are quite robust in that they have a strong tendency toward convergence of the ecological information which they produce.

Information transfer is controlled by two basically different transformations in most ordinations. The first yields resemblance values from raw data for input in the second which produces the ordination co-ordinates. Whereas no new information can be generated in the process, a great deal of information may be lost when the transformations are inefficient.

When information is transferred from one form into another with potential losses along the way, it is logical to ask the question: *what can possibly justify an analysis which wastes information?* The answer is that in an ordination valuable information may come to light about trends and classes of vegetational variation, and their environmental controls, which could not otherwise be detected in the data. A given ordination's success will of course depend on the efficiency of the transformations which it incorporates. In this respect the properties of the distance function and the method of co-ordinate extraction are uppermost in importance. We can recognize at least four types of distortions, related to transformations:

1. *Type A distortion.* When a vegetation sample characterized by specific nonlinear trends is ordinated on the basis of a linear or unfitting non-linear model, a certain amount of distortion can be anticipated. The problem with inappropriate models is that the ordination axes do not respond to the existing non-linearities in the sample, and therefore, existing trends in the data may not be recognized. A practical question arises at this point with regard to two often used ordination techniques. *Can the information associated with non-linear trends in a sample be represented or will it be lost in such linear ordinations as component analysis or the* BRAY & CURTIS *method?* We have already answered this question indirectly in our discussion of Fig. 3-6. The following can be observed further in this connection:

a. Non-linear correlations between species yield curved point configuration in sample space.

b. Different resemblance measures define different configurations.

c. Neither component analysis nor the BRAY & CURTIS method diminishes non-linearity.

After observing these we can make the following generalization: any abstract spatial configuration of points, linear or non-linear, which can be completely described by a distance matrix, can be embedded in the geometric space of component analysis, or of the BRAY & CURTIS ordination, without scrambling the original point distances if the distance function is Euclidean and if the ordination space has sufficient dimensions. It is implied here that the information associated with any trend under the specified constraints can be retained by these ordinations given sufficient dimensions, but at the same time, the linear constraints will render the ordinations potentially inefficient.

2. *Type B distortion.* When a t-dimensional point configuration is projected into an ordination space of less than t dimensions, an amount of information

will be lost due to distortions by projection. Construction of two-dimensional scatter diagrams is a typical example in this connection in which normally a great deal of *Type B* distortion must be anticipated.

3. *Type C distortion.* This is intrinsic in the distance function's own distorting effect. We give as an example the metric

$$s(j, k) = (2(1 - (\chi^2_{jk}/p)^{1/2}))^{1/2}$$

where χ^2_{jk}/p represents the mean square contingency for two quadrats. The distortion, in this case, is a consequence of the *signum* transformation which $s(j, k)$ incorporates. After such a transformation only that portion of the information is retained in the data which is associated with species presence and absence.

4. *Type D distortion.* This occurs when the resemblance function is incompatible with the ordination geometry. For example, the different versions of the BRAY & CURTIS (1957) ordination include operations with triangles which assume that the resemblance function is Euclidean. Now, when a non-Euclidean distance is exposed to such operations, such as in BEALS' (1960) version, the original point configuration is forced into an ordination space where it cannot fit. The result is an amount of *Type D* distortion.

It is common ecological practice to evaluate an ordination's success on the basis of the results which it happened to produce under the circumstances. The usual criteria stress the 'ecological meaningfulness' of the results, notwithstanding the fact that there may be weaknesses in the ordination which may make any search for ecological meaningfulness completely pointless. Furthermore, some ecological meaning can be interpreted in most ordinations, especially when no concrete objectives are set *a priori* for the ordination to accomplish. Therefore, it is important that an evaluation minimize the need for subjective value judgements, and use objective criteria instead. A reliable system of evaluation should emphasize axiomatic and other measurable properties in providing reliable answers to two pertinent questions:

1. *Is ordination an appropriate method for data analysis under the existing circumstances?*
2. *If it is, which kind of resemblance function should be chosen for ordination in association with which method of axis construction?*

Regarding these questions we must clearly define the objectives. Furthermore, we must consider the various sources of potential distortion. The *Type A* distortion weighs heavily in this connection. Unfortunately, a satisfactory solution to the problems springing from such a distortion is not a simple matter, and may have to be attempted by some indirect means. We may, for instance, restrict the sampling to stands which are characterized by an overall linearity of species correlations. It has been suggested that the linearity condition is likely to be satisfied if sampling units are selected from a relatively narrow segment of a predominant environmental gradient (AUSTIN & NOY-MEIR, 1971; GAUCH & WHITTAKER, 1972). When evidence indicates that species correlations are non-linear, and the non-linearity is suspected to be strong, a linear ordination alone is inappropriate. If performed it should be followed up by other analyses that can reveal the intrinsic non-linear trends in the data. Methods for non-linear ordination, which have potential in reducing the *Type A* distortion, were mentioned earlier. However, it is relevant to note that non-linear ordinations which assume a specific kind of non-linearity in the sample will certainly have no more generality in ecological applications than the linear models. Such non-linear models are preferred which require no assumption about the type of the non-linearity.

While conventional methods, such as component analysis, may be of little help to prevent information loss by the *Type A* distortion, the BRAY & CURTIS method comes out worst in controlling the *Type B* distortion. The reason is that the ordination axes, produced by this method, and the principal directions of variation in the sample lack any predictable relationship. The *Type B* distortion is effectively controlled in linear data structures when the analysis is based on an eigenvalue and vector method, such as component analysis and principal axes analysis. When the data structure is non-linear an efficient ordination cannot be achieved by these methods.

The *Type C* distortion is entirely preventable by choice of an appropriate resemblance function. The *Type D* distortion is also preventable provided that the distance function and the ordination geometry are compatible. Compatibility should be understood in such a sense that the function qualifies as a valid spatial parameter in the sample space of the ordination model. In component analysis, and also in the BRAY & CURTIS ordination, especially poor choices are the semimetrics, surpassed in lack of appropriateness only by nonmetric distances. For these ordinations Euclidean measures are preferred: $e(j, k)$ or $a(j, k)$ when the influence of absolute species quantity is to be retained, and $c(j, k)$ or $u(j, k)$ when the distance measure is to be in a relative form.

The sequence in which the potential sources of information loss are discussed in the foregoing text is not intended to indicate their relative importance. Their importance should be weighted with a view to achieving specific objectives. We may wish, for instance, to summarize vegetational variation on a new set of variables, or equivalently, transform the data into new forms which qualify as co-ordinates on certain axes, in order to achieve a parsimonious representation of linear or non-linear data structures. The definition of efficiency is straightforward in the linear data structures where it means summarization on axes with zero covariances. But it is not so straightforward in the non-linear case where it may mean different things depending on the type

99

of non-linearity present as we have seen in our earlier discussions. The object-ives may require derivation of co-ordinates for individuals for which only resemblance values are available. The co-ordinates are obtained based on some method of ordination. Those methods should be preferred which can efficient-ly represent the given data structure. Existing vegetation trends may have to be revealed and correlated with changes in the environment. Since vegetation response is most likely non-linear, methods that can efficiently represent non-linear data structures have special appeal in achieving these objectives.

When the objective is summarization, it is logical to consider the success of the analysis in terms of the total variation accounted for by the ordination axes. This is an intrinsic condition in the data and in the method of analysis. Similarly, when the goal is multidimensional scaling, the logical condition for evaluating an ordination's success is the degree to which it succeeded in repre-senting the existing data structure in the fewest possible dimensions. In neither case would it be necessary to inject external criteria in the evaluations, or to try to define 'meaningfulness' in the sense of what the results may mean in ecological terms. Ecological meaningfulness is of course a necessary criterion in evaluating an ordination's success when the objectives call for revealing ecological information. Among the different methods component analysis stands out as the single most efficient technique to summarize continuous linear data structures. While this function is performed by component analysis extremely well, this method is not very helpful when the data structure is non-linear. The method of principal axes analysis is mathematically similar to com-ponent analysis, and it has similar limitations, except that it is somewhat more open regarding the admissible resemblance functions. The RQ-technique, similarly to component analysis and principal axes analysis, incorporates a linear definition of the data structure in the sample. This means a serious con-straint when it comes to actual applications. The principal justification at the basis of the BRAY & CURTIS method is its relative computational simplicity and the option for personal choice of ordination poles. This method, however, is a poor substitute for component analysis when the objective is summariza-tion. Nevertheless, it may still render a useful service for those who like to preselect poles to define ordination axes. While position vectors ordination is potentially more efficient than the BRAY & CURTIS method in summarizing linear data structures, and computationally simpler than component analysis, it is not expected to be any more helpful when the data structure is non-linear. The KRUSKAL method, the SHEPARD & CARROLL method and SNEATH's method represent a special class of ordinations. The SHEPARD & CARROLL method and the SNEATH technique also have the added advantage in being capable of handling data structures which are not linear.

I assume that the user will choose a method after careful considerations of its suitability for the purpose in hands. No single method should be regarded as a 'general preference' method or used indiscriminately in connection with different objectives. Ordinations should be treated as highly specialized methods which can provide optimal performance with respect to a few specific goals under particular circumstances.

3.9 References

AUSTIN, M.P. & NOY-MEIR, 1971. The problem of non-linearity in ordination: experiments with two gradient models. *J. Ecol.* 59: 763-773.
BEALS, E. 1960. Forest bird communities in the Apostle Islands of Wisconsin. *The Wilson Bulletin* 72: 156-181.
BENZÉCRI, J.P. 1969. Statistical analysis as a tool to make patterns emerge from data. *In:* S. WATANABE (ed.), *Methodologies of Pattern Recognition,* pp. 35-74. New York, Academic Press.
BRAY, R.J. & J.T. CURTIS. 1957. An ordination of the upland forest communities of southern Wisconsin. *Ecol. Monogr.* 27: 325-349.
DALE, M.B. & D.J. ANDERSON. 1973. Inosculate analysis of vegetation data. *Aust. J. Bot.* 21: 253-276.
ESCOFIER-CORDIER, B. 1969. L'analyse factorielle des correspondances. *Cab. Bur. univ. Rech. opér. Univ. Paris,* 13.
GAUCH, H.G. & R.H. WHITTAKER. 1972. Comparison of ordination techniques. *Ecology* 53: 868-875.
GOWER, J.C. 1966. Some distance properties of latent root and vector methods used in multivariate analysis. *Biometrika* 53: 325-338.
GREIG-SMITH, P. 1964. *Quantitative Plant Ecology,* 2nd ed. London, Butterworths.
HATHEWAY, W.H. 1971. Contingency-table analysis of Rain Forest vegetation. *In:* G.P. PATIL *et al.* (eds.), *Statistical Ecology*, Vol. 3, pp. 271-307. London, Pennsylvania State Univ. Press.
HILL, M.O. 1973. Reciprocal averaging: an eigenvector method of ordination. *J. Ecol.* 61: 237-249.
HOTELLING, H. 1933. Analysis of a complex of statistical variables into principal components. *J. Educational Psychology* 24: 417-441, 498—520.
KRUSKAL, J.B. 1964a. Multidimensional scaling by optimizing goodness of fit to a nonmetric hypothesis. *Psychometrika* 29: 1-27.
KRUSKAL, J.B. 1964b. Nonmetric multidimensional scaling: a numerical method. *Psychometrika* 29: 115-229.
KRUSKAL, J.B. & F. CARMONE. 1971. How to use M-D-SCAL (Version 5M) and other useful information. Bell Telephone Laboratories. Murray Hill, New Jersey, U.S.A., and University of Waterloo, Waterloo, Ontario, Canada.
MAAREL, van der E. 1969. On the use of ordination models in phytosociology. *Vegetatio* 19: 21-46.
MORRISON, D.F. 1967. *Multivariate Statistical Methods.* New York, McGraw-Hill.
NEAL, M.W. & K.A. KERSHAW. 1973. Studies on lichen dominated systems. III. Phytosociology of a raised beach system near Cape Henrietta Maria, Northern Ontario. *Can. J. Bot.* 51: 1115-1125.
ORLÓCI, L. 1966. Geometric models in ecology. I. The theory and application of some ordination methods. *J. Ecol.* 54: 193-215.
ORLÓCI, L. 1967. Data centering: a review and evaluation with reference to component analysis. *Syst. Zool.* 16: 208-212.
PIELOU, E.C. 1969. *An Introduction to Mathematical Ecology.* New York, Wiley Interscience.

SHEPARD, R.N. & J.D. CARROLL. 1966. Parametric representation of nonlinear data structures. *In:* P.R. KRISHNAIAH (ed.), *Multivariate Analysis,* pp. 561-592. London, Academic Press.

SNEATH, P.H.A. 1965. A method for curve seeking from scattered points. *Computer Journal* 8: 383-391.

SWAN, J.M.A., R.L. DIX & C.F. WEHRHAHN. 1969. An ordination technique based on the best possible stand-defined axes and its application to vegetation analysis. *Ecology* 50: 206-212.

WHITTAKER, R.H. 1956. Vegetation of the Great Smoky Mountains. *Ecol. Monogr.* 26: 1-80.

WHITTAKER, R.H. 1960. Vegetation of the Siskiyou Mountains, Oregon and California. *Ecol. Monogr.* 30: 279-338.

WHITTAKER, R.H. 1967. Gradient analysis of vegetation. *Biol. Rev.* 42: 207-264.

WILLIAMS, E.J. 1952. Use of scores for the analysis of association in contingency tables. *Biometrika* 39: 274-289.

IV. CLASSIFICATIONS

The process which produces new classes constitutes a classification. This should be clearly distinguished from identification which finds the class, among a number of established classes, that represents the most likely parent population for a new individual. In this chapter we shall consider classifications — the concepts, objectives, methods and conditions of application.

4.1 Classical Approaches

Classifications have traditionally played a central role in phytosociology (see WHITTAKER, 1962). The classical schools tended to group themselves about distinct classificatory approaches of which some are still practiced:

1. *The zonal approach.* Broad regional units are recognized in the vegetation, closely corresponding to broad climatic and soil zones. This approach reached an early climax with DOKUCHAEV's (1899) work on Natural Zones.

2. *The dynamic or successional approach.* The main concern in this lies in the recognition of developmental stages in the vegetation, and on that basis, establishment of classification systems. This approach culminated with the work of CLEMENTS (1916, and other publications).

3. *The type or association approach.* In this vegetation units are recognized on the basis of the most abundant species in the undergrowth (CAJANDER, 1909), dominant species (TANSLEY, 1939), or diagnostic species (BRAUN-BLANQUET, 1928, 1951).

4. *The holistic or ecosystem approach.* In this, as KRAJINA (1933, 1960) asserts, the ecologist assumes that discrete ecosystems exist and that via the ecosystem units a joint classification of vegetation and environment is possible.

Our account of classifications is devoted entirely to the formal procedures which are the product of recent methodological advances.

4.2 The Medium

Ecologists hold opposing views regarding the basic aspects of the vegetation which they observe. They often assume, directly in line with the views advocated by the Zurich-Montpellier School, that the vegetation is actually discontinuous, consisting of discrete units existing as 'natural' types. The type, in this case, is an abstraction comparable to a population. While this viewpoint has been challenged repeatedly in the past (see McINTOSH, 1967, and references therein), this did not deter many phytosociologists from continued erection of classificatory systems based on natural types.

Whereas the assumption that natural types exist is vital in importance in the traditional classificatory approach, the assumption of vegetation continuum, or the denial that the vegetation is an aggregate of natural types, is just as fundamental in the early ordination approach advocated by the Wisconsin School. In this the objectives are concerned with the discovery and quantification of continuous trends in vegetational variation.

It is quite relevant to the prevailing arguments, whether they promote one or another of the classical views, that in the main they have relied on arbitrary definitions for natural types, or as a matter of fact, for vegetational continua. It can be suggested that any attempt to prove or disprove the existence of natural types, as discrete populations, has yet to resolve many difficulties:

1. *The difficulty of scale.* At which scale should one look for distinguishable types? Should it be a scale at which only gross vegetational differences can be detected, or should it be a much more refined scale at which even the very fine details of vegetational structure can be recognized?

2. *The difficulty of measurement.* How accurately should one measure the vegetation before one can be satisfied that the conclusions drawn from the measurements can be accepted with confidence?

3. *The difficulty of continuously changing systems.* Species, communities, or even environments, are not static. The time factor is important. When should the observations take place? What is the expected time span of an observation as a valid fact?

4. *The difficulty of complexity.* The vegetation and the environment have the potential of great degrees of complexity. How much of the total complexity must then be taken into account before any statement about the existence, or non-existence, of natural types can be firmly supported?

5. *The difficulty of population size.* A plant community may have an extent far beyond the possibility of complete enumeration. One may have to be satisfied with statistical estimation (rather than exact determination) of the population parameters. How much error in the estimates is permitted before rendering the results inacceptable in drawing conclusions about the existence of natural types?

6. *The difficulty for the 'intelligent ignoramus'.* One's conclusions about the existence of natural types are affected by experience and personal bias. Which person's views, therefore, should be accepted with confidence in the absence of hard, objective evidence?

In our presentations the validity of the classical views will not be argued, but rather, it will be assumed that a classification has to be done in order to achieve certain utilitarian goals. The principal question thus facing us at this point is not whether a classification can be done, but *how* should it be done so that it can best serve certain objectives.

4.3 Why Classify?

It is quite appropriate to ask this question for two specific reasons. Firstly, classifications represent only one of the many possible ways in which vegetational data may be analysed. Secondly, the user must be satisfied that classifications can do something uniquely well under the circumstances which could not be done so well by any other method. What then are the objectives that may call for a classification? These commonly fall into three categories:
1. Problem solving (prediction, hypothesis testing, etc.).
2. Problem recognition (hypothesis generation).
3. Data reduction, inventory, etc.

Regarding objectives in the first category, correlations may be sought between the vegetation and the environment to facilitate the use of vegetation classes as predictors of certain environmental conditions. We may consider, as an example, an allocation of n units to k classes based on vegetation data, and then, an allocation of the same units to m classes based on soil data. The extent to which certain vegetation classes tend to hold units in common with certain soil classes is an indication of the predictive potential of the vegetation classes. While classifications can be used to perform a predictive function reasonably well, they are generally not suited to serve as a basis for testing hypotheses about the existence of natural types (McINTOSH, 1967). As a matter of fact, just because a sample of vegetation units can be partitioned into groups by some method of classification, one should not conclude that the vegetation must consist of discrete types (PIELOU, 1969). Furthermore, a complete circularity of argument would be involved if we hypothesized that the groups of stands, recognized in a classification based on their species content, are samples from discrete types, and went about testing this hypothesis knowing that the different stands are assigned to the groups in such a manner that the groups must come out distinct in terms of vegetation. However, it would be perfectly valid to test hypotheses about the statistical indistinguishability of these groups in terms of environmental variables. The justification for such a test is that the criteria which form the groups, and the criteria on the basis of which their indistinguishability is tested, are different.

WILLIAMS & DALE (1965) assert that classifications can serve as hypothesis generating systems. Others believe that there are potential dangers in hypothesis generation on this basis. They reason that because the groups are a product of partitions, when no natural groups exist a classification will force the data "into a strait jacket which restricts the domain of possible hypotheses and suggests that some will be generated by the fact of dissection rather than by the data" (CORMACK, 1971).

Among the many uses to which classifications are put data reduction is by far the most prominent. But here, unlike in ordinations where data reduction is by axes, data reduction is by allocations to groups on the basis of suitably chosen criteria. Such groups may serve as a basis for inventory, mapping, organization of future research, and many other utilitarian objectives. In this sense a classification can provide concise descriptions of the complexity in the data which may lead to more efficient communication about relevant class properties. New information may be revealed in the process which in turn can illuminate such class properties which may not otherwise become apparent (GREIG-SMITH, 1964).

4.4 Classification or Ordination?

Ecologists advocate opposing views about the fundamental characteristics of the vegetation, and their views often determine their preference for one or another of the methods. The proponents of the classificatory approach tend to look upon classification not as a technique but rather as a general strategy. In their frame of reference classification is so fundamental that to them without classification there can be no science of vegetation (KRAJINA, 1961). In direct contrast stand those ecologists who assume a continuum. To them "vegetation changes continuously and is not differentiated, except arbitrarily, into sociological entities" (McINTOSH, 1967). To the holders of the continuum concept of vegetation classifications have no strong appeal; to them ordination represents the preferred strategy.

GREIG-SMITH (1964) asserts that ordination and classification as approaches "are, in theory, quite distinct" but then he adds that "in practice the divergence is not so great as may appear". McINTOSH (1967) makes a similar point when he claims that to many ecologists ordination and classification are not necessarily incompatible techniques. In line with these opinions we may add that ordinations and classifications should be thought of not as some preferential strategies, associated with rigid assumptions, but rather, as techniques which among other techniques of data analysis can help the user to accomplish certain objectives. It seems that there is no need for the ecologist to commit the analysis to one or another of the classical hypotheses prior to a vegetation study. On the contrary, an analysis may be best approached without an *a priori* commitment to one or another of such broad hypotheses. What the ecologist must do is to try to state clearly the objectives to be achieved, and then select an appropriate method for sampling, and a suitable method for data analysis. When the objectives are clearly defined, and the methodological implications understood, the choice between ordination and classification should not be too difficult.

4.5 On Terminology

When should a partition of a sample be called a *classification?* WILLIAMS & DALE (1965) answer that question by laying down three axioms. Their first axiom requires that individuals in any one group must share one or more common characteristics. Their second axiom states that group size is not a relevant characteristic, and that allocations must be open-ended in the sense that the classification will in no way limit the number of individuals per group. The third axiom restricts classifications to such subdivisions which produce non-overlapping groups. A partition which conforms to the first two of these axioms, but not the third, may be called *clumping* to indicate the presence of overlapping groups. When a completely continuous sample is classified, the resulting groups represent *dissections* (KENDALL, 1966).

4.6 Types of Classifications

According to what has been said in the preceding section, a distinction can be made between the following types of classifications:
1. *Non-overlapping groups.* The groups may be arranged *hierarchically* whereby the small groups are further combined according to their similarities into broader groups. The results of a hierarchic classification can be presented in the form of a dendrogram (classification tree). In some classifications non-overlapping groups are recognized at a single level and presented without showing hierarchic relationships.
2. *Overlapping groups.* In the present treatment we do not describe methods whose specific objective is clumping. These methods are considered in detail by JARDINE & SIBSON (1971). We recognize, of course, that a classification which forms non-overlapping groups of individuals may perform clumping in an indirect sense with regard to properties associated with the individuals. For example, when quadrats of vegetation are allocated to non-overlapping groups, the groups will almost certainly represent overlapping groups for the species which occur in the quadrats. In an analogous sense, in a classification of species with non-overlapping groups, the groups may certainly overlap in terms of the quadrats in which the species occur.

Classifications may be categorized further according to the characters on the basis of which the partitions are recognized. SNEATH (1962), for example, distinguishes *monothetic* and *polythetic* classifications which respectively partition a sample on the basis of the presence of one or more common characters, or the amount of shared character states or values. Classifications may be *subdivisive,* when groups are formed by subdivisions, or *agglomerative,* when groups are formed on the basis of fusions. Opinions divide on the relative merits of subdivisive and agglomerative classifications. For instance, WILLIAMS

& DALE (1965) advocate the use of the subdivisive methods, but GOWER (1967) finds them undesirable in general because they can irreparably dismember existing groups too early in the classificatory process.

4.7 The Model

The spatial analogy which we used with ordinations has direct relevance in classifications under particular circumstances. However, the mathematical model need not be of the usual metric kind. In some ways it may represent other abstractions which use non-metric spatial parameters.

4.8 Selected Techniques

Without attempting to provide a broad review of classifications, which CORMACK (1971) has done in a long article, we shall focus attention on three methods that can satisfy many of the classificatory needs in vegetation surveys, and consider others only in brief:

A. Average linkage clustering

This method has been suggested by SOKAL & MICHENER (1958) to perform a classification which is polythetic, agglomerative, and hierarchical. Individuals or groups are fused when their average similarity is the greatest. The formula for average similarity will be given later. We illustrate the method in an example on the data in Table 2-1. The objective is a hierarchical classification of quadrats:

1. As the first step we compute quadrat similarities. This has been done for the sample and the results are given in the matrix,

$$
\mathbf{S} = \begin{bmatrix} S_{11} & S_{12} & S_{13} & S_{14} & S_{15} \\ S_{21} & S_{22} & S_{23} & S_{24} & S_{25} \\ S_{31} & S_{32} & S_{33} & S_{34} & S_{35} \\ S_{41} & S_{42} & S_{43} & S_{44} & S_{45} \\ S_{51} & S_{52} & S_{53} & S_{54} & S_{55} \end{bmatrix} = \begin{bmatrix} 1.00 & 0.94 & 0.42 & 0.18 & 0.00 \\ 0.94 & 1.00 & 0.61 & 0.39 & 0.15 \\ 0.42 & 0.61 & 1.00 & 0.97 & 0.87 \\ 0.18 & 0.39 & 0.97 & 1.00 & 0.95 \\ 0.00 & 0.15 & 0.87 & 0.95 & 1.00 \end{bmatrix}
$$

The elements in $\mathbf{S}$ represent cosine separations of quadrat vectors according to the formula,

$$
S_{jk} = \sum_h X_{hj} X_{hk} / \left[\sum_h X_{hj}^2 \sum_h X_{hk}^2 \right]^{1/2} , \quad h = 1, ..., p \tag{4.1}
$$

(There is no compelling reason for choosing this particular formula other than convenience. Any other symmetric similarity measure could have been chosen if called for by some specific objective.)

2. The first operation on **S** involves finding the highest similarity value (excluding self comparisons indicated by unities in the diagonal cells). After inspecting **S** we find that $S_{34} = 0.97$ is the highest similarity indicating fusion between quadrats $3, 4$. In anticipation of work on large matrices it is advisable to keep a fusion register for quadrat labels and similarities.

3. We compute a reduced similarity matrix next. In this, columns (rows) 3 and 4 are replaced by a new third column (row) of average similarities; the fourth column (row) is wiped out. If we designate as $(3 + 4)$ the new third group, formed by the fusion of quadrats 3 and 4, the average similarity between any quadrat j and the third group accords with the GOWER (1967) formula,

$$S_{j(3+4)} = (N_3/(N_3 + N_4))S_{j3} + (N_4/(N_3 + N_4))S_{j4}$$
$$+ (N_3N_4/(N_3 + N_4)^2)(1 - S_{34}) = S_{j3}^*$$

The S symbols represent quadrat similarities, the N symbols signify group sizes, and $S_{j(3+4)}$ or S_{j3}^* represents the average similarity of quadrat j and the new third group $(3 + 4)$. For quadrat 1 this quantity becomes

$$S_{13}^* = (1/2)S_{13} + (1/2)S_{14} + (1/4)(1 - S_{34})$$
$$= (1/2)(0.42) + (1/2)(0.18) + (1/4)(1 - 0.97) = 0.31$$

The remaining values S_{23}^* and S_{53}^* are similarly computed to obtain a new matrix S^*:

$$S^* = \begin{bmatrix} 1 & 0.94 & 0.31 & - & 0.00 \\ 0.94 & 1 & 0.51 & - & 0.15 \\ 0.31 & 0.51 & 1 & - & 0.92 \\ - & - & - & - & - \\ 0.00 & 0.15 & 0.92 & - & 1 \end{bmatrix}$$

$$N = (1 \quad 1 \quad 2 \quad 0 \quad 1 \,)$$

The elements in vector **N** indicate group sizes after the first fusion. We inspect the reduced matrix and find that the highest similarity is $S_{12} = 0.94$; thus we fuse quadrats 1 and 2 to obtain a new first group $(1 + 2)$. The quadrat labels are entered in the register and also the average similarity. Following this we replace columns (rows) *1* and *2* by a new first column (row) of average similarities and wipe out the second column (row) in S^*.

4. The average similarity of any group j and the new first group $(1 + 2)$ is defined in symbolic terms by

$$S^*_{j(1+2)} = (N_1/(N_1 + N_2))S^*_{j1} + (N_2/(N_1 + N_2))S^*_{j2}$$
$$+ (N_1 N_2/(N_1 + N_2)^2)\ (1 - S^*_{12}) = S^{**}_{j1}$$

The S^* symbols in this expression indicate similarity values in matrix S^*. For group *3* the average similarity with the new first group is

$$S^{**}_{31} = (1/2)(0.31) + (1/2)(0.51) + (1/4)(1 - 0.94) = 0.43$$

and for group *5*, $S^{**}_{51} = 0.09$. The entire S^{**} matrix becomes:

$$S^{**} = \begin{bmatrix} 1 & - & 0.43 & - & 0.09 \\ - & - & - & - & - \\ 0.43 & - & 1 & - & 0.92 \\ - & - & - & - & - \\ 0.09 & - & 0.92 & - & - \end{bmatrix}$$

$$N\ =\ (2 \quad 0 \quad 2 \quad 0 \quad 1\ )$$

Vector N has the group sizes after the second fusion. In S^{**} the maximum similarity is $S^{**}_{35} = 0.92$; thus we fuse groups *3* with *5* to obtain the new third group.

5. The average similarity of group *1* with the new third group $(3 + 5)$ is computed according to

$$S^{***}_{13} = (N_3/(N_3 + N_5))S^{**}_{13} + (N_5/(N_3 + N_5))S^{**}_{15}$$
$$+ (N_3 N_5/(N_3 + N_5)^2)\ (1 - S^{**}_{35})$$
$$= (2/3)(0.43) + (1/3)(0.09) + (2/9)(1 - 0.92) = 0.33$$

The complete S^{***} matrix thus consists of

$$S^{***} = \begin{bmatrix} 1 & - & 0.33 & - & - \\ - & - & - & - & - \\ 0.33 & - & 1 & - & - \\ - & - & - & - & - \\ - & - & - & - & - \end{bmatrix}$$

$$N\ =\ (\ 2 \quad 0 \quad 3 \quad 0 \quad 0\ )$$

110

Vector **N** indicates the sizes of the groups after the third fusion. The fourth and last fusion is between groups *1* and *3* at an average similarity of 0.33.

We now summarize the steps by indicating changes in group contents and similarities. This information is found in the fusion register which we update after each fusion. Initially the register contains,

Group	Quadrats in group	Fusion similarity
1	1	
2	2	
3	3	
4	4	
5	5	

After the first fusion the register indicates the changes:

1	1	
2	2	
3	3,4	0.97
4	–	
5	5	

After the second fusion:

1	1,2	0.94
2	–	
3	3,4	0.97
4	–	
5	5	

After the third fusion:

1	1,2	0.94
2	–	
3	3,4,5	0.92
4	–	
5	–	

After the final fusion:

1	1,2,3,4,5	0.33
2	–	
3	–	
4	–	
5	–	

The clustering results are summarized in dendogram form in Fig. 4-1. I give a program ALC in the Appendix which automatically performs the computations.

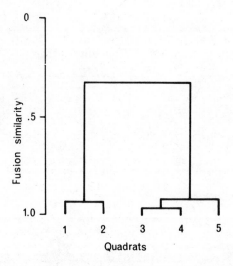

Fig. 4-1. Dendrogram indicating hierarchy for quadrats in *Table 1-1* constructed on the basis of average linkage clustering.

The reader should notice that the GOWER expression (formula (4.1)) for averaging similarities reduces to

$$S_{j(A+B)} = 0.5(S_{jA} + S_{jB}) + 0.25(1 - S_{AB}) \qquad (4.2)$$

for group j and the union group $(A + B)$ when group sizes are not considered. Whether to use formula (4.1) or (4.2) in the averaging is a choice dependent on the user.

B. Sum of squares clustering

In average linkage clustering fusions depend on the average similarity of the groups. The method, to be described next, selects fusions that minimize the within group sum of squares. What do we mean by 'sum of squares' in this particular instance? An answer is provided in the following text.

Let X_m represent a $p \times N_m$ matrix of data elements for p species in N_m quadrats. Let X_{hjm} designate an individual data element in matrix X_m. The subscripts h, j, m identify respectively species, quadrat, and group. The mean of species h in group m is $\bar{X}_{hm}$. In terms of these symbols, we define the sum of squares as the quantity,

$$Q_m = \sum_j \sum_h (X_{hjm} - \bar{X}_{hm})^2 = \sum_j d^2(j, \bar{X}_m),$$
$$j = 1, ..., N_m; \ h = 1, ..., p$$

This quantity gives the sum of squared distances of quadrats from their common group centroid specified by the co-ordinates,

$$\bar{X}_m = \begin{bmatrix} \bar{X}_{1m} \\ \vdots \\ \bar{X}_{pm} \end{bmatrix}$$

Vector $\bar{X}_m$ is called a *group mean vector*.

The quantity Q_m can be computed directly from the quadrat distances,

$$Q_m = (1/N_m) \sum_j \sum_k d^2(j, k; m), j = 1, ..., N_m - 1, \ k = j + 1, ..., N_m$$

where $d^2(j, k; m)$ is the squared Euclidean distance of quadrat j and k in group m.

Let us consider now two groups A, B and their fusion $(A + B)$. We can define the sum of squares within $(A + B)$ in terms of the expression,

$$Q_{A+B} = (1/(N_A + N_B)) \sum_j \sum_k d^2(j, k; A + B),$$
$$j = 1, ..., N_A + N_B - 1; \ k = j + 1, ..., N_A + N_B$$

All j, k are members in group $(A + B)$. The symbols N_A, N_B and $d^2(j,k; A + B)$ indicate group sizes in A and B, and the squared distance of quadrats j and k within the fusion group $(A + B)$. In clustering we minimize the quantity

$$Q_{AB} = Q_{A+B} - Q_A - Q_B = (N_A N_B/(N_A + N_B)) \sum_h (\bar{X}_{hA} - \bar{X}_{hB})^2$$
$$= (N_A N_B/(N_A + N_B)) \ d^2(A, B), \ h = 1, ..., p \tag{4.3}$$

113

where $d^2(A, B)$ is the squared Euclidean distance of the group centroids (tips of group mean vectors). The quantity Q_{AB} has been used as a clustering criterion in vegetational classification (ORLÓCI, 1967) and elsewhere (WARD, 1963; WARD & HOOK, 1963; EDWARDS & CAVALLI-SFORZA, 1965).

With such a definition of group distances and sum of squares in mind, we can perform a cluster analysis in the following manner:

1. The quadrats to be clustered are those listed in Table 2-1. We assume that *a priori* considerations call for the use of the chord distance (formula (2.2)) to measure quadrat distances. Having chosen this definition of distance we obtain distances from the S matrix in the preceding example according to

$$d^2(j, k) = 2(1 - S_{jk})$$

with corresponding numerical values,

$$\mathbf{D}^2 = \begin{bmatrix} 0.00 & 0.12 & 1.16 & 1.64 & 2.00 \\ 0.12 & 0.00 & 0.78 & 1.22 & 1.70 \\ 1.16 & 0.78 & 0.00 & 0.06 & 0.26 \\ 1.64 & 1.22 & 0.06 & 0.00 & 0.10 \\ 2.00 & 1.70 & 0.26 & 0.10 & 0.00 \end{bmatrix}$$

In the initial step, when the groups contain only a single quadrat each, the clustering criterion (formula (4.3)) reduces to

$$Q_{AB} = (1/2)d^2(A,B)$$

i.e. one half of the squared Euclidean distance. The minimum value occurs between quadrats *3, 4*. The labels *3, 4* are entered in a register and also the value $Q_{34} = Q_{3+4} = (1/2)(0.06) = 0.03$ for the new third group *(3 + 4)*. Note that $Q_{34} = Q_{3+4}$ holds true only because groups *3* and *4* represent a single quadrat each. The same condition would be true also if the groups contained two or more quadrats, provided that all quadrats within a group were identical.

2. Having completed the first fusion we now compute values for criterion Q_{j3}, involving comparisons between any quadrat *j* and the new third group *(3 + 4)*. Taking quadrat *1* first, we have

$$Q_{13} = Q_{1+3} - Q_1 - Q_3$$
$$= (1/(N_1 + N_3))(d^2(1,3) + d^2(1,4) + d^2(3,4)) - 0 - (1/N_3)d^2(3,4)$$
$$= (1/3)(1.16 + 1.64 + 0.06)(1/2)(0.06) = 0.92$$

114

Another way of calculating Q_{13} would be from the co-ordinates (Table 2-1),

$$Q_{13} = (N_1N_3/(N_1 + N_3)) (2 (1 - \sum_h X_{h1}\bar{X}_{h3}/ \left[\sum_h X_{h1}^2 \sum_h X_{h3}^2 \right]^{1/2}))$$

$$= (2/3)(2(1 - ((2)(1.5) + (0)(3.5) + (3)(0.05)) /$$

$$\sqrt{((4 + 0 + 9)(2.25 + 12.25 + 0.25))))}$$

$$= (2/3)(2(1 - 4.5/\sqrt{((13)(14.75))))) = 0.90}$$

There are two things to be noted here. One is the discrepancy in the value of Q_{13} calculated by the two methods; this is a consequence of rounding errors. Another is that the computation is much more tedious.

We determine the Q_{j3} values for all quadrats and place the values in the third column (row) of matrix $\mathbf{Q}$. The values, not in the third column (row) accord with formula $(1/2)d^2(j,k)$. The entire matrix is given by

$$\mathbf{Q} = \begin{bmatrix} 0.00 & 0.06 & 0.92 & - & 1.00 \\ 0.06 & 0.00 & 0.66 & - & 0.85 \\ 0.92 & 0.66 & 0.00 & - & 0.11 \\ - & - & - & - & - \\ 1.00 & 0.85 & 0.11 & - & 0.00 \end{bmatrix}$$

$$\mathbf{N} = (\quad 1 \quad\quad 1 \quad\quad 2 \quad\quad 0 \quad\quad 1 \quad)$$

The elements in vector $\mathbf{N}$ indicate group sizes after the first fusion. After inspection of the sum of squares we find that the next fusion is between quadrats 1 and 2 for which $Q_{1+2} = 0.06$ represents a minimum.

3. The labels 1, 2 and $Q_{1+2} = 0.06$ are marked down and a new $\mathbf{Q}$ matrix is constructed by computing values Q_{jl} for the first new group $(1 + 2)$ and any other group j. For the third group $(3, 4)$ we have

$$Q_{31} = Q_{3+1} - Q_3 - Q_1 = (1/(N_1 + N_3)) (d^2(1,2) + d^2(1,3)$$

$$+ d^2(1,4) + d^2(2,3) + d^2(2,4) + d^2(3,4)) - (1/N_3)d^2(3,4)$$

$$- (1/N_1)d^2(1,2) = (1/4)(0.12 + 1.16 + 1.64 + 0.78 + 1.22 + 0.06)$$

$$- (1/2)(0.06) - (1/2)(0.12) = 1.16$$

For the last group (including only quadrat 5),

$$Q_{51} = Q_{5+1} - Q_5 - Q_1 = (1/(N_1 + N_5))(d^2(1,2) + d^2(1,5) + d^2(2,5))$$

$$- 0 - (1/N_1)d^2(1,2)$$

$$= (1/3)(0.12 + 2.0 + 1.7) - (1/2)(0.12) = 1.21$$

The next **Q** matrix holds the elements,

$$\mathbf{Q} = \begin{bmatrix} 0.00 & - & 1.16 & - & 1.21 \\ - & - & - & - & - \\ 1.16 & - & 0.00 & - & 0.11 \\ - & - & - & - & - \\ 1.21 & - & 0.11 & - & 0.00 \end{bmatrix}$$

$$\mathbf{N} = (\; 2 \quad 0 \quad 2 \quad 0 \quad 1 \;)$$

Vector **N** indicates group sizes after the second fusion. The minimum value in the last matrix **Q** is $Q_{35} = 0.11$ indicating the next fusion between the third and fifth group. The labels *3* and *5* are entered in the register, and also Q_{3+5} = (1/3)(0.06 + 0.26 + 0.1) = 0.14, the within group sum of squares in the new third group (*3 + 5*).

4. There are only two groups remaining, group *1* including quadrats *1, 2* and group *3* including quadrats *3, 4, 5*. For these, the within group sum of squares is

$$Q_{1+3} = (1/(N_1 + N_3))\,(d_2^2(1,2) + d^2(1,3) + d^2(1,4) + d^2(1,5) + d^2(2,3)$$
$$+ d^2(2,4) + d^2(2,5) + d^2(3,4) + d^2(3,5) + d^2(4,5))$$
$$= (1/5)(0.12+1.16+1.64+2.00+0.78+1.22+1.70+0.06+0.26+0.10)$$
$$= 1.81$$

The corresponding between group sum of squares is $Q_{13} = 1.81 - 0.06 - 0.14 = 1.61$.

The information about changing group contents and sum of squares is contained in the register. Initially the register indicates,

Group	Quadrats in group	Within group sum of squares
1	1	0
2	2	0
3	3	0
4	4	0
5	5	0

After the first fusion:

1	1	0
2	2	0
3	3,4	0.03
4	–	–
5	5	0

After the second fusion:

1	1,2	0.06
2	–	–
3	3,4	0.03
4	–	–
5	–	–

After the third fusion:

1	1,2	0.06
2	–	–
3	3,4,5	0.14
4	–	–
5	–	–

Finally:

1	1,2,3,4,5	1.81
2	–	–
3	–	–
4	–	–
5	–	–

From these results a dendrogram is constructed which I give in Fig. 4-2. The computations in sum of squares clustering are automatically accomplished by program SSA in the Appendix.

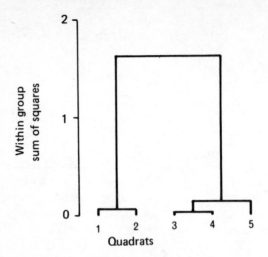

Fig. 4-2. Dendrogram constructed on the basis of sum of squares agglomeration from data given in *Table 1-1*.

It should be noted in connection with formula (4.3) that the Q_{AB} quantity is influenced by group size. When it is not important to consider the size of the groups, a decision which the user has to make, the clustering procedure reduces to *centroid clustering* in which two groups are fused when the distance between their centroids is the smallest. Such a clustering method has been described by DUCKER, WILLIAMS & LANCE (1965).

The dependence of the fusion criterion in sum of squares clustering on group size has an interesting consequence. To show this consider Q_{Aj} and Q_{Bj} both defined on the basis of formula (4.3). Assume that A and B represent groups of N_A and N_B quadrats respectively, while j designates a single quadrat not in A or B. Now allocate j to either group A or group B depending on the size of Q_{Aj} or Q_{Bj}. Fuse j with group A if the condition

$$N_A/(N_A + 1)\, d^2(A, j) < N_B/(N_B + 1)\, d^2(B,j)$$

is true, and with B when the reverse is true. From this we can deduce that,
1. When $N_A = N_B$ the condition for allocation reduces to $d(A, j) < d(B, j)$, the criterion for centroid clustering.
2. When $d(A, j) = d(B, j)$ the allocation of j to group A or B will depend solely on the sizes of $N_A/(N_A + 1)$ and $N_B/(N_B + 1)$.
The latter implies that the allocations are biased in favour of the smallest

118

group, so that quadrats tend to be added onto the small groups, even though they may be located closer in distance terms to a large group's centroid. This can reduce the chaining effect whereby the size of a large group can increase more rapidly as it actually increases.

Sum of squares clustering is a polythetic, hierarchical, agglomerative technique. It forms groups by fusing individuals or groups. We can see that average linkage clustering and sum of squares clustering have several properties in common. On the basis of the examples given we may even expect them to produce similar dendrograms. These methods differ nevertheless from one another in several important respects:
1. Whereas sum of squares clustering is limited to a Euclidean distance function, practically any similarity measure is admissible in average linkage clustering.
2. Sum of squares clustering is a special purpose method of classification, appropriate when the analysis is committed to a covariance structure. But average linkage clustering is more of a general purpose classification with little restriction on applications.

Sum of squares clustering has a closely related ally in the subdivisive method of EDWARDS & CAVALLI-SFORZA (1965). This method has some ideal properties but is otherwise hopeless for computation. It has been estimated that clustering in a modest sample of let us say 30 or 40 individuals by this method would need thousands of years even for the fastest electronic computer to complete.

C. JANCEY's (1974) method

Most clustering algorithms find clusters in a sample irrespective of the existence, or non-existence, of actual discontinuities. While these algorithms can be very useful when the goal is simply a dissection, they will be of little help when we try to discover discontinuities, or equivalently, recognize natural groups in a sample.

If we accept the definition that *a group is discrete if all of its members have their nearest neighbour within the group* then it is quite logical that a clustering algorithm which will find such groups incorporate single linkage clustering (SNEATH, 1957) performed iteratively at increasing maximum nearest neighbour distances. Such an algorithm has been proposed by JANCEY (1974) for which I give a computer program (TRGRUP) in the Appendix.

Regarding the JANCEY (1974) algorithm it should be stressed that the objective is to search the sample for discrete groups under the hypothesis that it naturally divides into R recognizable parts, against the alternative that it does not. The groups, which we have in mind, are separated from one another by discontinuities measured in terms of the maximum nearest neighbour distance.

119

The initial linkage parameter C, its stepwise increments D, and also R the number of groups sought, are specified *a priori*. Specification of the minimum acceptable group size S is reguired. The linkage parameter C then is incremented by D in steps and a new clustering cycle is performed after each increment. The analysis is terminated when one of two things happens:

1. R groups are found.
2. Only one group is found.

If a solution does not exist under the R group hypothesis, but a solution exists at the next higher number of groups, the next higher and the next lower number of groups are found and described. If a solution is not found at a higher number of groups, the value of R is decremented in steps and the sample is reanalysed at each reduced value of R until a termination is indicated.

The principal value of JANCEY's (1974) clustering algorithm appears to be his definition of a discrete group, and two other things which the algorithm does that normally are not done so well by other clustering techniques:

1. Natural groups are found if they exist, and if no groups can be found at the specified constraints *(R, C, D)* groups will not be formed.
2. The method can find groups at a specified minimum groups size S if a solution is possible under the specified contraints R, C, D.

Because the clustering is basically single linkage, the method is sensitive to aberrant individuals which may link the otherwise discrete groups. This problem is difficult to overcome and the user may have to resort to various arbitrary methods to locate and eliminate the aberrant individuals. Apart from this difficulty, the JANCEY algorithm appears from the example given by JANCEY (1974) himself to have considerable potential in vegetation classifications. The data which JANCEY used in his example are reproduced in Fig. 4-3. This figure incorporates several dense clusters of points, one of which is completely enveloped by a high-density ring. The computations by TRGRUP (see the Appendix) reveal all groups including the high-density ring as separate entities. The parameters and results in the analysis are summarized below:

Total number of points   85
Number of attributes   2
Minimum group size *(S)*   4
Number of groups sought *(R)*   4
Linkage parameter *(C)*   0.033
Increment *(D)*   0.06
Group *1*:   High-density ring of 58 points
Group *2*:   Cluster of 4 points in right lower corner
Group *3*:   Cluster of 8 points in center
Group *4*:   Elongated cluster of 15 points

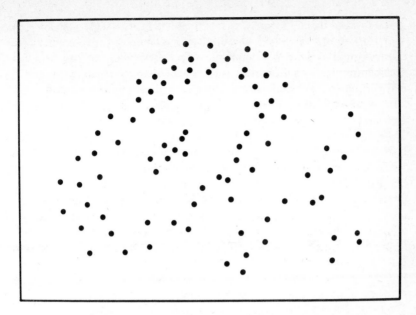

Fig. 4-3. Scatter diagram from point co-ordinates listed under program
TRGRUP as file RAWD4 in the Appendix. The analysis is described
in the main text. Diagram reproduced after JANCEY (1974) with
the permission of the Editors of Vegetatio.

Trials performed on other data sets, simulated and real, indicate the versatility
of the algorithm and suggest possible applications when the objectives call for
recognition of vegetation types or classes of habitats as a prelude to vegetation
mapping, habitat mapping, or inventory in the course of a general survey. The
method is little restricted regarding the resemblance function. It can be any
symmetric distance or similarity measure which retain a uniform scale within
the same sample. Program TRGRUP uses the Euclidean distance.

There are many other classification methods which may be considered for
vegetation analysis. In this connection the reader may consult for further information the brief review of methods below and the references therein.

4.9 Miscellaneous Methods

A. *Information clustering*

The clustering procedures described in section 4.8 may be associated with different information theory quantities as clustering parameters. These quantities
may measure the heterogeneity within the groups, or the information diver-

gence between them. Examples of functions (ORLÓCI, 1970) include:

1. $I(A;B)$ of formula (2.35). This divergence is computed from count or frequency data. It represents a simple sum of p individual bits of information, each contributed by a different species. Such a simple summation of terms may, of course, be objectionable if the species are not independent. We can build a clustering algorithm about $I(A;B)$, similarly as in sum of squares clustering, in which fusions are selected to minimize $I(A;B)$.

2. $I(A;B)$ of formula (2.36). This function is computed from counts or frequencies. No assumptions are required about species independence. The clustering algorithm is similar to sum of squares clustering.

3. $r(F_h;F_i)$ of formula (2.28). When the data represent quantities of some arbitrary scale, such as the data in Table 2-2, the coherence coefficient is a convenient measure of resemblance between the entities. The coherence coefficient can be analyzed in average linkage clustering. Although formula (2.28) defines the coherence coefficient for species, it can be defined also for pairs of quadrats.

B. Methods of successive cluster formation

These include techniques in which one cluster is completely formed before the formation of another cluster begins. The different techniques (see CARLSON, 1970, and references therein) initially select:

1. A pivot character with the highest number of significant correlations with all other characters.
2. A pair of mutually most similar individuals.
3. A pivot individual with the largest number of similarities in excess of a specified limit.

In the subsequent steps an individual is assigned to a cluster if it carries a given pivot character, if it is sufficiently similar to a pivot individual, or to some other members in the group. Once a cluster is completed, its members are removed from the sample, and the classification is performed once again on the remaining individuals. The process is repeated over and over again until all the individuals are clustered. We may consider GOODALL's (1953) method as an example:

1. Find the most frequent species having the largest number of significant correlations with other species of the sample.
2. Group together all quadrats containing that species.
3. Analyse this group of quadrats to find the species with the highest number of significant correlations with the other species.
4. Continue with step 2. Stop when a group is found in which no significant species correlations remain.
5. Remove this group from the sample and reanalyse the residual sample starting with step 1. Continue until all quadrats are clustered.

A quite unique feature of this method is the reliance for the accuracy of correlations on large groups, and the use of significance tests to control the contents of the groups. The appropriateness of a conventional significance test on species correlations may, however, be in doubt considering that groups are not formed in a random clustering process, and as a consequence of this, the correlation coefficient may not have the sampling distribution which is assumed in the statistical test.

C. Clustering based on ordination

Open model factor analysis (CATTELL, 1965), component analysis, and other ordination techniques are commonly used as a basis for cluster recognition. The methods may differ considerably. Some will collect individuals in a common group if their factor loadings are similar on all factors, or form groups of those characters which show a high affinity to a given factor (e.g. DAGNELIE, 1960). Others rely on inspection of scatter diagrams and recognition of clusters on that basis (e.g. GITTINS, 1965).

Classifications based on ordinations, however, must be rather inefficient. Reasons have been given by CARLSON (1970):
1. Ordinations produce axes and not clusters.
2. The rotated axes may dismember groups.
3. The number of groups emerging from the analysis is restricted by the number of axes extracted from the data.

We may add to these that scatter diagrams based on the extracted axes present a potentially distorted projection of clusters of individuals, and therefore, a classification based on groups recognized in a scatter diagram may itself be distorted.

D. Latent structure clustering

This method was proposed by GIBSON (1959) as an adaptation of LAZARS-FELD's latent structure analysis to class recognition. It is aimed at creating classes of individuals in which the characters are uncorrelated. While such a definition of a class is quite attractive, and has also been advocated in connection with vegetation classifications (e.g. GOODALL, 1953), the GIBSON method as it appears from the 1959 publication cannot handle more than a few classes at a time depending on the number of uncorrelated dimensions.

E. GOODALL's (1966) probability clustering

This method differs from any of those so far considered because it takes into account the rank order of the parameter rather than its actual magnitude when deciding on a fusion.

123

F. Similarity clustering

In the most restrictive case, groups are sought, like the natural taxa of SNEATH (1961), in which any individual is more like any other in the group than any other outside the group. Because such a definition of a group, or taxon, may be far too restrictive in practical situations, two alternative strategies are readily conceived:
1. Define a group as a class in which every individual is less similar to every outsider than a fixed similarity value.
2. Permit deviations from perfect homogeneity by allowing any individual to have higher similarity to $\alpha\%$ of the individuals outside the group than a chosen similarity value which describes a current state of homogeneity within the group.

The first of these appears to be the condition used in many clustering methods, among these the graph theory clustering of WIRTH, ESTABROOK & ROGERS (1966), and the single linkage technique of JANCEY (1974). The second allows $\alpha\%$ of the individuals to be deviants. This has been used by CARLSON (1970). None of these methods incorporates statistical tests on the similarity measure. They also possess the attractive properties provided by explicit definitions of group, relative simplicity of algorithms, and flexibility in the choice of a similarity function.

G. Clustering by positive association

The methods of this group use the χ^2 function to seek classes of positively associated species (AGNEW, 1961). The broader literature is reviewed by McINTOSH (1973). Note that the clustering is quite arbitrary because there is reliance on arbitrary limits of significance.

H. Methods that form a specified number of groups

The problem here amounts to sorting individuals into groups when the number of groups to be formed is given. The method of JANCEY (1966) may be mentioned as an example. His method works through successive iterative cycles of fitting centroids to the sample in such a manner that the between group centroid distances are maximized in the final configuration.

I. Methods for large samples and other specialized techniques

The classification techniques which we considered may be not quite suitable for handling very large samples when the number of individuals is in the order of several thousands. Even if one had free access to the largest digital computer the vastness of core space required may force the user to consider other procedures. A method which may help in this connection is described by BAUM & LEFKOVITCH (1971) in connection with a taxonomic study.

It is quite conceivable that in vegetation research special circumstances may call for the use of specialized methods. When the objective is to construct a dichotomous key, for instance, the method of WILLIAMS & LAMBERT (1959) may be considered. This is a monothetic, subdivisive, hierarchical method in which groups of quadrats are split into subgroups based on the presence or absence of strategically chosen species. The division criterion is basically a sum of squares criterion under constraint of the condition that each subdivision must maximize the between groups sum of squares based on a single species.

While classifications most often are used deterministically in ecology, the probabilistic uses are also known to have relevance. For instance, it may be desired to attach probabilities to the allocation so that statements can be made about the 'goodness' of fit of an individual in a specified class. Such probabilities are the basis of allocations in GOODALL's (1968) affinity analysis.

The estimative use of classifications can be another objective which requires special methods. When, for example, the concept of estimative classification is understood in the sense that from sample class values population class values are estimated, there may be serious difficulties with the estimation, because the classes are not constructed by a random sorting process, but rather, they combine individuals of maximum similarity. It follows then that the sample class values are likely to be biased. MACNAUGHTON-SMITH (1965) has considered this problem and suggested a solution:
1. Derive a classification for the first random half of the sample, and then
2. Impose the derived classification upon the second half.
Because the two halves have no individuals in common, membership in one or the other half of the sample is the consequence of chance alone, the class values in the second half will hopefully represent unbiased estimates of the population class values. Imposition of an existing classification on the individuals of another sample may be accomplished on the basis of given diagnostic species when the first random sample is classified in terms of some species-based monothetic classification (*e.g.* WILLIAMS & LAMBERT, 1959), or on the basis of some multivariate assignment function when the first classification is polythetic (see Chapter V for details).

4.10 Evaluation of Clustering Results

A. Recognition of types

Classifications normally use devices which monitor the efficiency of the classification at any stage during the clustering process. Such a device may be a relative measure of heterogeneity between the groups, often a ratio of sum of squares or information, or some other quantity such as for instance a fusion similarity. Considering Fig. 4-2 as an example, classification efficiency at the 2-type level, based on sum of squares, can be determined via the following analysis:

Source of sum of squares	Sum of Squares	% of total
Between groups	$1.81 - 0.06 - 0.14 = 1.61$	89
Within groups	$0.06 + 0.14 = 0.20$	11
Total	1.81	100

There are few other measures on which a similar additive analysis could be performed. Information is one of them, but average similarity is not. The additive property of sum of squares and information will hold true regardless of the number of groups involved.

When a dendrogram is given, and the goal is to recognize vegetation types, the dendrogram may be intercepted at a level corresponding to a specified classification efficiency, and the intercepted stems may be used to delineate vegetation types. The criterion for choosing groups, however, need not specify classification efficiency, but simply, it may specify the number of vegetation types to be formed, in which case, the dendrogram is intercepted at a level incorporating the required number of stems.

There are classifications where no hierarchy is constructed. JANCEY's (1966) method is a good example of this. In his method the number of groups to be formed is specified, and the dissections will stop only after all individuals were allocated to the groups. In JANCEY's 1966 method groups will be formed regardless of the existence or non-existence of natural groups in the sample. In JANCEY's (1974) other method groups will be formed only if the data structure is discontinuous. In other words, the groups must actually exist as discrete entities, separated by sharp discontinuities, before they are recognized as such.

Still other methods may specify an *a priori* maximum for the tolerated heterogeneity within groups and a group is regarded complete once the specified heterogeneity limit is reached. In other cases a subdivision would not be made if the value of the heterogeneity measure, such as χ^2 (WILLIAMS & LAMBERT, 1959), correlation r (GOODALL, 1953), information I (MACNAUGHTON-SMITH, 1965) or the variance ratio F (EDWARDS & CAVALLI-SFORZA, 1965) dropped below a given threshold limit. Similar stopping rules may also be associated with agglomerative clustering methods. In either case, as a general rule, heterogeneity measures such as χ^2, r, I, or F should not really be used as probabilistic criteria for testing hypotheses about heterogeneity because within the groups they may not possess the sampling distributions assumed by statistical tests.

B. Comparison of types

We should base group comparisons on variables other than those which formed the groups. For example, when the groups are represented by vegetation types delimited in terms of species composition, a comparison may be based on environmental variables. Materials for such a comparison are given in Table 4-1 and Fig. 4-4.

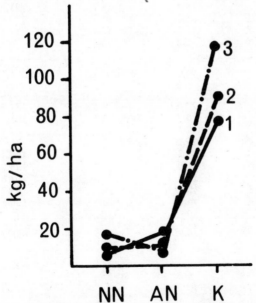

Fig. 4-4. Soil chemical profiles of vegetation types *(1,2,3)*. Vertical scale indicates mean values within the types. *Legend to symbols: NN* – nitrate nitrogen; *AN* – ammoniacal nitrogen; *K* – potassium. All elemental, in kg/ha units.

Table 4-1. Some soil chemical properties in three vegetation types. Replicates are soil samples from quadrats. Entries in table represent quantities in kg/ha units

Type	Replicate	Elementary Nitrate N	Variable Elementary Ammonical N	Elementary K	Total
1	1	7.5	20.1	42.0	69.6
	2	10.9	20.4	43.2	74.5
	3	10.8	17.9	40.4	69.1
	4	12.2	18.0	84.3	114.5
	5	5.1	15.4	69.5	90.0
	6	6.2	12.1	99.8	118.1
	7	3.0	21.0	110.4	134.4
	8	6.6	16.1	101.4	124.1
	9	12.9	13.8	87.7	114.4
	10	4.0	18.0	115.2	137.2
Total		79.2	172.8	793.9	1045.9
2	1	15.2	11.0	94.7	120.9
	2	11.7	13.5	70.8	96.0
	3	9.1	7.8	87.5	104.4
	4	7.0	10.9	125.6	143.5
	5	8.9	15.1	71.0	95.0
	6	11.7	15.3	133.5	160.5
	7	10.1	13.8	77.7	101.6
	8	6.2	16.0	70.3	92.5
Total		79.9	103.4	731.1	914.4
3	1	20.6	9.6	121.9	152.1
	2	20.8	4.1	101.0	125.9
	3	17.1	5.8	83.3	106.2
	4	15.1	12.1	121.4	148.6
	5	16.3	8.9	105.4	130.6
	6	14.9	11.9	128.8	155.6
	7	17.3	5.8	103.6	126.7
	8	13.7	8.7	163.3	185.7
	9	15.1	10.0	126.5	151.6
Total		150.9	76.9	1055.2	1283.0
Grand Total		310.0	353.1	2580.2	3243.3

Let X_{jmh} define in symbolic terms a data element in Table 4-1, and let j, m, h identify respectively a quadrat in which the soil sample is taken, vegetation type in which the quadrat is taken, and variable. For example, $X_{213} =$

43.2 is the quantity of elementary potassium (variable *3*) in the second quadrat of type *1*. The values are totalled within rows as well as columns and these totals are given in the marginal cells. The symbol $X_{jm.}$ represents the *j*th row total in type *m*, and symbol $X_{.mh}$ the *h*th column total in the same type. The total in type *m* is $X_{.m.}$ and the total within the *h*th column $X_{..h}$. The grand total for the table is designated by $X_{...}$, the number of replicates in type *m* by n_m, and in all types by $n_1 + ... + n_k = N$. Symbol *k* designates the number of types and *p* the number of variables.

The procedure to be outlined requires the assumption that the populations from which the samples derive are multivariate normal. This means, in terms of our earlier spatial analogy, that the points form linear clusters of uniform density. Under this assumption we can stipulate different hypotheses about the *k* types:

H_0 : The types are indistinguishable in terms of the *p* environmental variables.

H_{01} : The point clusters, which represent the types, are indistinguishable based on their size, shape, or orientation.

H_{02} : The type mean vectors estimate the same population mean vector.

The general hypothesis of type indistinguishability H_0 has two components H_{01} and H_{02}. It is quite logical to begin with H_{01} because the test on H_{02} requires the assumption that H_{01} is true. The criterion that describes the shape, size and orientation of linear point clusters is the covariance matrix. Let S_m represent the *m*th sample covariance matrix of the variables. This matrix has $p \times p$ elements. A characteristic element of S_m is S_{him}, relating the *i*th and *h*th variables in type *m*. Because the covariance matrix completely describes a linear cluster, less its location, a test on H_{01}, against an alternative hypothesis which negates H_{01}, is equivalent to a test on the null hypothesis

$$H_{01} : E(S_1) = ... = E(S_k)$$

which stipulates that the *k* population covariance matrixes are equal, against the alternative that at least some of them are not. The letter E indicates expectation. The test criterion is MC^{-1} which we compute according to

$$M = \sum_m (n_m - 1) \ln |S| - \sum_m (n_m - 1) \ln |S_m|, \; m = 1, ..., k$$

and

$$C^{-1} = 1 - \frac{2p^2 + 3p - 1}{6(p + 1)(k - 1)} \left[\sum_m \frac{1}{n_m - 1} - \frac{1}{\sum_m (n_m - 1)} \right], \; m = 1, ..., k$$

129

In these expressions $|S|$ is the determinant of the pooled covariance matrix whose elements are defined by

$$S_{hi} = \frac{\sum_m (n_m - 1) S_{him}}{\sum_m (n_m - 1)}, \quad m = 1, ..., k$$

where S_{him} is the covariance of variable h and i in type m, and $|S_m|$ is the determinant of the mth covariance matrix S_m; n_m represents the number of samples taken from type m; k is the number of types; and p the number of variables. We accept H_{01} at α probability if the condition

$$MC^{-1} < \chi^2_{\alpha;\,(k-1)p(p+1)/2}$$

is satisfied. Otherwise we reject H_{01}.

Based on the data in Table 4-1 we use program TSTCOV in the Appendix to compute the following numerical results:

$$k = 3 \quad n_1 = 10 \quad n_2 = 8 \quad n_3 = 9 \quad p = 3$$

$$S_1 = \begin{bmatrix} 12.5218 & -1.0784 & -52.3609 \\ -1.0784 & 8.5351 & -26.6524 \\ -52.3609 & -26.6521 & 840.434 \end{bmatrix}$$

$$|S_1| = 53538.4$$

$$S_2 = \begin{bmatrix} 8.3270 & -1.1854 & 7.9813 \\ -1.1854 & 7.8564 & -12.6739 \\ 7.9813 & -12.6739 & 634.510 \end{bmatrix}$$

$$|S_2| = 39020.0$$

$$S_3 = \begin{bmatrix} 6.2525 & -3.9396 & -30.7371 \\ -3.9396 & 7.7628 & 34.7115 \\ -30.7371 & 34.7115 & 515.228 \end{bmatrix}$$

$$|S_3| = 10549.9$$

$$S = \begin{bmatrix} 9.2085 & -2.0633 & -27.5532 \\ -2.0633 & 8.0797 & -2.1207 \\ -27.5532 & -2.1207 & 671.971 \end{bmatrix}$$

$$|S| = 40718.9$$

130

$$M = 24 \ln 40718.9 - 9 \ln 53538.4 - 7 \ln 39020.0 - 8 \ln 10549.9$$
$$= 8.6396$$
$$C^{-1} = 1 - \frac{18+8}{6(4)(2)}\left[\frac{1}{9} + \frac{1}{7} + \frac{1}{8} - \frac{1}{24}\right] = 1 - 0.1827 = 0.8173$$

From these we have $MC^{-1} = 7.061$. Because $\chi^2_{0.05\,;\,12} = 21.03$, the condition

$$MC^{-1} < \chi^2_{0.05\,;12}$$

is true, and H_{01} is accepted. We thus declare indistinguishability on the shape, size and orientation of the k clusters. The question remains: are the mean vectors distinguishable?

The test on the equality of covariance matrices clears the way for a test on the type mean vectors about which we hypothesized under H_{02}. This hypothesis can be restated as

$$H_{02} = E(\bar{X}_1) = \ldots = E(\bar{X}_k)$$

where $\bar{X}_m = (\bar{X}_{m1} \ldots \bar{X}_{mp})$ is the mean vector of type m whose elements $\bar{X}_{m1}, \ldots, \bar{X}_{mp}$ represent the variate means. The letter E indicates expectation. H_{02} is tested against an alternative hypothesis which negates H_{02}. The procedure is based on the multivariate analysis of variance which partitions sum of squares and cross products. We define the cross products of variable h and i in the total sample, irrespective of types, as

$$S_{hi} = \sum_m \sum_j X_{jmh}X_{jmi} - X_{..h}X_{..i}/N, \quad m = 1, \ldots, k;\ j = 1, \ldots, n_m$$

Any such cross product can be partitioned into a between *(H)* and within *(E)* component:

$$H_{hi} = \sum_m X_{.mh}X_{.mi}/n_m - X_{..h}X_{..i}/N, \quad m = 1, \ldots, k$$
$$E_{hi} = \sum_m \left[\sum_j (X_{jmh}X_{jmi}) - X_{.mh}X_{.mi}/n_m\right], \quad m = 1, \ldots, k;\ j = 1, \ldots, n_m$$

To test the hypothesis of equal type mean vectors we extract the largest eigenvalue λ of HE^{-1} where H is a $p \times p$ matrix of elements H_{hi} and E is a $p \times p$ matrix of elements E_{hi}. The test criterion $\theta = \lambda/(1 + \lambda)$ is referred to the approriate HECK (1960) chart at α probability and parameters $s = \min(k-1, p)$, $m = (|k-p-1|-1)/2$, and $n = (N-k-p-1)/2$. H_{02} is accepted at α probability if the condition

$$\theta < \theta_{\alpha;\,s,m,n}$$

is satisfied. Other wise H_{02} is rejected.

Based on the data in Table 4-1 the following results emerge by an analysis based on program EMV in the Appendix:

$$\bar{X}_1 = \begin{bmatrix} 7.9 \\ 17.3 \\ 79.4 \end{bmatrix} \qquad \bar{X}_2 = \begin{bmatrix} 10.0 \\ 12.9 \\ 91.4 \end{bmatrix} \qquad \bar{X}_3 = \begin{bmatrix} 16.8 \\ 8.5 \\ 117.2 \end{bmatrix}$$

$$S = \begin{bmatrix} 617.101 & -412.991 & 995.941 \\ -412.991 & 555.647 & -1610.02 \\ 995.941 & -1610.02 & 23113.2 \end{bmatrix}$$

$$H = \begin{bmatrix} 396.096 & -363.471 & 1657.22 \\ -363.471 & 361.733 & -1559.13 \\ 1657.22 & -1559.13 & 6985.90 \end{bmatrix}$$

$$E = \begin{bmatrix} 221.005 & -49.5202 & -661.277 \\ -49.5202 & 193.913 & -50.8975 \\ -661.277 & -50.8975 & 16127.300 \end{bmatrix}$$

$$E^{-1} = \begin{bmatrix} 0.00555111 & 0.00147857 & 0.000232282 \\ 0.00147857 & 0.00555505 & 0.0000781584 \\ 0.000232282 & 0.0000781584 & 0.0000717777 \end{bmatrix}$$

$$HE^{-1} = \begin{bmatrix} 2.04630 & -1.30392 & 0.182549 \\ -1.84497 & 1.35017 & -0.168066 \\ 8.51681 & -5.66470 & 0.764574 \end{bmatrix}$$

$\lambda = 12.1929$
$\theta = 12.1929/13.1929 = 0.924$
$s = \min(2,3) = 2$
$m = (|3 - 3 - 1| - 1)/2 = 0$
$n = (27 - 3 - 3 - 1)/2 = 10$

Because the chart value $\theta_{0.05\,;\,2\,0,10} = 0.375$ is less than the calculated value θ we reject H_{02} and declare that at least two of the type mean vectors are significantly different.

132

As the next step after rejection of H_{02} we could examine mean vectors in pairs to determine which are significantly different and which are not, and we could also consider the question of which variables are contributing most strongly to the differences. We shall limit the subsequent discussions to tests concerned with the hypotheses:

$$H_{021} : E(\overline{X}_1) = E(\overline{X}_2)$$

$$H_{022} : E(\overline{X}_1) = E(\overline{X}_3)$$

$$H_{023} : E(\overline{X}_2) = E(\overline{X}_3)$$

The test criterion is

$$T_{mz}^2 = \frac{n_m n_z}{n_m + n_z} \, (\overline{X}_m - \overline{X}_z)' \, S^{-1} (\overline{X}_m - \overline{X}_z)$$

for any m or z where n_m and n_z indicate the number of samples from types m and z, $\overline{X}_m$ and $\overline{X}_z$ are type mean vectors, and S is the pooled covariance matrix for the two types. The quantity

$$F = (n_m + n_z - p - 1) \, T^2 \, / ((n_m + n_z - 2)p)$$

has the variance ratio distribution with degrees of freedom p and $n_m + n_z - p - 1$. For type 1 and 2 the criterion becomes:

$$T_{12}^2 = \frac{80}{18}(7.9 - 10.0 \quad 17.3 - 12.9 \quad 79.4 - 91.4)$$

$$\begin{bmatrix} 0.133227 & 0.0354857 & 0.00557475 \\ 0.0354857 & 0.133321 & 0.00187579 \\ 0.00557475 & 0.00187579 & 0.00172266 \end{bmatrix} \begin{bmatrix} 7.9 - 10.0 \\ 17.3 - 12.9 \\ 79.4 - 91.4 \end{bmatrix}$$

$$= 12.37 \text{ and } F_{12} = \frac{14}{48} 12.37 = 3.61$$

To explain further these results we note that in this particular example we use the inverse of the pooled covariance matrix S which we computed in the test for equality of covariance matrices. We do use the same inverse because it is convenient, and also, justified. Firstly, the inverse of S is already available as it had to be computed before the determinant of S could be found. Secondly, we have theoretical justification springing from the test of H_{01}: when we accepted H_{01} we implied that pooling S_1, S_2, S_3 is justified because they are all estimates of a common population covariance matrix.

133

Similar computations yield the remaining values of T_{13}^2 and T_{23}^2. The complete set of results are summarized in the following table:

Types	F	Degrees of freedom	$F_{0.05;p,\, n_m+n_z-p-1}$	Hypothesis H_{02} rejected (R)
1,2	3.61	3,14	3.34	R
1,3	28.0	3,15	3.29	R
2,3	11.3	3,13	3.41	R

We conclude that all pairs of mean vectors differ significantly. The difference is smallest between types *1* and *2*, and greatest between *1* and *3*.

Some further comments should be made about these results. Longhand computations, even in the present example where only three variables are involved and only three groups, are not really recommended. The computations should be performed by a computer. Regarding precision, it is logical that we retain not more than one decimal when we give the mean vectors. This is the precision in the measurements themselves. However, in the intermediate results, such as in the inverse of any matrix, we retain six significant digits. This is the computer's precision. In the test quantities such as F and χ^2 the number of decimals retained coincide with the numbers given in a relevant statistical table.

C. Predictive use of classifications

A specific kind of test is needed when there are two classifications of the same set of quadrats and we intend to use one to predict the properties in the other. For example, we may recognize classes on the basis of species abundance, and we may wish to use these classes to predict given environmental properties. This we would do in such a way that we could make statements about the environmental conditions in a new quadrat once its affiliation with a vegetation class has been established. The question is how reliably can a given vegetational classification be used for such a prediction?

This question can, of course, be answered only with local relevance based on a survey of both the vegetation and environment. Let us assume that such a survey is completed and that subsequent analyses of the survey data yield two classifications of the same set of N quadrats. Let us further assume that the vegetational classification consists of k classes, and that there are t classes in the classification derived from environmental data. We wish to test the hypothesis that the k vegetation classes have no predictive value for the conditions in the t environmental classes.

134

To illustrate the procedure we shall consider the data in Table 4-2. In this

Table 4-2. Comparison of classifications. Entries represent quadrat
counts in classes of vegetation *(A, B, C, D)*, in classes of soil
texture *(a, b, c, d)*, and in common between the two

Soil textural class	Vegetation class				Total
	A	B	C	D	
a	4	1	19	8	32
b	5	27	3	4	39
c	8	16	6	20	50
d	12	2	1	1	16
Total	29	46	29	33	137

table the same set of 137 quadrats are sorted according to two sets of classificatory criteria. The first set *A, B, C, D* signifies vegetation classes, and the second set *a, b, c, d* represents soil textural classes. The entries in the body of the table signify the number of quadrats which are common to the respective classes. In the marginal cells the values indicate the total number of quadrats in the individual classes.

The degree to which the soil textural classes are unpredictable from the vegetation classes is entirely dependent on the degree to which the two classifications are independent. The criterion, particularly suited for testing independence in such a contingency table, is the mutual information, given by

$$2I(\text{vegetation; soil texture}) = 2 \sum_h \sum_i f_{hi} \ln \frac{f_{hi} f_{..}}{f_{h.} f_{.i}}$$

The summations are taken from $h = a$ to d and $i = A$ to D. The remaining symbols are defined as follows: f_{hi} element in hi cell, $f_{h.}$ hth row total, $f_{.i}$ ith column total, $f_{..}$ grand total for the table. The working formula to be used in the computations accords with

$$2I(\text{vegetation; soil texture}) = 2 \sum_h \sum_i f_{hi} \ln f_{hi} + f_{..} \ln f_{..}$$

$$- \sum_h f_{h.} \ln f_{h.} - \sum_i f_{.i} \ln f_{.i}$$

$$= 2(2(4 \ln 4) + 19 \ln 19 + 2(8 \ln 8) + 5 \ln 5 + 27 \ln 27 + 3 \ln 3$$

$$+ 16 \ln 16 + 6 \ln 6 + 20 \ln 20 + 12 \ln 12 + 2 \ln 2 + 137 \ln 137$$

$$- 32 \ln 32 - 39 \ln 39 - 50 \ln 50 - 16 \ln 16 - 2(29 \ln 29)$$

$$- 46 \ln 46 - 33 \ln 33)$$

$$= 2(346.868 + 674.037 - 493.745 - 486.805)$$

$$= 80.706$$

This quantity is referred to the χ^2 distribution with 9 degrees of freedom. Because $\chi^2_{0.05\,;9} = 16.919$ is less than $2I$, we reject the hypothesis of independence, and accept the alternative hypothesis that the two classifications are related. What we can conclude from the text about the strength of the relationship between the two classifications is that the probability of obtaining an I-divergence of the magnitude as ours, when the population classifications indeed are independent, is less than 5%. This is a rather weak statement, and we prefer in addition something quantitative in terms of a relative scale. For this purpose we may compute the coherence coefficient. In the case of our contingency table RAJSKI's metric is defined by

$$d(vegetation;\ soil\ texture) = 1 - \frac{I(vegetation;\ soil\ texture)}{I(vegetation,\ soil\ texture)}$$

$$= 1 - \frac{\sum\limits_{h}\sum\limits_{i} f_{hi} \ln f_{hi}f_{..}/(f_{h.}f_{.i})}{-\sum\limits_{h}\sum\limits_{i} f_{hi} \ln f_{hi}/f_{..}}$$

with summations $h = 1, ..., n;\ i = 1, ..., c$, where n and c indicate respectively the number of rows and columns in the contingency table. The corresponding numerical value is given by

$$d(vegetation;\ soil\ texture) = 1 - \frac{40.355}{327.169} = 0.877$$

From this we compute the coherence coefficient

$$r(vegetation;\ soil\ texture) = \sqrt{(1 - d^2)} = \sqrt{(1 - 0.877^2)} = 0.481$$

This indicates a reasonably high average affinity between the two classifications. We may then conclude that on the average the vegetation class affiliation of quadrats and their membership in a soil class are quite strongly related, and with regard to our original question, that the predictive value of the vegetational classification for soil texture is reasonably high.

One further question flows from what we have said so far: which vegetation class has a high predictive value for which soil textural class? To answer this we partition $2I(vegetation;\ soil\ texture)$ into components specific to A, B, C, or D and look at them individually. The relevant results for A are the following:

$$2I(A;\ soil\ texture) = 2\sum\limits_{h} f_{hA} \ln \frac{f_{hA}f_{..}}{f_{h.}f_{.A}}$$

$$= 2\sum\limits_{h} f_{hA} \left[\ln \frac{f_{hA}}{f_{.A}/n} - \ln \frac{f_{h.}}{f_{..}/n} \right]$$

The working formula accords with

$$2I(A; soil\ texture) = 2 \sum_h f_{hA} \ln f_{hA} + f_{.A} \ln f_{..} - \sum_h f_{hA} \ln f_{h.}$$

$$- f_{.A} \ln f_{.A} = 2(4 \ln 4 + 5 \ln 5 + 8 \ln 8 + 12 \ln 12$$
$$+ 29 \ln 137 - 4 \ln 32 - 5 \ln 39 - 8 \ln 50$$
$$- 12 \ln 16 - 29 \ln 29)$$
$$= 2(60.047 + 142.679 - 96.748 - 97.652) = 16.652$$

This can be compared to χ^2 at 3 degrees of freedom for significance. In such a comparison $\chi^2_{0.05;\ 3} = 7.815$ is exceeded by the value $2I$. Hence we declare significance on $2I$ conditional on vegetation class A. The test indicates that $2I(A; soil\ texture)$ significantly differs from zero. Although this may be an interesting fact, it does not tell us much about the extent to which A can predict soil texture relative to B, C, or D. We can, of course, compute A's specific share in RAJSKI's metric and the corresponding coherence value, and use these as a measure for A's weakness or strength of prediction. These are given by

$$d(A; soil\ texture) = 1 - \frac{I(A; soil\ texture)}{I(vegetation, soil\ texture)}$$

$$= 1 - \frac{8.327}{327.169} = 0.975$$

$$r(A; soil\ texture) = \sqrt{(1 - 0.975^2)} = 0.222$$

Similar computations yield components specific to B, C, D. The results are given below:

$$2I(B; soil\ texture) = 2(27 \ln 27 + 16 \ln 16 + 2 \ln 2 + 46 \ln 137$$
$$- \ln 32 - 27 \ln 39 - 16 \ln 50 - 2 \ln 16 - 46 \ln 46)$$
$$= 2(134.735 + 226.319 - 170.519 - 176.118)$$
$$= 28.834$$

$$d(B; soil\ texture) = 1 - \frac{14.417}{327.169} = 0.956$$

$$r(B; soil\ texture) = \sqrt{(1 - 0.956^2)} = 0.293$$

$$2I(C; \text{ soil texture}) = 2(19 \ln 19 + 3 \ln 3 + 6 \ln 6 + 29 \ln 137 +$$
$$- 19 \ln 32 - 3 \ln 39 - 6 \ln 50 - \ln 16 - 29 \ln 29)$$
$$= 2(69.991 + 142.679 - 103.084 - 97.652)$$
$$= 23.868$$

$$d(C; \text{ soil texture}) = 1 - \frac{11.934}{327.169} = 0.964$$

$$r(C; \text{ soil texture}) = \sqrt{(1 - 0.964^2)} = 0.266$$

$$2I(D; \text{ soil texture}) = 2(8 \ln 8 + 4 \ln 4 + 20 \ln 20 + 33 \ln 137 - 8 \ln 32$$
$$- 4 \ln 39 - 20 \ln 50 - \ln 16 - 33 \ln 33)$$
$$= 2(82.095 + 162.359 - 123.393 - 115.385)$$
$$= 11.352$$

$$d(D; \text{ soil texture}) = 1 - \frac{5.676}{327.169} = 0.983$$

$$r(D; \text{ soil texture}) = \sqrt{(1 - 0.983^2)} = 0.184$$

The partial results are summarized below:

Source	Component of information $2I$	Degrees of freedom (DF)	$x^2_{0.05;DF}$	Component of RAJSKI's metric	Coherence coefficient
A	16.652	3	7.815	0.975	0.222
B	28.834	3		0.956	0.293
C	23.868	3		0.964	0.266
D	11.352	3		0.983	0.184
A+B+C+D	80.706			0.877	0.481

Several comments are in order regarding these results. Firstly, we should point out that the sum of the individual components of $2I$ should be equal to $2I(\text{vegetation; soil texture})$. Secondly, the one-complement of the sum of one-complements of the components of RAJSKI's metric is equal to $d(\text{vegetation; soil texture})$, i.e. $1 - ((1 - 0.975) + (1 - 0.956) + (1 - 0.964) + (1 - 0.982)) = 0.877$. We further note that all $2I$ values represent significant divergences. On this basis we can give the following characterizations:

1. Vegetation class B is the best single predictor for soil texture. When a quadrat is identified as a member in vegetation class B it most likely is also a

member of soil texture class b. This is a consequence of the frequencies in Table 4-2.

2. Vegetation class C is the second best predictor for soil texture. When a quadrat is identified as a member in C, it most likely is also a member in soil texture class a.

3. Vegetation class A is the third ranking predictor for soil texture. When a quadrat is identified as a member in A, it most probably is also a member in soil texture class d.

4. The least reliable predictor is vegetation class D. A quadrat identified as a member of D most probably comes as a member in soil texture class c.

If we use the coherence coefficient to measure how much reliance can be placed on a classification as a predictor of conditions indicated by another classification, we may also use RAJSKI's metric as our heuristic measure for uncertainty in the prediction. In these terms, when two classifications are identical, the prediction of one based on the other is without uncertainty, and thus their mutual information – *i.e.* 2*I(vegetation; soil texture)* in the example – is maximal, the value of RAJSKI's metric is zero, the value of the coherence coefficient is one. At the other extreme, when the two classifications are completely different and it is impossible to make predictions from one about the other, the mutual information is zero, RAJSKI's metric is one, and the coherence coefficient is zero.

D. Comparison of dendrograms

Dendrograms may be described in different ways. A description of the levels at which the fusions occur is one possibility, but it may prove to be too restrictive because there would be too much weight attributed to quantitative differences among dendrograms which otherwise may be quite similar in terms of their fusion topology. There is much to be said for the PHIPPS (1971) method which describes dendrograms by their fusion topology. Such a description is based on counts, symbolically represented by $t_{11}, t_{12}, ..., t_{hi}, ...$ in which the general element t_{hi} specifies the number of fusions that must occur before individuals h and i unite in a common group. Counts of this sort can provide unique descriptions for dendrograms and a suitable basis for comparisons.

Let the count t_{mhi} represent the h, i element in matrix $\mathbf{T}_m$ of group m. We shall refer to $\mathbf{T}_m$ as the mth topology matrix. Dendrograms whose topology matrices are equivalent are said to have identical topologies. Such dendrograms may nevertheless differ with respect to other descriptors such as the levels at which the fusions occur. Considering topology matrices they are characterized by certain common properties:

1. The elements are positive integer numbers and symmetric. Because of the symmetry property it is sufficient to give the counts in one half above or below the principal diagonal in a topology matrix.

2. The elements are not independent. The degree of freedom in a dendrogram is less than the actual number of fusions.

3. With a decrease in the number of individuals the number of possible dendrograms is reduced and the differences between the dendrograms become restricted to less and less variation.

The fact that fusion counts are not completely independent have a consequence of fundamental importance. Non-independence means that for example when three objects A, B, C give rise to fusions $A + B$ and $A + B + C$ with a topology matrix

	A	B	C
A	–	1 .	2
B		–	2
C			–

once t_{AB} is determined to be one, the value of t_{AC} or t_{BC} is also determined. Similar non-independence exists between certain elements in any larger topology matrix irrespective of its actual order. When the objective is to compare dendrogram topologies the non-independence of fusion counts removes from consideration certain statistics, such as for instance χ^2, which assume that the elements are independent. The problem is that because the fusion counts are not independent the sampling distribution of a statistical index will probably not conform to the stipulated theoretical distribution, and the true distribution will be unknown under the circumstances. When the sampling distribution is unknown we can tell in no way whether an observed value of the statistic is small or large from the point of view of accepting or rejecting null hypotheses.

When the sampling distribution of a statistic cannot be derived from basic principles it still can be determined on empirical grounds. For example, we may generate a large number of dendrograms under the assumption that the null hypothesis of equal topology matrices is true, compute the statistic for each pair of dendrograms, and then, use the distribution of the computed values as the sampling distribution of the statistic. We derive in the following example such a distribution for

$$I(m;o) = \sum_h \sum_i \left[t_{mhi} \ln \frac{2t_{mhi}}{t_{mhi} + t_{moi}} + t_{ohi} \ln \frac{2t_{ohi}}{t_{mhi} + t_{ohi}} \right] \qquad (4.4)$$

where m and o are two dendrograms with topology matrices $\mathbf{T}_m$, $\mathbf{T}_o$ and characteristic elements t_{mhi}, t_{ohi}. We proceed like this:

1. Sort individuals at random between quadrats based on the observed quantities of species.

140

2. Analyse the data into a dendrogram m.
3. Describe the dendrogram by a topology matrix T_m.
4. Repeat steps 1 through 3 a large number of times, designated by E, but not in excess of the possible maximum number of distinct dendrograms that can be derived from the data under the chosen fusion strategy.
5. Compute $I(m; o)$ values for all distinct pairs of topology matrices. There will be $E(E - 1)/2$ such values.
6. Order the $I(m; o)$ values in a sense of increasing magnitude and determine by counting probability points. An α probability point $I(m; o)_\alpha$ is such that the probability of a larger or equal $I(m; o)$ value is α.

Once probability points are determined for $I(m; o)$ we can use these points to test the null hypothesis that the two population topology matrices corresponding to any sample topology matrices T_m, T_o are identical. Because the empirical distribution of $I(m; o)$ is generated under the assumption that the null hypothesis is true, we accept the null hypothesis with α probability if the condition

$$I(m; o) < I(m; o)_\alpha$$

is true, and reject it if

$$I(m; o) \geqslant I(m; o)_\alpha$$

is true.

Let us assume that the objects to be classified are species with total counts of individuals, given in Table 4-3, estimated to the nearest thousand within

Table 4-3. Estimated numbers of individuals within survey site

Species	Total
1. Poa compressa	1994000
2. Andropogon scoparius	473000
3. Artemisia campestris	48000
4. Melilotus alba	37000
5. Artemisia caudata	21000
6. Panicum virgatum	12000
7. Equisetum hyemale	8000

the survey site. We can use programs SSSIM2 and SSSIM3 to compute an empirical sampling distribution for $I(m; o)$ based on these species quantities. We

141

note that there are 25 quadrats in the sample. After the computation of 30 dendrograms and 435 values for $I(m; o)$, in accord with steps 1 to 6, and after counting the ordered values, we find the following probability points

α	.975	.95	.90	.10	.05	.025
$I(m; o)_\alpha$	.638	.750	1.007	8.065	8.627	9.136

An entry $I(m; o)_\alpha$ in this table corresponds to the limit such that the probability of a larger or equal value in the empirical distribution of $I(m; o)$ is α. Let us assume that an analysis of samples from two soil types in the survey site for Table 4-3 yields dendrograms for the seven species with topology matrices,

$$\mathbf{T}_1 = \begin{bmatrix} 0 & 1 & 2 & 3 & 2 & 2 & 3 \\ & 0 & 2 & 3 & 2 & 2 & 3 \\ & & 0 & 2 & 1 & 1 & 2 \\ & & & 0 & 1 & 1 & 1 \\ & & & & 0 & 1 & 2 \\ & & & & & 0 & 2 \\ & & & & & & 0 \end{bmatrix}$$

$$\mathbf{T}_2 = \begin{bmatrix} 0 & 1 & 2 & 1 & 1 & 4 & 5 \\ & 0 & 2 & 1 & 1 & 3 & 4 \\ & & 0 & 1 & 1 & 3 & 4 \\ & & & 0 & 1 & 3 & 4 \\ & & & & 0 & 3 & 4 \\ & & & & & 0 & 2 \\ & & & & & & 0 \end{bmatrix}$$

The information divergence (formula (4.4)) of $\mathbf{T}_1$ and $\mathbf{T}_2$ is $I(1; 2) = 5.954$. We now wish to test the null hypothesis of equal population topology matrices. In other words, we want to decide whether 5.954 is a large enough number to declare significant the difference of $\mathbf{T}_1$ and $\mathbf{T}_2$. We choose $\alpha = 0.05$ as the rejection probability. Because the value $I(1; 2) = 5.954$ is less than $I(m; o)_\alpha = 8.627$ we accept the null hypothesis and declare $\mathbf{T}_1$ and $\mathbf{T}_2$ statistically indistinguishable. But when we consider the topology matrices,

$$\mathbf{T}_3 = \begin{bmatrix} 0 & 1 & 2 & 3 & 1 & 2 & 1 \\ & 0 & 2 & 3 & 1 & 2 & 1 \\ & & 0 & 2 & 1 & 1 & 1 \\ & & & 0 & 2 & 1 & 2 \\ & & & & 0 & 2 & 1 \\ & & & & & 0 & 2 \\ & & & & & & 0 \end{bmatrix}$$

$$T_4 = \begin{bmatrix} 0 & 1 & 2 & 3 & 4 & 5 & 6 \\ & 0 & 2 & 3 & 4 & 5 & 6 \\ & & 0 & 2 & 3 & 4 & 5 \\ & & & 0 & 2 & 3 & 4 \\ & & & & 0 & 2 & 3 \\ & & & & & 0 & 2 \\ & & & & & & 0 \end{bmatrix}$$

we have to reject the null hypothesis. In this case $I(3, 4) = 11.547$ which exceeds the α rejection limit.

4.11 References

AGNEW, A.D.Q. 1961. The ecology of *Juncus effusus L.* in North Wales. *J. Ecol.* 49: 83-102.

BAUM, B.R. & L.P. LEFKOVITCH. 1971. A model for cultivar classification and identification with reference to oats (Avena). I. Establishment of the groupings by taximetric methods. *Can. J. Bot.* 50: 121-130.

BRAUN-BLANQUET, J. 1928. *Pflanzensoziologie. Grundzuge der Vegetationskunde.* 1. Auflage., Springer, Berlin.

BRAUN-BLANQUET. J. 1951. *Pflanzensoziologie. Grundzuge der Vegetationskunde.* 2. Auflage, Springer-Verlag, Wien.

CAJANDER, A.K. 1909. Über Waldtypen. *Acta Forestalia Fennica* 1: 1-175.

CARLSON, K.A. 1970. *A Multivariate Classification of Reformatory Inmates.* Ph.D. thesis. University of Western Ontario, London, Canada.

CATTELL, R.B. 1965. Factor analysis: an introduction to essentials. *Biometrics* 21: 190-215, 405-435.

CLEMENTS, F.E. 1916. Plant succession: an analysis of the development of vegetation. *Carnegie Inst. Washington, Publ.* 242: 1-512.

CORMACK, R.M. 1971. A review of classification. *J. Roy. statis. Soc. Series A,* 134: 321-353.

DAGNELIE, P. 1960. Contribution à l'étude des communautés végétales par l'analyse factorielle. *Bull. Sérv. Carte Phytogéogr. Ser. B.* 5: 7-71, 93-195.

DOKUCHAEV, V.V. 1899. *On the Theory of Natural Zones.* St. Petersburg.

DUCKER, S.C., W.T. WILLIAMS & G.N. LANCE. 1965. Numerical classification of the Pacific forms of *Chlorodesmis* (Chlorophyta). *Aust. J. Bot.* 13: 489-499.

EDWARDS, A.W.F. & L.L. CAVALLI-SFORZA. 1965. A method for cluster analysis. *Biometrics* 21: 362-375.

GIBSON, W.A. 1959. Three multivariate models: factor analysis, latent structure analysis, latent profile analysis. *Psychometrika* 24: 229-252.

GITTINS, R. 1965. Multivariate approaches to a limestone grassland community. III. A comparative study of ordination and association analysis. *J. Ecol.* 53: 411-425.

GOODALL, D.W. 1953. Objective methods for the classification of vegetation. I. The use of positive interspecific correlation. *Aust. J. Bot.* 1: 39-63.

GOODALL, D.W. 1966. Numerical taxonomy of bacteria – some published data reexamined. *J. gen. Microbiol.* 42: 25-37.

GOODALL, D.W. 1968. Affinity between an individual and a cluster in numerical taxonomy. *Biometrie-Praximetrie* 9: 52-55.

GOWER, J.C. 1967. A comparison of some methods of cluster analysis. *Biometrics* 23: 623-637.

GREIG-SMITH, P. 1964. *Quantitative Plant Ecology.* 2nd ed. London, Butterworths.
HECK, D.L. 1960. Charts of some upper percentage points of the distribution of the largest characteristic root. *The Annals of Math. Statistics* 31: 625-642.
JANCEY, R.C. 1966. Multidimensional group analysis. *Aust. J. Bot.* 14: 127-130.
JANCEY, R.C. 1974. Algorithm for detection of discontinuities in data sets. *Vegetatio* (in press).
JARDINE, N. & R. SIBSON. 1971. *Mathematical Taxonomy.* London, Wiley.
KENDALL, M.G. 1966. Discrimination and classification. *In:* P.R. KRISHNAIAH (ed.), *Proc. Symp. Multiv. Analysis, Dayton, Ohio,* pp. 165-185. New York, Academic Press.
KRAJINA, V.J. 1933. Die Pflanzengesellschaften des Mlynica Tales in den Vysoke Tatry (Hohe Tatra). Mit besonderer Berucksichtigung der okologischen Verhaltnisse. *Bot. Centralbl., Abt.* 2, 50: 744-957, 51: 1-244.
KRAJINA, V.J. 1960. Ecosystem classification of forests. *Silva Fennica* 105: 107-110, 123-138.
KRAJINA, V.J. 1961. Ecosystem classification of forests. Summary. *In: Recent Advances in Botany,* pp. 1599-1603. Toronto, Univ. Toronto Press.
LAZARSFELD, P.F. 1950. The logical and mathematical foundations of latent structure analysis. *In:* S.A. STOUFFER *et al.* (eds.), *Measurement and Prediction,,*pp. 362-413. Princeton, Princeton. Univ. Press.
MACNAUGHTON-SMITH, P. 1965. Some statistical and other numerical techniques for classifying individuals. London, Her Majesty's Stationary Office.
McINTOSH, R.P, 1967. The continuum concept of vegetation. *Bot. Rev.* 33: 130-187.
McINTOSH, R.P. 1973. Matrix and plexus techniques. *In:* R.H. WHITTAKER (ed.), *Handbook of Vegetation Science,* Vol. 5, pp. 157-191. The Hague, W. Junk.
ORLÓCI, L. 1967. An agglomerative method for classification of plant communities. *J. Ecol.* 55: 193-205.
ORLÓCI, L. 1970. Analysis of vegetation samples based on the use of information. *J. theoret. Biol.* 29: 173-189.
PHIPPS, J.B. 1971. Dendrogram topology. Syst. Zool. 20: 306-308.
PIELOU, E.C. 1969. *An Introduction to Mathematical Ecology.* New York, Wiley-Inter-Science.
SNEATH, P.H.A. 1957. The application of computers to taxonomy. *J. Gen. Microbiol.* 17: 201-226.
SNEATH, P.H.A. 1961. Recent developments in theoretical and quantitative taxonomy. *Syst. Zool.* 10: 118-139.
SNEATH, P.H.A. 1962. The construction of taxonomic groups. *In:* G.C. AINSWORTH & P.H.A. SNEATH (eds.), *Microbiol Classification, 12th Symposium of the Society for General Microbiology,* pp. 289-332. Cambridge, Cambridge Univ. Press.
SOKAL, R.R. & C.D. MICHENER. 1958. A statistical method for evaluating systematic relationships. *Univ. Kansas Sci. Bull.* 38: 1409-1438.
TANSLEY, A.G. 1939. *The British Islands and their Vegetation.* Cambridge, Cambridge Univ. Press.
WARD, J.H. 1963. Hierarchical grouping to optimize an objective function. *J. Amer. Statist. Ass.* 58: 236-244.
WARD, J.H. & M.E. HOOK. 1963. Application of an hierarchical grouping procedure to a problem of grouping profiles. *Education and Psychological Measurement* 23: 69-82.
WHITTAKER, R.H. 1962. Classification of natural communities. *Bot. Rev.* 28: 1-239.
WILLIAMS, W.T. & J.M. LAMBERT. 1959. Multivariate methods in plant ecology.
I. Association analysis in plant communities. *J. Ecol.* 47: 83-101.
WILLIAMS, W.T. & M.B. DALE. 1965. Fundamental problems in numerical taxonomy. *Adv. Bot. Res.* 2: 35-68.
WIRTH, M., G.F. ESTABROOK & D.J. ROGERS. 1966. A graph theory model for systematic biology, with an example for the Oncidiinae (Orchidaceae). *Syst. Zool.* 15: 59-69.

V. IDENTIFICATION

In Chapter IV we have considered methods whose objective is to partition a sample of objects into groups. In the present chapter we proceed on the assumption that the groups are formed and the remaining objective amounts to finding the group that is most likely to represent a parent population for a given individual. The problem thus is one of identification. It will be seen that the solution requires an appropriate measure of affinity. We shall consider several alternatives.

5.1 Identification Based on Generalized Distance

In statistical applications of the generalized distance it is assumed that the population distribution is multivariate normal. This implies, as we have seen already, that the groups can be represented by linear clusters of points. Such a cluster is ellipsoidal in shape, has uniform density, and for these reasons can be completely described by a mean vector and covariance matrix. Let us assume that the points represent quadrats embedded within a reference system of species. With n_m quadrats and p species in group m, and with sample mean vector

$$\bar{\mathbf{X}}_m = \begin{bmatrix} \bar{X}_{1m} \\ \vdots \\ \bar{X}_{pm} \end{bmatrix} \quad ,$$

and covariance matrix

$$\mathbf{S}_m = \begin{bmatrix} S_{11} & S_{12} & \dots & S_{1p} \\ S_{21} & S_{22} & \dots & S_{2p} \\ - & - & - & - \\ S_{p1} & S_{p2} & \dots & S_{pp} \end{bmatrix}$$

the generalized distance of a new quadrat

$$\mathbf{X} = \begin{bmatrix} X_1 \\ \vdots \\ X_p \end{bmatrix}$$

from group m can be computed according to

$$d(X, \bar{X}_m) = ((X - \bar{X}_m)'S_m^{-1} (X - \bar{X}_m))^{1/2} \tag{5.1}$$

where S_m^{-1} is the inverse of S_m. Under the null hypothesis that X represents a random sample from a multivariate normal population from which group m is a random sample,

$$F_m = \frac{n_m d^2 (X; \bar{X}_m)(n_m - p)}{(n_m + 1)p(n_m - 1)} \tag{5.2}$$

has the F distribution with p and $n_m - p$ degrees of freedom. When the computed value F_m satisfies the condition

$$F_m < F_{\alpha; p, n_m - p} \tag{5.3}$$

at given probability α, we declare group m a likely parent population for X. If more than one group satisfies this condition, X may be assigned to either group or to the group from which its distance is smallest.

Let us consider an example. We want to determine if either one of three compartments could represent a parent population for a given vegetation quadrat. The compartments are described on the basis of two species in random samples of 24, 31 and 20 quadrats respectively. The compartment mean vectors are given by

$$\bar{X}_1 = \begin{bmatrix} \bar{X}_{11} \\ \bar{X}_{21} \end{bmatrix} = \begin{bmatrix} 2.1 \\ 4.8 \end{bmatrix} \qquad \bar{X}_2 = \begin{bmatrix} \bar{X}_{12} \\ \bar{X}_{22} \end{bmatrix} = \begin{bmatrix} 3.9 \\ 4.6 \end{bmatrix}$$

$$\bar{X}_3 = \begin{bmatrix} \bar{X}_{13} \\ \bar{X}_{23} \end{bmatrix} = \begin{bmatrix} 2.2 \\ 1.1 \end{bmatrix}$$

and the covariance matrices by

$$S_1 = \begin{bmatrix} 1.043 & 0.042 \\ 0.042 & 0.931 \end{bmatrix} \qquad S_2 = \begin{bmatrix} 1.503 & 0.165 \\ 0.165 & 0.265 \end{bmatrix}$$

$$S_3 = \begin{bmatrix} 0.974 & 0.707 \\ 0.707 & 1.050 \end{bmatrix}$$

A newly acquired vegetation quadrat is specified by its data vector,

$$X = \begin{bmatrix} X_1 \\ X_2 \end{bmatrix} = \begin{bmatrix} 2 \\ 1 \end{bmatrix}$$

We compute the affinity of X and the compartments in terms of formula (5.1). In the first step we determine the inverses of S_1, S_2, and S_3 which are found to be,

$$S_1^{-1} = \begin{bmatrix} 0.961 & -0.043 \\ -0.043 & 1.076 \end{bmatrix} \qquad S_2^{-1} = \begin{bmatrix} 0.714 & -0.445 \\ -0.445 & 4.051 \end{bmatrix}$$

$$S_3^{-1} = \begin{bmatrix} 2.008 & -1.352 \\ -1.352 & 1.862 \end{bmatrix}$$

Based on these results we proceed with the calculation of the $d^2(X, \overline{X}_m)$ values for the different compartments:

Compartment 1:

$$(X - \overline{X}_1)' = (2 - 2.1 \quad 1 - 4.8) = (-0.1 \quad -3.8)$$

$$d^2(X, \overline{X}_1) = (-0.1 \quad -3.8) \begin{bmatrix} 0.961 & -0.043 \\ -0.043 & 1.076 \end{bmatrix} \begin{bmatrix} -0.1 \\ -3.8 \end{bmatrix} = 15.514$$

$$F = \frac{(24)(15.514)(24-2)}{(24+1)(2)(24-1)} = \frac{8191.392}{1150} = 7.12$$

Because F exceeds the $\alpha = 0.05$ probability point $F_{0.05; \, 2,22} = 3.44$, the condition in formula (5.3) remains unsatisfied. We conclude that compartment 1 cannot represent a parent population for quadrat X.

Compartment 2:

$$(X - \overline{X}_2)' = (2 - 3.9 \quad 1 - 4.6) = (-1.9 \quad -3.6)$$

$$d^2(X, \overline{X}_2) = (-1.9 \quad -3.6) \begin{bmatrix} 0.714 & -0.445 \\ -0.445 & 4.051 \end{bmatrix} \begin{bmatrix} -1.9 \\ -3.6 \end{bmatrix} = 48.991$$

$$F = \frac{(31)(48.991)(29)}{(32)(2)(30)} = 22.94$$

At $\alpha = 0.05$ probability $F_{0.05; 2,29} = 3.33$. The condition in formula (5.3) still remains unsatisfied.

Compartment 3:

$$(X - \overline{X}_3)' = (2 - 2.2 \quad 1 - 1.1) = (-0.2 \quad -0.1)$$

$$d^2(X, \overline{X}_3) = (-0.2 \quad -0.1) \begin{bmatrix} 2.008 & -1.352 \\ -1.352 & 1.863 \end{bmatrix} \begin{bmatrix} -0.2 \\ -0.1 \end{bmatrix} = 0.0449$$

$$F = \frac{(20)(0.0449)(18)}{(21)(2)(19)} = 0.02$$

Because at $\alpha = 0.05$ probability $F_{0.05; 2,18} = 3.55$, the condition in formula (5.3) is satisfied, indicating that compartment 3 is a most likely parent population for quadrat X. The average misclassification probability is $(24P(F > 7.12) + 31P(F > 22.94))/ 55 < 0.002$. We note that:

1. Irrespective of the number of reference groups we deal with the groups individually. We compute the distance $d(X, \overline{X}_m)$ on the basis of the mth covariance matrix S_m; in this respect we differ from other users who recommend pooling the group covariance matrices and then computing the generalized distance based on the pooled covariance matrix. While pooling has practical advantages in simplifying the computations, it also puts an additional constraint on the method manifested in the assumption that the population group covariance matrices are equal.

2. The distance $d(X, \overline{X}_m)$ can be associated with a standard statistical distribution when the samples are drawn at random from a multivariate normal population. Otherwise it will serve only as a deterministic measure of absolute separation.

3. Because an inverse of the covariance matrix is incorporated in the formula for distance $d(X, \overline{X}_m)$, a standardization occurs which is not applied directly to the species, but rather indirectly to their linear compound. This is obvious from the equivalent expression of formula (5.1),

$$d(X, \overline{X}_m) = \left[\sum_i Y_i^2 / \lambda_i \right]^{1/2}, \quad i = 1, ..., t \tag{5.4}$$

where t indicates the number of non-zero eigenvalues of the covariance matrix, λ_i the ith eigenvalue, and Y_i the ith component score for quadrat X.

Let us consider the last point further on the basis of a numerical example. The data are given in Table 5-1. It can be seen from Fig. 5-1 that the data

Table 5-1. Co-ordinates for the points in Fig. 5-1

Species									Quadrat						
	1	2	3	4	5	6	7	8	9	10	11	12	13	14	15
X_{1m}	2	3	2	3	4	3	3	4	5	6	5	5	4	4	5
X_{2m}	2	2	3	3	3	4	5	4	3	4	4	5	5	6	6

	16	17	18	19	20	21	22	23	24	25	$\bar{X}_{im}$
	6	7	6	7	8	7	6	5	7	8	5
	5	5	6	6	7	7	7	7	8	8	5

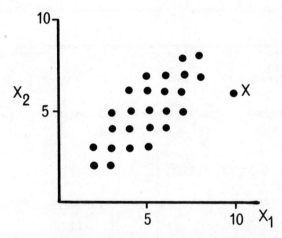

Fig. 5-1. Scatter diagram for quadrats of a hypothetical sample. X_1 and X_2 represent species. Point X signifies an external quadrat.

define a linear cluster of points of reasonably uniform density. Such a cluster can be described reasonably well by a mean vector

$$\bar{\mathbf{X}}_m = \begin{bmatrix} 5 \\ 5 \end{bmatrix}$$

and covariance matrix

$$\mathbf{S}_m = \begin{bmatrix} 3.167 & 2.417 \\ 2.417 & 3.167 \end{bmatrix}$$

149

The inverse of S_m is

$$S_m^{-1} = \begin{bmatrix} 0.756 & -0.577 \\ -0.577 & 0.756 \end{bmatrix}$$

The separation of individual

$$X = \begin{bmatrix} 10 \\ 6 \end{bmatrix}$$

from group m is

$$d^2(X, \overline{X}_m) = (5 \quad 1) \begin{bmatrix} 0.756 & -0.577 \\ -0.577 & 0.756 \end{bmatrix} \begin{bmatrix} 5 \\ 1 \end{bmatrix} = 13.886$$

or

$$d(X, \overline{X}_m) = 3.726$$

The same generalized distance may be derived from the component scores which we compute for X based on the formulae,

$$Y_{1X} = (X - \overline{X}_m)'b_1 = (5 \quad 1) \begin{bmatrix} 0.707 \\ 0.707 \end{bmatrix} = 4.242$$

$$Y_{2X} = (X - \overline{X}_m)'b_2 = (5 \quad 1) \begin{bmatrix} -0.707 \\ 0.707 \end{bmatrix} = -2.828$$

where b_1, b_2 hold the component coefficients of S_m. From the component scores and eigenvalues $\lambda_1 = 5.583$, $\lambda_2 = 0.750$, we obtain according to formula (5.4)

$$d(X, \overline{X}_m) = \left[\frac{Y_{1X}^2}{\lambda_1} + \frac{Y_{2X}^2}{\lambda_2} \right]^{1/2} = \left[\frac{4.242^2}{5.583} + \frac{(-2.828)^2}{0.750} \right]^{1/2} = 3.726$$

This is the same quantity as the one computed by formula (5.1). According to formula (5.2), we have

$$F_m = \frac{(25)(3.726)^2 (25-2)}{(25 + 1)(2)(25 - 1)} = 6.40$$

150

Because $F_m > F_{0.05;\ 2,23} = 3.42$, the hypothesis that quadrat **X** is from a population represented by group m must be rejected. It is interesting to note that when we plot points, based on the component scores in Table 5-2, we obtain a point cluster exactly like the one in Fig. 5-1. When, however, the component scores are standardized the point cluster becomes circular in shape (Fig. 5-2).

Table 5-2. Component scores of quadrats based on data in Table 5-1

Component	Quadrat						
	1	2	3	4	5	6	7
Y_{1m}	−0.866	−0.722	−0.722	−0.577	−0.433	−0.433	−0.289
Y_{2m}	0.000	−0.144	0.144	0.000	−0.144	0.144	0.289
	8	9	10	11	12	13	14
	−0.289	−0.289	0.000	−0.144	0.000	−0.144	0.000
	0.000	−0.289	−0.289	−0.144	0.000	0.144	0.289
	15	16	17	18	19	20	21
	0.144	0.144	0.289	0.289	0.433	0.722	0.577
	0.144	−0.144	−0.289	0.000	−0.144	−0.144	0.000
	22	23	24	25	λ_1		
	0.433	0.289	0.722	0.866	5.583		
	0.144	0.289	0.144	0.000	0.750		

5.2 Identification Based on Rank Order

Identification based on the use of generalized distance is burdened by the restrictive assumption of multivariate normality and a rather involved computational procedure. If nothing else, these aspects could explain its infrequent use in vegetation ecology. Rather than rely on methods in which identifications are based on the actual magnitude of a distance, the ecologist may consider using other methods which rely on rank order in a manner as suggested by GOODALL (1968). A variant is outlined below in connection with a numerical example:

1. Assuming that a sample of quadrats has been drawn from a vegetation type m whose sample mean vector is $\overline{\mathbf{X}}_m$, and that the elements of $\overline{\mathbf{X}}_m$ represent

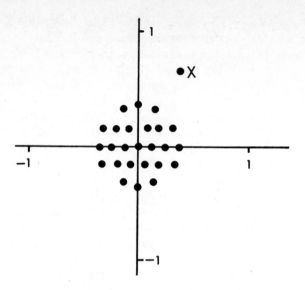

Fig. 5-2. Scatter diagram for standardized component scores.

sample means $\bar{X}_{1m}, ..., \bar{X}_{tm}$ for species, compute the dissimilarity between a quadrat j in type m and the type mean vector $\bar{\mathbf{X}}_m$ with respect to species h as the quantity,

$$\delta_{hjm} = |X_{hjm} - \bar{X}_{hm}|$$

Similarly for the external quadrat $\mathbf{X}$ whose type affiliation is sought compute

$$\delta_{hXm} = |X_{hX} - \bar{X}_{hm}|$$

2. Compute the affinity of $\mathbf{X}$ and vegetation type m with respect to species h as the quantity.

$$p_{hXm} = P(\delta \geqslant \delta_{hXm})$$

This is the proportion of quadrats in type m which are at least as far away from the centroid of type m as the external quadrat $\mathbf{X}$ with respect to species h. 3. Determine the total affinity A_{Xm} of $\mathbf{X}$ by combining the proportions p_{hXm} for the t species as a simple product to obtain,

$$\chi^2_{Xm} = -2 \ln (p_{1Xm} \cdots p_{tXm})$$

and then refer χ^2_{Xm} to the chi square distribution to obtain

$$A_{Xm} = P(\chi^2 \geqslant \chi^2_{Xm})$$

with $2t$ degrees of freedom. The affinity A_{Xm} thus measures a probability that any member of type m is at least as dissimilar to the common type mean vector $\bar{X}_m$ as X to $\bar{X}_m$. Because we form a simple product of the probabilities, we must assume that the individual probabilities are additive, or equivalently in our case, that the species are uncorrelated. Zero terms in the product will cause indeterminacy. To avoid this the zeros should be omitted. When all terms are zero, A_{Xm} is set at 0.

4. Determine through similar manipulations the affinity of X to each vegetation type which may represent a parent population. Following this, identify m as the parent population for X if A_{Xm} is the highest affinity among all affinity values. Alternatively, make the identification conditional not on the actual size of A_{Xm} but rather on A_{Xm} being in excess of a given threshold value α.

We shall base the illustrations on data given in

Type A

Species			Quadrat			$\bar{X}_{hA}$
	1	2	3	4	5	
X_1	5	4	5	3	3	4
X_2	1	2	0	1	1	1
X_3	2	3	2	2	1	2

$$X = \begin{bmatrix} 2 \\ 2 \\ 3 \end{bmatrix}$$

At this point we could replace the species by sets of component scores to remove the effect of species correlations from the measurement of affinities. However, for the purpose of illustration it will be simpler if we proceed with the data as presented. We begin with computing the δ_{hjA} values,

$$\begin{bmatrix} \delta_{11A} & \delta_{12A} & \delta_{13A} & \delta_{14A} & \delta_{15A} \\ \delta_{21A} & \delta_{22A} & \delta_{23A} & \delta_{24A} & \delta_{25A} \\ \delta_{31A} & \delta_{32A} & \delta_{33A} & \delta_{34A} & \delta_{35A} \end{bmatrix} = \begin{bmatrix} 1 & 0 & 1 & 1 & 1 \\ 0 & 1 & 1 & 0 & 0 \\ 0 & 1 & 0 & 0 & 1 \end{bmatrix}$$

We compute the δ_{hXA} values next

$$\begin{bmatrix} \delta_{1XA} \\ \delta_{2XA} \\ \delta_{3XA} \end{bmatrix} = \begin{bmatrix} 2 \\ 1 \\ 1 \end{bmatrix}$$

From these we obtain the p_{hXA} values,

$$\begin{bmatrix} p_{1XA} \\ p_{2XA} \\ p_{3XA} \end{bmatrix} = \begin{bmatrix} 0 \\ 2/5 \\ 2/5 \end{bmatrix}$$

We find the affinity index, after omitting the single zero term and reducing the degrees of freedom from $2t$ to $2(t-1)$ so that $\chi^2_{XA} = -2 \ln 4/25 = 3.665$ with 4 degrees of freedom, to be $A_{XA} = P(\chi^2 \geqslant 3.665) \approx 0.55$. When we set the critical α to 0.05 the condition $A_{XA} > \alpha$ is satisfied and type A is declared a likely parent population for $\mathbf{X}$. When several reference types are given, the assignment of $\mathbf{X}$ to one of them is based on the criteria which were discussed under item 4 of the preceding enumeration.

5.3 Identification Based on Information

Identifications may be based on the I-divergence information of formula (2.22) when the data are categorical. When a reference class is described as a p-valued probability distribution,

$$\mathbf{P}_j = (P_{j1} \ldots P_{jp})$$

we can use the quantity

$$2I(\mathbf{F};\mathbf{P}_j) = 2\Sigma_i f_i \ln f_i/(f \, P_{ji}), \quad i = 1, \ldots, p$$

to evaluate the null hypothesis that an observed distribution

$$\mathbf{F} = (f_i \ldots f_p)$$

represents a random sample from a population completely described by $\mathbf{P}_j$, against the alternative hypothesis that it does not. Under the null hypothesis $2I(\mathbf{F};\mathbf{P}_j)$ may be referred to the chi square distribution with

154

p- 1 degrees of freedom. We note that the totals for distribution **F** and P_j are respectively f and 1.

Let the frequency distribution **F** = (58 62 70) describe a new quadrat whose class affiliation is in question. In **F** the elements define species quantities. Let the distributions P_1 = (0.260 0.300 0.440) and P_2 = (0.318 0.290 0.392) specify the relative proportions of the same three species in two vegetation types which can be considered as possible parent populations for **F**. Our decision regarding the class affiliation of **F** may take several possible forms:

Assign **F** to type 1 with α probability if the condition

$$2I(\mathbf{F};P_1) < 2I(\mathbf{F};P_2)$$

is true provided that the conditions

$$2I(\mathbf{F};P_1) < \chi^2_{\alpha,\,p\text{-}1}$$

$$2I(\mathbf{F};P_2) \geqslant \chi^2_{\alpha,\,p\text{-}1}$$

are true also. In these expressions $\chi_{\alpha,\,p\text{-}1}$ is the α probability point of the chi square distribution with p-1 degrees of freedom. If these conditions are reversed, an assigment of **F** to type 2 is indicated. Furthermore, when $2I$ exceeds the corresponding chi square probability point in both types, no assignment is made. Conversely, when they both are smaller than the stipulated probability point, an assignment to either type may be justified.

For the example we have the numerical values: $2I(\mathbf{F};P_1)$= 4.187 and $2I(\mathbf{F};P_2)$ = 1.203. Because both of these quantities are smaller than the specified probability point $\chi^2_{0.05,2}$= 5.991 we conclude that an assignment to either type can be justified.

Several comments are in order at this point:
1. Strictly speaking $2I(\mathbf{F};P_j)$ should be used as a statistic only when there is good reason to assume that the species in **F** are non-interacting in the sampled populations. This may rarely be the case, and therefore, we should normally anticipate the actual but unknown value of $2I(\mathbf{F};P_j)$ to be less than the observed value.
2. It directly follows from the presence of species interactions that the assignments based on $2I(\mathbf{F};P_j)$ are likely to be conservative; we may decide to reject the null hypothesis on the basis of an observed value when in fact the actual values of $2I(\mathbf{F};P_j)$ may indicate that it should be accepted.
3. We cannot tell whether **F** as a random sample happened to incorporate all the species which actually occur in the sampling site. Furthermore, **F**

may display a species list which does not match the species list in the reference types. These raise problems on different counts. Firstly, zeros are introduced in $\mathbf{F}$ and $\mathbf{P}_j$. However, the zeros cannot be uniquely interpreted; some will indicate that certain species, present in the sampling site, were missed by sampling, while others signify actual absences in the survey site. Secondly, when the zeros indicate that species were actually missed, the nominal value of $2I(\mathbf{F};\mathbf{P}_j)$ can be either smaller or larger than the actual value. Because we do not know in which way the bias occurs, we cannot tell its influence on our evaluation of the null hypothesis.

4. The problems which arise because of indeterminacy in the presence of zeros dictate that identifications be based on sets of shared species. But then it should be clearly understood that the analysis will have relevance with respect only to these species.

The problems raised in the foregoing comments are in no way unique to identifications which use information. The fact of the matter is that zeros in the data can lead to similar problems in most methods of data analysis.

5.4 Further Remarks on Identification

We have to choose an affinity measure before we could implement an analysis with the objective of identification, and our choice may depend on the method of cluster analysis which produced the reference groups. If, for instance, the groups were recognized based on average linkage, it may be quite logical under specific circumstances to use average linkage as a criterion for measuring affinity. Similarly, if the groups were recognized on the basis of a sum of squares criterion, the same criterion may serve as a measure for affinity in identifications.

It is quite possible, however, that we recognize reference groups using one set of criteria, and then, redescribe the groups in terms of some new criteria which then provide a basis for identification. When such is the case the criteria which produce the reference groups have no relevance in the identifications and a measure of affinity can be more freely chosen. The following examples will help illuminate these points:

Case 1. N quadrats are selected at random in an area of vegetation. Each quadrat is described in terms of species composition. The sample is subdivided into k groups by the method of sum of squares clustering. If $\mathbf{X}$ represents a new quadrat from the same area, described in terms of the same set of species, the minimum value of the function

$$\frac{n_m}{n_m+1} \sum_h (X_h - \bar{X}_{hm})^2 , \quad m = 1, ..., k$$

is a logical criterion for identifying the best fitting group for $\mathbf{X}$.

156

Case 2. Types are recognized based on the method of sum of squares clustering. Each type then is mapped and resampled in the field for the yield of given tree species within given sized quadrats. An additional quadrat is chosen whose type affiliation is sought in terms of the yield data and some affinity measure which in this case need not be the sum of squares. The reason is that the sum of squares no longer is a relevant criterion because the types are redescribed by means of new characters different from those which formed the type limits. Here the user has more freedom than in Case 1 to choose an affinity measure. When there is good reason to commit the analysis to a covariance structure the generalized distance of formula (5.1) or (5.5) is a logical choice. When, however, there is no compelling reason to prefer one affinity measure over another, the identification based on rank order or information may have special appeal.

5.5 Reference

GOODALL, D.W. 1968. Affinity between an individual and a cluster in numerical taxonomy, *Biometrie-Praximetrie* 9: 52-55.

VI. MULTIVARIATE ANALYSIS – A DISCUSSION

6.1 Choice of Method

We have described in the preceeding chapters methods which have at least one property in common: they are suitable to analyse multidimensional data, and thus, to reveal information about correlations. In the measurement of correlations we relied on different objective functions that are based on, or can be derived from, the covariance, information, or probability. We characterized the methods as 'multivariate' to signify that they deal with several correlated variables simultaneously.

To appreciate what methods of this sort can do for the ecologist, it is sufficient to consider what data analysis would be like if data analysis had to rely entirely on univariate techniques. Firstly, variables would be analysed individually. Secondly, variable correlations would be ignored. And thirdly, all conclusions would be limited to a single variable at a time.

When we analyse variables individually efficiency suffers. Consider, for example, a comparison between several diagnostic categories such as the different vegetation types in an area. We may wish to compare the vegetation types under the null hypothesis that they are indistinguishable on the basis of p environmental variables. Should we decide to follow a univariate approach in the testing, we would proceed as follows:

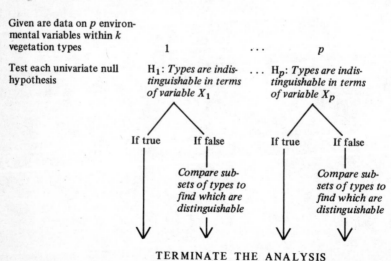

Given are data on p environmental variables within k vegetation types

1 ... p

Test each univariate null hypothesis

H_1: *Types are indistinguishable in terms of variable X_1* ... H_p: *Types are indistinguishable in terms of variable X_p*

If true   If false   If true   If false

Compare subsets of types to find which are distinguishable   *Compare subsets of types to find which are distinguishable*

TERMINATE THE ANALYSIS

It is quite obvious that the univariate test will have to be repeated for each variable separately. When the overall test on a single variable in the k types lead to rejection of the null hypothesis, the analysis is continued with comparison of the types in subsets to discover which of them differ significantly and which do not. Considering k types the last step may at worst require $k(k-1)/2$ paired comparisons on each variable. An essential feature of these tests, and a reason for their potential inefficiency, is their reliance on a single variable at a time, even though the problem itself is typically multivariate. A more parsimonious analysis may, in the first place, subject all k types to a single test on a multivariate null hypothesis based on the use of all p variables simultaneously, in the same manner as illustrated in section 4.10. Only if the null hypothesis is rejected should testing continue with more specific hypotheses — some of which may be univariate.

The logistic advantage of a multivariate approach is quite obvious. But besides the increased logistic efficiency, there are also other advantages to be gained as a direct consequence of analysing variables as correlated entities in a group. The power of the analysis increases, and in turn, the conclusions of the analysis become broad in relevance. Clearly then, what makes the multivariate methods so well suited for use in vegetation studies is the important fact that they are efficient, can convey information about correlations, and their results have broad relevance.

The multivariate techniques, however, just as any other method of data analysis, cannot be utilized to their fullest advantage, unless they are embedded in a general procedure characterized by strict internal consistency. The statements —
1. Definition of the problem in workable terms,
2. Data collection based on a statistical sampling design,
3. Data analysis based on a multivariate method,
4. Statistical inference
— exemplify a procedure for the embedding of a multivariate method. We realize, of course, that the parts of this procedure are interrelated. The choice of a method of multivariate analysis must follow constraints imposed on it by decisions regarding the problem, sampling design, and method of inference.

The mode of implementation of a multivariate method depends on local circumstances. We may reason along two basically different lines in this connection: If all population units can be located and measured, or the sample has not been derived by random sampling, necessarily the approach is deterministic, and the multivariate methods must be applied as mathematical techniques with the sole objective of deriving precise descriptions of the materials in hands. The question of statistical estimation and inference does not arise. If, however, the sample has been randomly chosen, the approach will have to be statistical involving an estimation of unknown population parameters and tests of null hypotheses about them. However, it should be clear that in either case the underlying mathematical technique may be precisely the same; only the manner of implementation different.

We must choose a method with a clear understanding of the objectives to be achieved. We may recognize as objectives such things as summarization, multidimensional scaling, trend seeking, cluster recognition, identification, etc. When summarization is accomplished on axes, and also in the case of multidimensional scaling or trend seeking, the assumption of a continuous data structure is implicit. Axes are sought, representing straight lines or curves, that can serve as a basis for simple, efficient representations. The methods that have primary relevance in this connection are known under the collective name 'ordinations'. Class recognition is a matter for classification techniques which may dissect a perfectly continuous sample arbitrarily into groups, or alternatively, delimit natural groups separated by clear discontinuities. In other cases identifications may be sought. These entail the finding of a class which represents the most probably parent population for a questionable individual.

Once the relevant class of method is identified, a further choice within the class may depend on the data structure in the sample. Four broad categories may be recognized:

1. In the first category the data structures are linear and continuous. These mean that the points form a single ellipsoidal cluster of uniform density. Although, such data structures are believed to be rare in vegetation samples, it is conceivable that a sample from a relatively narrow segment of a predominant environmental gradient may exhibit a nearly linear, continuous data structure.

2. The data structures in the second category are curved and continuous with points arranged evenly within a single curved solid or on the surface of some manifold. It may be suggested that this type of structure occurs in samples taken from broad segments of a predominant environmental gradient.

3. The third category includes data structures which contain several linear clusters separated by discontinuities. This may be the case when a sample encompasses several short segments of separate parallel gradients.

4. The fourth category contains data structures with points arranged in several curved clusters. Such curved and continuous data structures are probably the commonest in samples originating in vegetation surveys encompassing broadly different environmental conditions.

We understand, of course, that the foregoing categorization of data structures, while relevant in the ordination methods which we described, may have little relevance in some other analyses. The reason is that in certain methods the concept of linearity, or as a matter of fact non-linearity, may have no significance. Some classificatory techniques are examples in this connection in which only the continuity or discontinuity property is relevant. When ordination is intended, several specific objectives may be served on which the choice of a particular method will have to depend. Some contingencies are given below:

Objective to be achieved	Data structure in sample	Method indicated
Data reduction through summarization of variation on axes	Linear, continuous	Component analysis
	Curved, continuous	SHEPARD & CARROLL (1966)*
	Linear or curved, disjoint	SNEATH (1966)*
Multidimensional scaling	As above, except that when linearity is suspected principal axes analysis is indicated. Other linear scaling techniques may be useful under specific circumstances. For instance, when it is essential to preselect the ordination poles the modified BRAY & CURTIS method (section 3.4) is a logical choice. When there is concern about the computational difficulties with principal axes analysis, the use of other simple methods (*e.g.* position vectors ordination) may be appropriate. It is conceivable, that under certain circumstances, we may wish to do an ordination in which the ordination configuration is a given non-linear function of the actual data structure in the sample. When such is the case we may consider applying some variants of the KRUSKAL method (KRUSKAL & CARMONE, 1971).	
Trend seeking – a single species, several environmental variables	Linear or curved, continuous	Multiple regression analysis
– several species, no environmental variables	Linear, continuous	Component analysis, principal axes analysis, etc.
	Curved, continuous	The method of SHEPARD & CARROLL and like techniques*
	Linear or curved, disjoint	SNEATH's method*
Reciprocal ordering – species scores given	Linear, continuous	WILLIAMS (1952), WHITTAKER (1960)
– species scores to be estimated from species abundance data	Linear, continuous	*RQ*-technique (WILLIAMS, 1952, HATHEWAY, 1971, HILL, 1973)

* There is no sufficient evidence to reliably appraise these methods in vegetation studies.

It should be clear that ordinations, in general, are recommended for handling samples which are continuous, and conversely, a classificatory analysis is not a logical objective in an ordination. We have quoted reasons for this in the preceding chapters. It will be sufficient here to stress one further point. If we have ordination objectives, and a discontinuous data structure in the sample, it may be wise to classify the sample first and then ordinate within the classes. Because we have to make decisions about the data structure, whose exact shape may not be known, it may happen that the method of ordination which is first chosen is not the best method available. We may have to make several trials before a satisfactory method is found. 'Satisfactory' means that the method, besides satisfying certain norms of mathematical acceptability, is also valid statistically and acceptable ecologically.

In the group of classificatory analyses the methods can accomplish their task in different ways. The hierarchical techniques will normally produce classes irrespective of the existence or non-existence of discrete groups in the sample. To this extent the hierarchical techniques are prone to produce dissections. However, we have seen already that certain techniques can find groups if they actually exist, or will signal the user if there are no groups that would satisfy their criteria.

Identification involves the measurement of affinity between a reference class and an external individual, and then, assignment of the individual to the class with which its affinity is greatest. The choice of an affinity measure is crucial. Two distinct cases must be distinguished. In the first case, identifications are based on the variables and measures which formed the reference classes. For instance, when the reference classes are the product of average linkage clustering of species data, the identifications may rely on average linkage, as a measure of affinity, and the same kind of species data. In the second case, identifications are sought in terms of variables and measures which have not been used in the delimitation of the reference classes. An example in this connection includes several environmental classes to which new sampling units (quadrats) are assigned on the basis of vegetation data. While in the first example the affinity measure is predetermined, in the second it can be more freely chosen.

We have used in the text different formal procedures for testing hypotheses which rely on statistical indices of known sampling distribution including F, χ^2, etc. While such indices can provide elegant tests, their scope of application is rather limited for reasons of implicit assumptions about distributions. A method of testing statistical significance, however, need not be based on a standard statistical index. It is quite possible to proceed heuristically involving random simulations in which a sampling distribution is determined empirically. We have seen an example for this when we compared dendrograms in section 4.10.

It seems appropriate to suggest that vegetation science is in a transitional stage. A novel and essentially objective outlook is emerging to serve the new objectives. The trend, in fact, seems to point to wide-spread future uses of methods founded upon mathematics and probability theory, in association with elaborate computer-based systems of sampling, data anlysis and inference. The principal value of such systems, as noted by SHUBIK (1954) in connection with political behaviour, is that it should render the complex problems manageable, while also providing facilities for exact repetition, and also, precision and speed in the computations.

It seems appropriate to finish our task with this section, before we turn to some bibliographic notes, by paraphrasing some informal comments of PIELOU (1971) in which she contrasts soft science and hard science:

An example of hard science is celestial mechanics. It provides astronomers with the means to make predictions about comets, like Halley's. The astronomer's predictions are precise. The comet proves it when it turns up at the right place on time. This is what we expect from a hard science. Its predictions are precise and confident. Ecology is a soft science. What this really means is that in ecology we cannot normally predict things with such high degrees of accuracy. The difficulties are rooted in the fact that good ecological data are difficult to obtain, that ecological data carry excessive random variation which can obscure the things about which we wish to make predictions, and that the ecological objects do not have the good behaviour, like comets. Furthermore, ecological problems are usually complex. They cannot be reasoned out as neatly as the orbital path of comets or the trajectory of a space module.

These thoughts should warn against overestimating the limits to which statistical and other mathematical methods can be put to useful service in plant ecology or in other domains of *soft science*.

6.2 Bibliographic Notes

An exhaustive list of publications using mathematical methods in vegetation ecology and in related fields, up to 1962, has been compiled by GOODALL (1962). Recent surveys appear in various textbooks and monographs including SOKAL & SNEATH (1963, 1973), GREIG-SMITH (1964), LAMBERT & DALE (1964), KERSHAW (1964), WILLIAMS & DALE (1965), McINTOSH (1967a), GOODALL (1970), CROVELLO (1970), CROVELLO & MOSS (1971), SHIMWELL (1971) and WILLIAMS (1971), among others. A series of essays by JUHÁSZ-NAGY (1966a, b, 1968) treats the conceptual framework and provides references on that topic. The underlying mathematical and/or statistical theory is explained by: SEARLE (1966) and REKTORYS (1969) for mathematics; SAMPFORD (1962) for sampling theory; OSTLE (1963), SOKAL & ROHLF (1969) and DAGNELIE (1969) for univariate statistical methods; KULLBACK (1959) and KULLBACK *et al.* (1962) for information theory; SEAL (1964), MORRISON (1967), ANDERSON (1958), BARTLETT (1965), DEMPSTER (1969) and RAO (1972) for multivariate statistical methods; and BARTLETT (1960) and PIELOU (1969) for stochastic population processes and pattern. Computer programs are described by COOLEY & LOHNES (1962), GRENCH & THACHER (1965), LANCE & WILLIAMS (1967, 1968), WISHART (1969), COLE (1969), GOLDSTEIN & GRIGAL (1972) and others.

Regarding procedure, ecologists will find the commentary of SOKAL (1965), LAMBERT & DALE (1964), WILLIAMS & DALE (1965) and GREIG-SMITH (1971) most informative. Specific aspects of character selection are considered by DALE (1968), and of sampling by GREIG-SMITH (1964),who also review the relevant literature. Resemblance functions are reviewed by GOODMAN & KRUSKAL (1954, 1959), SOKAL & SNEATH (1963, 1973), WILLIAMS & DALE (1965), ČEŠKA (1968), CROVELLO (1970), ORLÓCI (1972) and GOODALL (1973a). The first published work on metrics is apparently due to FRECHET (1906). Recent treatments can be found in textbooks on topology, *e.g.* SIMMONS (1963). Some statistical aspects of distance are discussed by MAHALANOBIS (1936), and their role in eigenvalue and vector methods by GOWER (1966). The weighting of characters in distance measures is considered by MACNAUGHTON-SMITH *et al.* (1964) and WILLIAMS *et al.* (1964), and the sampling properties of some similarity measures by GOODALL (1967) and HOLGATE (1971). The literature on information theory metrics and other information divergences include such fundamental treatments as KULLBACK (1959), RAJSKI (1961), RÉNYI (1961), FRASER (1965) and SIBSON (1969), in addition to those concerned with taxonomic and ecological applications including MARGALEF (1958), PIELOU (1966a, b), McINTOSH 1967b), ESTABROOK (1967), JUHÁSZ-NAGY (1967), ORLÓCI (1969a, b, 1970a, b, 1971, 1962), DALE (1971) and HILL (1973). Trend seeking, gradient recognition, multidimensional scaling and hypothesis generation in ordinations are treated by GREIG-SMITH (1964), GROENEWOUD (1965), WHITTAKER (1967), McINTOSH (1967a), ARMSTRONG (1967), GITTINS (1968, 1969), GOODALL (1970), ANDERSON (1971), WHITTAKER & GAUCH (1973), COTTAM *et al.* (1973) and ORLÓCI (1973). Other ordination references deal with specific methodological problems such as revisions of the underlying mathematical procedure (GOWER, 1966; AUSTIN & ORLÓCI, 1966; ORLÓCI, 1966, 1967) and investigation of the non-linearity property (SHEPARD & CARROLL, 1966; SNEATH, 1966; SWAN, 1790; NOY-MEIR & AUSTIN, 1970; AUSTIN & NOY-MEIR, 1971; and GAUCH, 1973). The classical approaches to vegetation classifications are reviewed by WHITTAKER (1962) and the classificatory approach in general by CORMACK (1971) and GOODALL (1973b). GREIG-

SMITH (1964), WILLIAMS & DALE (1965), PIELOU (1969), JACKSON (1969), BALL (1970), LERMAN (1970), JARDINE & SIBSON (1971), EMDEN (1971), WILLIAMS (1971) and SNEATH & SOKAL (1973) treat specific aspects of theory and applications. Identification in the sense of discriminant analysis, profile analysis, etc., are discussed in most advanced texts on multivariate statistics (e.g. RAO, 1952; MORRISON, 1967). These also treat hypothesis testing.

6.3 References

ANDERSON, A.J.B. 1971. Similarity measure for mixed attribute types. *Nature* 232: 416-417.
ANDERSON, T.W. 1958. *An Introduction to Multivariate Statistical Analysis.* New York, Wiley.
ARMSTRONG, J.S. 1967. Derivation of theory by means of factor analysis or Tom Swift and his electric factor analysis machine. *The American Statistician* 21: 17-21.
AUSTIN, M.P. & I. NOY-MEIR. 1971. The problem of non-linearity in ordination: experiments with two gradient models. *J. Ecol.* 59: 763-773.
AUSTIN, M.P. & L. ORLÓCI. 1966. Geometric models in ecology. II. An evaluation of some ordination techniques. *J. Ecol.* 54: 217-227.
BALL, G.H. 1970. Classification analysis. SRI Stanford Research Institute, Menlo Park, California 94025, U.S.A.
BARTLETT, M.S. 1965. Multivariate statistics. *In:* T.H. WATERMAN & H.J. MOROWITZ (eds.), *Theoretical and Mathematical Biology*, pp. 201-224. New York, Blaisdell.
BARTLETT, M.S. 1960. *Stochastic Population Models in Ecology and Epidemiology.* London, Methuen.
ČEŠKA, A. 1968. Application of association coefficients for estimating the mean similarity between sets of vegetation relevés. *Folia geobot. phytotax. Praha* 3: 57-64.
COLE, A.J. 1969. *Numerical Taxonomy.* London, Academic Press.
COOLEY, W.W. & P.R. LOHNES, 1962. *Multivariate Procedures for the Behavioral Sciences.* New York, Wiley.
CORMACK, R.M. 1971. A review of classification. *J. Roy. Statist. Soc. Series* A, 134: 321-353.
COTTAM, G., F.G. GOFF & R.H. WHITTAKER. 1973. Wisconsin comparative ordination. *In:* R.H. WHITTAKER (ed.), *Handbook of Vegetation Science,* Vol. V, pp. 193-221. The Hague, W. Junk.
CROVELLO, T.J. 1970. Analysis of character variation in ecology and systematics. *Annual Rev. Ecol. Syst.* 1: 55-98.
CROVELLO, T.J. & W.W. MOSS. 1971. A bibliography on classification in diverse disciplines. *Classification Society Bulletin.* Vol. 2, No. 3, pp. 29-45.
DAGNELIE, P. 1969. *Théorie et Méthodes Statistiques,* Vol. 1, 2. Gembloux, Duculot.
DALE, M.B. 1968. On property structure, numerical taxonomy and data handling. *In:* V.H. HEYWOOD (ed.), *Modern Methods in Plant Taxonomy,* pp. 185-197. London, Academic Press.
DALE, M.B. 1971. Information analysis of quantitative data. *In:* G.P. PATIL *et al.* (eds.), *Statistical Ecology,* Vol. 3, pp. 133-148. London, Pennsylvania State Univ. Press.
DEMPSTER, A.P. 1969. *Elements of Continuous Multivariate Analysis.* Reading, Massachusetts, Addison-Wesley.
EMDEN, M.H. VAN. 1971. *An Analysis of Complexity.* Mathematisch Centrum, Amsterdam.

ESTABROOK, G.F. 1967. An information theory model for character analysis. *Taxon* 16: 86-97.
FRASER, D.A.S. 1965. On information in statistics. *Ann. Math. Statist.* 36: 890-896.
FRECHET, M. 1906. Sur quelques points du calcule functionel. *Rend. Math. di Palermo* 22: 1-74.
GAUCH, H.G. 1973. The relationship between sample similarity and ecological distance. *Ecology* 54: 618-622.
GITTINS, R. 1968. Trend-surface analysis of ecological data. *J. Ecol.* 56: 845-869.
GITTINS, R. 1969. The application of ordination techniques. *In:* R.H. RORISON (ed.), *Ecological Aspects of the Mineral Nutrition of Plants,* pp. 37-66, London, Blackwell.
GOLDSTEIN, R.A. & D.F. GRIGAL. 1972. Computer programs for the ordination and classification of ecosystems. Ecological Sciences Division Publication No. 417. Oak Ridge National Laboratory, Oak Ridge, Tennesee, U.S.A.
GOODALL, D.W. 1962. Bibliography of statistical plant sociology. *Excerpta Sect. B,* 4: 253-322.
GOODALL, D.W. 1967. The distribution of the matching coefficient. *Biometrics* 23: 647-656.
GOODALL, D.W. 1970. Statistical plant ecology. *Annual Rev. Ecol. Syst.* 1: 99-124.
GOODALL, D.W. 1973a. Sample similarity and species correlation. *In:* R.H. WHITTAKER (ed.), *Handbook of Vegetation Science,* Part V, pp. 105-156. The Hague, W. Junk.
GOODALL, D.W. 1973b. Numerical Classification. *In:* R.H. WHITTAKER (ed.), *Handbook of Vegetation Science,* Part V, pp. 575-615. The Hague, W. Junk.
GOODMAN, L.A. & W.H. KRUSKAL. 1954. Measures of association for cross classifications. *J. Amer. Stat. Ass.* 49: 732-764.
GOODMAN, L.A. & W.H. KRUSKAL. 1959. Measures of association for cross classifications. II. Further Discussion and Reference. *J. Amer. Stat. Ass.* 54: 123-338.
GOWER, J.C. 1966. Some distance properties of latent root and vector methods used in multivariate analysis. *Biometrika* 53: 325-338.
GREIG-SMITH, P. 1964. *Quantitative Plant Ecology.* 2nd ed. London, Butterworths.
GREIG-SMITH, P. 1971. Analysis of vegetation data: the user viewpoint. *In:* G.P. PATIL *et al.* (eds.), *Statistical Ecology,* Vol. 3, pp. 149-166. London, Pennsylvania State Univ. Press.
GRENCH, R.E. & H.C. THACHER. 1965. *Collected Algorithms 1960-1963 from the Communications of the Association for Computing Machinery.* Clearing House for Federal Scientific and Technical Information, U.S. Department of Commerce, Springfield, Virginia.
GROENEWOUD, H. VAN. 1965. Ordination and classification of Swiss and Canadian coniferous forests by various biometric and other methods. *Ber. geobot. Inst. ETH, Stiftg. Rübel,* Zürich 36: 28-102.
HATHEWAY, W.H. 1971. Contingency-table analysis of rain forest vegetation. *In:* G.P. PATIL *et al.* (eds.), *Statistical Ecology,* Vol. 3, pp. 271-307. London, Pennsylvania State Univ. Press.
HILL, M.O. 1973. Diversity and evenness: a unifying notation and its consequences. *Ecology* 54: 427-432.
HOLGATE, P. 1971. Notes on the Marczewski-Steinhaus coefficient of similarity. *In:* G.P. PATIL *et al.* (eds.), *Statistical Ecology,* Vol. 3, pp. 181-193. London, Pennsylvania State Univ. Press.
JACKSON, D.M. 1969. Comparison of classifications. *In:* A.J. COLE (ed.), *Numerical Taxonomy,* pp. 91-113. London, Academic Press.
JARDINE, N. & R. SIBSON, 1971. *Mathematical Taxonomy.* London, Wiley.
JUHÁSZ-NAGY, P. 1966a. Some theoretical problems of synbotany. Part 1. Primary considerations on a conceptual network. *Acta Biologica Debrecina* IV, 59-66.
JUHÁSZ-NAGY, P. 1966b. Some theoretical problems of synbotany. Part 2. Preliminaries on an axiomatic model-building. *Acta Biologica Debrecina* IV, 67-81.
JUHÁSZ-NAGY, P. 1967. On association among plant populations. I. Multiple and partial association: a new approach. *Acta Biologica Debrecina* V, 43-56.

JUHÁSZ-NAGY, P. 1968. Some theoretical problems of synbotany. Part 3. The importance of methodology. *Acta Biologica Debrecina* VI, 65-77.
KERSHAW, K.A. 1964. *Quantitative and Dynamic Ecology.* London, Edward Arnold.
KRUSKAL, J.B. & F. CARMONE. 1971. How to use M-D-SCAL (Version 5M) and other useful information. Bell Telephone Laboratories, Murray Hill, New Jersey, U.S.A., and University of Waterloo, Waterloo, Ontario, Canada.
KULLBACK, S. 1959. *Information Theory and Statistics.* New York, Wiley, Chapman and Hall.
KULLBACK, S., M. KUPPERMAN & H.H. KU. 1962. Tests for contingency tables and Markov chains. *Technometrics* 4: 573-608.
LAMBERT, J.M. & M.B. DALE. 1964. The use of statistics in phytosociology. *Adv. ecol. Res.* 2: 59-99.
LANCE, G.N. & W.T. WILLIAMS. 1967. Mixed-data classificatory programs. I. Agglomerate systems. *Austral. Comput. J.* 1: 15-20.
LANCE, G.N. & W.T. WILLIAMS. 1968. Mixed-data classificatory programs. II. Divisive systems. *Austral. Comput. J.* 1: 82-85.
LERMAN, I.C. 1970. *Les Bases de la Classification Automatique.* Paris, Gauthier-Villars.
MACNAUGHTON-SMITH, P., W.T. WILLIAMS, M.B. DALE & L.G. MOCKETT. 1964. Dissimilarity analysis: a new technique of hierarchical sub-division. *Nature* 202: 1034-1035.
MAHALANOBIS, P.C. 1936. On the generalized distance in statistics. *Proc. Nat. Inst. Sci. India* 2: 49-55.
MARGALEF, D.R. 1958. Information theory in ecology. *Yearbook of the Society for General Systems Research* 3: 36-71.
MORRISON, D.F. 1967. *Multivariate Statistical Methods.* New York, McGraw-Hill.
McINTOSH, R.P. 1967a. The continuum concept of vegetation. *Bot. Rev.* 33: 130-187.
McINTOSH, R.P. 1967b. An index of diversity and the relation of certain concepts to diversity. *Ecology* 48: 392-404.
NOY-MEIR, I. & M.P. AUSTIN. 1970. Principal component ordination and simulated vegetation data. *Ecology* 51: 551-552.
ORLÓCI, L. 1966. Geometric models in ecology. I. The theory and application of some ordination methods. *J. Ecol.* 54: 193-215.
ORLÓCI, L. 1967. Data centering: a review and evaluation with reference to component analysis. *Syst. Zool.* 16: 208-212.
ORLÓCI, L. 1969a. Information theory models for hierarchic and non-hierarchic classifications. *In:* A.J. COLE (ed.), *Numerical Taxonomy.* pp. 148-164. London, Academic Press.
ORLÓCI, L. 1969b. Information analysis of structure in biological collections. *Nature* 223: 283-284.
ORLÓCI, L. 1970a. Analysis of vegetation samples based on the use of information. *J. theoret. Biol.* 29: 173-189.
ORLÓCI, L. 1970b. Automatic classification of plants based on information content. *Can. J. Bot.* 48: 793-802.
ORLÓCI, L. 1971. Information theory techniques for classifying plant communities. *In:* G.P. PATIL *et al.* (eds.), *Statistical Ecology,* Vol. 3, pp. 259-270. London, Pennsylvania State Univ. Press.
ORLÓCI, L. 1972. On objective functions of phytosociological resemblance. *Amer. Midland Nat.* 88: 28-55.
ORLÓCI, L. 1973. Ordination by resemblance matrices. *In:* R.H. WHITTAKER (ed.), *Handbook of Vegetation Science,* Part V, pp. 249-286. The Hague, W. Junk.
OSTLE, B. 1963. *Statistics in Research.* Ames, Iowa State Univ. Press.
PIELOU, E.C. 1971. Measurement of structure in animal communities. *In:* J.A. WIENS (ed.), *Ecosystems Structure and Function,* pp. 113-135. Seattle, Oregon State Univ. Press.
PIELOU, E.C. 1966a. Species-diversity and pattern-diversity in the study of ecological succession. *J. theoret. Biol.* 10: 370-383.

167

PIELOU, E.C. 1966b. The measurement of diversity in different types of biological collections. *J. theoret. Biol.* 13: 131-144.
PIELOU, E.C. 1969. *An Introduction to Mathematical Ecology.* New York, Wiley-Interscience.
RAJSKI, C. 1961. Entropy and metric spaces. *In:* C. CHERRY (ed.), *Information Theory,* pp. 41-45. London, Butterworths.
RAO, C.R. 1952. *Advanced Statistical Methods in Biometric Research.* New York, Wiley.
RAO, C.R. 1972. Recent trends of research work in multivariate analysis. *Biometrics* 28: 3-22.
REKTORYS, K. 1969. *Survey of Applicable Mathematics.* Cambridge, Massachusetts, M.I.T. Press.
RÉNYI, A. 1961. On measures of entropy and information. *In:* J. NEYMAN (ed.), *Proceedings of the 4th Berkeley Symposium on Mathematical Statistics and Probability,* Vol. I, pp. 547-561. Berkeley-Los Angeles, Univ. Calif. Press.
SAMPFORD, M.R. 1962. *An Introduction to Sampling Theory.* Edinburgh, Oliver and Boyd.
SEAL, H.L. 1964. *Multivariate Statistical Analysis for Biologists.* London, Methuen.
SEARLE, S.R. 1966. *Matrix Algebra for the Biological Sciences.* New York, Wiley.
SHEPARD, R.N. & J.D. CARROLL. 1966. Parametric representation of non-linear data structures. *In:* P.R. KRISHNAIAH (ed.), *Multivariate Analysis,* pp. 561-592. London, Academic Press.
SHIMWELL, D.W. 1971. *The Description and Classification of Vegetation.* Seattle, Univ. of Washington Press.
SHUBIK, M. 1954. *Readings in Game Theory and Political Behavior.* Garden City, N.Y., Doubleday.
SIBSON, R. 1969. Information radius. *I. Wahrscheinlichkeitstheorie & verw. Geb.,* 14: 149-160.
SIMMONS, G.F. 1963. *Introduction to Topology and Modern Analysis.* New York, McGraw-Hill.
SNEATH, P.H.A. 1966. A method for curve seeking from scattered points. *Computer Journal* 8: 383-391.
SNEATH, P.H.A. & R.R. SOKAL. 1973. *Numerical Taxonomy.* San Francisco, Freeman.
SOKAL, R.R. 1965. Statistical methods in systematics. *Biol. Rev.* 40: 337-391.
SOKAL, R.R. & F.J. ROHLF. 1969. *Biometry.* San Francisco, Freeman.
SOKAL, R.R. & P.H.A. SNEATH. 1963. *Principles of Numerical Taxonomy.* London, Freeman.
SWAN. J.M.A. 1970. An examination of some ordination problems by use of simulated vegetation data. *Ecology* 51: 89-102.
WHITTAKER, R.H. 1960. Vegetation of the Siskiyou Mountains, Oregon and California. *Ecol. Monogr.* 30: 279-338.
WHITTAKER, R.H. 1962. Classification of natural communities. *Bot. Rev.* 28: 1-239.
WHITTAKER, R.H. 1967. Gradient analysis of vegetation. *Biol. Rev.* 42: 207-264.
WHITTAKER, R.H. 1970. The population structure of vegetation. *In:* R. TÜXEN (ed.), *Gesellschaftsmorphologie,* pp. 39-59. The Hague, Junk.
WHITTAKER, R.H. & H.G. GAUCH. 1973. Evaluation of ordination techniques. *In:* R.H. WHITTAKER (ed.), *Handbook of Vegetation Science,* Part V, pp. 287-321. The Hague, W. Junk.
WILLIAMS, E.J. 1952. Use of scores for the analysis of association in contingency tables. *Biometrika* 39: 274-289.
WILLIAMS, W.T. 1971. Principles of clustering. *Annual Rev. Ecol. Syst.* 2: 303-326.
WILLIAMS, W.T. & M.B. DALE. 1965. Fundamental problems in numerical taxonomy. *Adv. bot. Res.* 2: 35-68.
WILLIAMS, W.T., M.B. DALE & P. MACNAUGHTON-SMITH. 1964. An objective method of weighting in similarity analysis. *Nature* 201: 426.
WISHART, D. 1969. An algorithm for hierarchical classifications. *Biometrics* 22: 165-170.

168

1. Introduction

The computer programs in this Appendix supplement the examples in the main text.
The programs use the BASIC computer language. This is a conversational language designed
to solve mathematical problems from a teletype console. The fundamentals of BASIC are
described by J.G. KEMENY & T.E. KURTZ in their manual "Basic" published at
Dartmouth College, Computing Center (1968), and a special adaptation to the PDP-10
Time-Sharing System, for which the present programs were written, in a manual published
under the title "Advanced Basic for the PDP-10" by Digital Equipment Corporation,
Maynard, Massachusetts, U.S.A.
A typical sequence of commands to run a BASIC program on the PDP-10 includes:

.R BASIC ↓
(READY)
OLD ↓
(OLD FILE NAME--) RANK ↓
(READY)
RUN ↓

The words between parentheses indicate computer response. The symbol ↓ signifies the
use of the return key on the teletype which echoes as a carriage return and line feed.
Upon receiving the RUN command the computer begins processing the program. It is
assumed that the program, in this example RANK, exists as a disk file.
For opening a disk file for a program the following commands give a typical example:

.R BASIC ↓
(READY)
NEW ↓
(NEW FILE NAME--) RANK ↓
(READY)
SAVE ↓
(READY)
10 PRINT "PROGRAM NAME --- RANK" ↓
.
. (Type all statements in program)
.
1290 END ↓
REPLACE ↓
(READY)

The SAVE command opens file RANK on disk. The REPLACE command causes the computer to transfer program RANK from user core to disk.

2. Brief Description of Programs

RANK — This program ranks species based on a sum of squares criterion. The method is
described in Chapter I.

STRESS — When run after program RANK this program computes stress analysis in a
manner described in Chapter I.

STRESC — This program computes stress analysis for count data following the steps as
outlined in Chapter I.

EUCD — Euclidean distance is computed in this program from raw observations or normalized data according to formula (2.1) or (2.2) as described in Chapter II.

CORRS — This program computes different vector scalar products in accordance with the
descriptions given in Chapter II.

OBLIK – This program should be run after CORRS has already been run with options $z = 1$ and $v = 1$. A Euclidean distance is computed based on oblique reference axes. The formula is explained in Chapter II.

GEND – This program computes generalized distance when run after program CORRS has been run with option $z = 0$. For descriptions see Chapter II.

PINDEX – A version of GOODALL's similarity index (Chapter II) is computed by this program.

INFC – This program computes different information quantities depending on the option selected by the user. The definitions are given in Chapter II and the options specified in the listing of the program.

PCAR – This program computes the R-algorithm for component analysis outlined in Chapter III.

PCAD – This program computes the D- or Q-algorithm of component analysis as described in Chapter III. The input data include Euclidean distances, generated in program EUCD, or vector scalar products computed in program CORRS.

PVO – Position vectors ordination (described in Chapter III) is computed by this program. Vector scalar products (from program CORRS) represent the input data.

RQT – This program computes the RQ-algorithm for reciprocal ordering. Counts of individuals represent the input data. The technique is described in Chapter III.

ALC – This program performs average linkage clustering on the data. A similarity matrix serves as input. The procedure is described in Chapter IV.

SSA – Sum of squares clustering (Chapter IV) is computed in this program. It uses the Euclidean distance as input data.

TRGRUP – This program tests the hypothesis that the sample divides into R natural groups. It uses JANCEY's 1974 algorithm based on single linkage described in Chapter IV.

EMV – Based on this program a test on the equality of mean vectors can be computed (see descriptions in Chapter IV).

TSTCOV – This program computes a test on the equality of covariance matrices. The method is described in Chapter IV.

SSSIM2 – This is a simulation program. It generates dendrograms and determines their topology matrices for input in SSSIM3. The procedure is described in Chapter IV.

SSSIM3 – An empirical distribution is computed for $I(m; o)$ from input originating in program SSSIM2. The method is described in Chapter IV.

3. Program Directory

4. A Note Regarding Programs

I have written these programs with a dual purpose in mind. Firstly, I want to help those who would like to apply the methods but are unable to write their own programs. Secondly, I want to give a clear and explicit statement of the algorithms. To avoid obscuring the computational steps certain parts of the programs do not provide for the simplest and most efficient computations. However, the inefficiencies are rather inconsequential in computations with small data sets. Those who wish to use the programs with extensively large volumes of data can have the programs revised to suit better their own specific needs.

I also want to draw the user's attention to some programming peculiarities, such as TRGRUP lines 1220-1420 in which the IF statements are fragmented. This has been done because of the inability of the local BASIC system to handle certain blocks of complex IF statements. Because the porgrams were tested on the local system I present them in the form in which they were tested.

```
00010 PRINT "PROGRAM NAME --- RANK"
00020 REM---    THIS PROGRAM RANKS SPECIES ACCORDING TO A SUM OF
00030 REM   SQUARES CRITERION.  THE INPUT DATA ARE STORED IN DISK
00040 REM   FILE RAWD AS P SETS OF N NUMBERS WHERE P INDICATES
00050 REM   THE NUMBER OF SPECIES AND N THE NUMBER OF QUADRATS.
00060 REM   SPECIES MUST NOT HAVE ZERO VARIANCE.
00070 PRINT "=========================================================
00080 FILES RAWD,STAD,ORD
00090 SCRATCH #2,3
00100 REM---FILES STAD AND ORD ARE WRITTEN IN THE PROGRAM.  STAD HOL
00110 REM   THE STANDARIZED DATA AND ORD THE RANK ORDER OF SPECIES F
00120 REM   INPUT IN PROGRAM STRESS
00130 DIM R(5,5),X(5,10),D(10,5),Y(5),K(5)
00140 REM
00150 REM
00160 REM---EXPLANATIONS TO ARRAY SYMBOLS:
00170 REM
00180 REM      R - A P*P ARRAY OF SUM OF SQUARES AND CROSS PRODUCTS
00190 REM      X - A P*P ARRAY OF RAW DATA
00200 REM      D - TRANSPOSE OF ARRAY X
00210 REM      K, Y - P-VALUED VECTORS
00220 REM
00230 MAT K=ZER
00240 REM
00250 REM
00260 REM---READ DATA
00270 PRINT "NUMBER OF SPECIES";
00280 INPUT P
00290 PRINT "NUMBER OF QUADRATS";
00300 INPUT N
00310 LET A=N
00320 LET N=P
00330 LET P=A
00340 FOR I= 1TO N
00350 FOR K= 1TO P
00360 READ #1,X(I,K)
00370 NEXT K
00380 NEXT I
00390 REM
00400 REM
00410 REM---CENTER, STANDARDIZE DATA WITHIN ROWS (SPECIES)
00420 PRINT "TYPE 1 IF STANDARDIZATION IS REQUIRED ELSE TYPE 0";
00430 INPUT Q
00440 FOR I= 1TO N
00450 LET M=0
00460 LET S=0
00470 FOR K= 1TO P
00480 LET M=M+X(I,K)
00490 LET S=S+X(I,K)^2
00500 NEXT K
```

```
00510 LET S=(S-M^2/P)
00520 FOR K= ITO P
00530 LET X(I,K)=X(I,K)-M/P
00540 IF Q=0 THEN 560
00550 LET X(I,K)=X(I,K)/SQR(S)
00560 WRITE#2,X(I,K)
00570 NEXT K
00580 NEXT I
00590 REM
00600 REM
00610 REM---GENERATE R MATRIX
00620 PRINT "TYPE I IF PRINTING OF R MATRIX IS REQUIRED"
00630 PRINT "ELSE TYPE O";
00640 INPUT Q
00650 PRINT "TYPE I IF PRINTING OF SUM OF SQUARED VECTOR"
00660 PRINT "PROJECTIONS IS REQUIRED ELSE TYPE O";
00670 INPUT Z
00680 MAT D=TRN(X)
00690 MAT R=X*D
00700 FOR I= ITO N
00710 LET A9=A9+R(I,I)
00720 NEXT I
00730 LET A=0
00740 LET M=0
00750 IF Q=0 THEN 840
00760 PRINT
00770 PRINT
00780 PRINT "R MATRIX OR RESIDUAL"
00790 MAT PRINT R;
00800 REM
00810 REM
00820 REM---COMPUTE SUM OF SQUARED PROJECTIONS OF VECTORS
00830 REM    ON A GIVEN SPECIES VECTOR
00840 FOR I= ITO N
00850 LET S=0
00860 IF R(I,I)=0 THEN 960
00870 FOR K= ITO N
00880 LET S=S+(R(I,K)^2)/R(I,I)
00890 NEXT K
00900 IF Z=0 THEN 930
00910 PRINT "THE SUM OF SQUARED PROJECTIONS OF SPECIES VECTORS"
00920 PRINT "ON SPECIES"I"IS"S
00930 IF M>=S THEN 960
00940 LET M=S
00950 LET L=I
00960 NEXT I
00970 IF L=0 THEN 1190
00980 LET A=A+I
00990 PRINT "SPECIES"L"RANK"A"SPECIFIC SUM OF SQUARES"M;
01000 PRINT "PER CENT"100*M/A9
```

```
01010 LET K(L)=A
01020 REM
01030 REM
01040 REM--COMPUTE RESIDUAL OF R
01050 FOR I= 1TO N
01060 LET Y(I)=R(I,L)/SQR(R(L,L))
01070 NEXT I
01080 FOR I= 1TO N
01090 FOR K=I TO N
01100 LET R(I,K)=R(I,K)-Y(I)*Y(K)
01110 LET R(K,I)=R(I,K)
01120 NEXT K
01130 LET R(L,I)=0
01140 LET R(I,L)= 0
01150 NEXT I
01160 LET L=0
0.1170 IF A=N THEN 1240
0.1180 GO TO 740
0.1190 FOR I= 1TO N
01200 IF K(I)>0 THEN 1230
01210 LET A=A+1
01220 LET K(I)=A
01230 NEXT I
01240 FOR L= 1 TO N
01250 WRITE#3,K(L)
01260 PRINT "SPECIES"L"RANK"K(L)
01270 NEXT L
01280 PRINT
01290 PRINT "CONTINUE WITH PROGRAM STRESS IF STRESS ANALYSIS";
01300 PRINT " IS REQUIRED"
01310 END


READY
OLD
OLD FILE NAME--RAWD

READY
LIST
```

```
01000    45,2,9,26,3,5,2,90,31,16,18,92,32,48,73,80,95,13,92,78
01010    3,40,5,83,68,27,2,17,1,23,10,61,11,3,32,2,39,2,8,6
01020    9,53,99,21,49,81,72,6,90,62
```

```
READY
OLD
OLD FILE NAME--RANK

READY
RUN

RANK            12:10           9-MAY-74



PROGRAM NAME --- RANK
==============================================================
NUMBER OF SPECIES ?5
NUMBER OF QUADRATS ?10
TYPE 1 IF STANDARDIZATION IS REQUIRED ELSE TYPE 0 ?0
TYPE 1 IF PRINTING OF R MATRIX IS REQUIRED
ELSE TYPE 0 ?0
TYPE 1 IF PRINTING OF SUM OF SQUARED VECTOR
PROJECTIONS IS REQUIRED ELSE TYPE 0 ?0
SPECIES 2 RANK 1 SPECIFIC SUM OF SQUARES 17027.2 PER CENT 46.2184
SPECIES 3 RANK 2 SPECIFIC SUM OF SQUARES 9061.53 PER CENT 24.5965
SPECIES 5 RANK 3 SPECIFIC SUM OF SQUARES 6281.31 PER CENT 17.0499
SPECIES 4 RANK 4 SPECIFIC SUM OF SQUARES 2956.14 PER CENT 8.0241
SPECIES 1 RANK 5 SPECIFIC SUM OF SQUARES 1514.55 PER CENT 4.11108
SPECIES 1 RANK 5
SPECIES 2 RANK 1
SPECIES 3 RANK 2
SPECIES 4 RANK 4
SPECIES 5 RANK 3

CONTINUE WITH PROGRAM STRESS IF STRESS ANALYSIS IS REQUIRED


TIME:  2.74 SECS.

READY
OLD
OLD FILE NAME--STRESS

READY
LIST


STRESS          12:14           9-MAY-74


00010 PRINT "PROGRAM NAME --- STRESS"
00020 REM---    RUN THIS PROGRAM AFTER PROGRAM RANK TO COMPUTE STRESS
00030 REM    ANALYSIS FOR SPECIES.
00040 PRINT "======================================================"
00050 FILES STAD, ORD, DIST
00060 SCRATCH #3
00070 DIM X(5,10), R(5)
```

```
00080 REM
00090 REM
00100 REM---EXPLANATIONS TO ARRAY SYMBOLS:
00110 REM        X - A P*N ARRAY WHERE P REPRESENTS THE NUMBER
00120 REM            OF SPECIES AND N THE NUMBER OF QUADRATS
00130 REM        R - A P-VALUED VECTOR
00140 REM
00150 REM
00160 REM---READ DATA
00170 PRINT "NUMBER OF SPECIES";
00180 INPUT P
00190 PRINT "NUMBER OF QUADRATS";
00200 INPUT N
00210 LET A=N
00220 LET N=P
00230 LET P=A
00240 FOR K= 1TO N
00250 READ #2,R(K)
00260 NEXT K
00270 FOR K=1 TO N
00280 LET R1=R(K)
00290 FOR J=1 TO P
00300 READ #1,A
00310 LET X(R1,J)=A
00320 NEXT J
00330 NEXT K
00340 REM
00350 REM
00360 REM---COMPUTE DISTANCES BASED ON P SPECIES
00370 LET N1=0
00380 FOR K=1 TO P-1
00390 FOR J=K+1 TO P
00400 LET A=0
00410 FOR H= 1TO N
00420 LET A=A+(X(H,K)-X(H,J))^2
00430 NEXT H
00440 WRITE#3,A
00450 NEXT J
00460 NEXT K
00470 REM
00480 REM
00490 REM---COMPUTE DISTANCES USING A REDUCED NUMBER OF SPECIES
00500 LET N1=N1+1
00510 LET S1=0
00520 LET S2=0
00530 LET S3=0
00540 LET S4=0
00550 LET S5=0
00560 RESTORE#3
00570 FOR K= 1TO P-1
00580 FOR J=K+1 TO P
00590 READ #3,A
00600 LET B=0
```

```
00610  FOR H=1 TO N1
00620  LET B=B+(X(H,K)-X(H,J))^2
00630  NEXT H
00640  LET S1=S1+A
00650  LET S2=S2+B
00660  LET S3=S3+A^2
00670  LET S4=S4+B^2
00680  LET S5=S5+A*B
00690  NEXT J
00700  NEXT K
00710  REM
00720  REM
00730  REM---COMPUTE CORRELATION AND STRESS
00740  LET A=(P*(P-1))/2
00750  LET S5=S5-S1*S2/A
00760  LET S3=S3-S1^2/A
00770  LET S4=S4-S2^2/A
00780  PRINT"NO OF SPECIES IN REDUCED SET "N1
00790  LET B=S5/SQR(S3*S4)
00800  PRINT"CORRELATION",B,   "STRESS"100*(1-B*B)
00810  PRINT
00820  IF N1=N THEN 840
00830  GO TO 500
00840  END
```

READY
RUN

PROGRAM NAME ---STRESS
===
NUMBER OF SPECIES ?5
NUMBER OF QUADRATS ?10
NO OF SPECIES IN REDUCED SET 1
CORRELATION   0.728787   STRESS 46.8869

NO OF SPECIES IN REDUCED SET 2
CORRELATION   0.728298   STRESS 46.9582

NO OF SPECIES IN REDUCED SET 3
CORRELATION   0.886349   STRESS 21.4386

NO OF SPECIES IN REDUCED SET 4
CORRELATION   0.920366   STRESS 15.2926

NO OF SPECIES IN REDUCED SET 5
CORRELATION   1.   STRESS -5.96046E-6

TIME: 3.09 SECS.

READY
OLD
OLD FILE NAME--STRESC

READY
LIST

STRESC   12:22   9-MAY-74


```
00010 PRINT "PROGRAM NAME --- STRESC"
00020 REM---   THIS PROGRAM COMPUTES STRESS IN COUNT DATA USING
00030 REM   K, THE MAXIMUM LIMIT FOR COUNTS, AS A VARIABLE.  THE
00040 REM   DATA ARE STORED IN DISK FILE RAWD AS P SETS OF N NUMBERS
00050 REM   WHERE P SPECIFIES THE NUMBER OF SPECIES AND N THE NUMBER
00060 REM   OF QUADRATS.
00070 PRINT "================================================="
00080 FILES RAWD, DIST
00090 SCRATCH #2
00100 DIM X(5,10)
00110 REM
00120 REM---EXPLANATION TO ARRAY SYMBOL:
00130 REM        X - A P*N ARRAY OF DATA
00140 REM
00150 REM
00160 REM---READ DATA
00170 PRINT "NUMBER OF SPECIES";
00180 INPUT P
00190 PRINT "NUMBER OF QUADRATS";
00200 INPUT N
00210 FOR I=1 TO P
00220 FOR J=1 TO N
00230 READ #1,A
00240 LET X(I,J)=A
00250 NEXT J
00260 NEXT I
00270 REM
00280 REM
00290 REM---COMPUTE DISTANCE MATRIX FROM TOTAL COUNTS
```

```
00300 LET NI=N*(N-1)/2
00310 LET S1=0
00320 LET S2=0
00330 FOR J=1 TO N-1
00340 FOR M=J+1 TO N
00350 LET S6=0
00360 FOR H=1 TO P
00370 LET S6=S6+(X(H,J)-X(H,M))^2
00380 NEXT H
00390 WRITE #2, S6
00400 LET S1=S1+S6
00410 LET S2=S2+S6^2
00420 NEXT M
00430 NEXT J
00440 REM
00450 REM
00460 REM---COMPUTE DISTANCE MATRIX FROM TRUNCATED COUNTS
00470 LET K=5
00480 LET S3=0
00490 LET S4=0
00500 LET S5=0
00510 RESTORE #2
00520 FOR J=1 TO N-1
00530 FOR M=J+1 TO N
00540 LET S6=0
00550 FOR H=1 TO P
00560 IF X(H,J)<=K THEN 590
00570 LET A=K
00580 GO TO 600
00590 LET A=X(H,J)
00600 IF X(H,M)<=K THEN 630
00610 LET B=K
00620 GO TO 640
00630 LET B=X(H,M)
00640 LET S6=S6+(A-B)^2
00650 NEXT H
00660 LET S3=S3+S6
00670 LET S4=S4+S6^2
00680 READ #2, A
00690 LET S5=S5+S6*A
00700 NEXT M
00710 NEXT J
00720 LET A=S2-S1^2/NI
00730 LET B=S4-S3^2/NI
00740 LET C=S5-S1*S3/NI
00750 LET D=C^2/(A*B)
00760 PRINT "K="K"  CORRELATION="SQR(D)"    STRESS="1-D
```

```
00770 LET K=K+5
00780 IF I-D>.01 THEN 480
00790 END
```

READY
OLD
OLD FILE NAME--RAWD

READY
LIST

RAWD   12:25   9-MAY-74

```
01000    45,2,9,26,3,5,2,90,31,16,18,92,32,48,73,80,95,13,92,78
01010    3,40,5,83,68,27,2,17,1,23,10,61,11,3,32,2,39,2,8,6
01020    9,53,99,21,49,81,72,6,90,62
```

READY
OLD
OLD FILE NAME--STRESC

STRESC   12:25   9-MAY-74

```
PROGRAM NAME --- STRESC
===========================================================
NUMBER OF SPECIES ?5
NUMBER OF QUADRATS ?10
K= 5    CORRELATION= 9.24958E-2 STRESS= 0.991445
K= 10   CORRELATION= 0.277735   STRESS= 0.922863
K= 15   CORRELATION= 0.379077   STRESS= 0.856301
K= 20   CORRELATION= 0.488919   STRESS= 0.760959
K= 25   CORRELATION= 0.569557   STRESS= 0.675604
K= 30   CORRELATION= 0.640074   STRESS= 0.590306
K= 35   CORRELATION= 0.715967   STRESS= 0.487391
K= 40   CORRELATION= 0.768257   STRESS= 0.409781
K= 45   CORRELATION= 0.817181   STRESS= 0.332215
K= 50   CORRELATION= 0.857721   STRESS= 0.264314
K= 55   CORRELATION= 0.889989   STRESS= 0.207919
K= 60   CORRELATION= 0.913295   STRESS= 0.165893
K= 65   CORRELATION= 0.936184   STRESS= 0.123559
K= 70   CORRELATION= 0.955287   STRESS= 8.74266E-2
K= 75   CORRELATION= 0.972166   STRESS= 5.48941E-2
```

180

```
K= 80    CORRELATION= 0.982968    STRESS= 3.37737E-2
K= 85    CORRELATION= 0.992263    STRESS= 1.54139E-2
K= 90    CORRELATION= 0.997155    STRESS= 5.68229E-3


TIME:  8.05 SECS.

READY
OLD
OLD FILE NAME--EUCD


READY
LIST


EUCD              13:38              9-MAY-74


00010 PRINT "PROGRAM NAME --- EUCD"
00020 REM-—     THIS PROGRAM COMPUTES EUCLIDEAN DISTANCE BETWEEN N
00030 REM     QUADRATS FROM RAW OR NORMALIZED DATA.  THE DATA ARE READ
00040 REM     FROM DISK FILE RAWD9 ARRANGED AS P SETS OF N NUMBERS.  P
00050 REM     SIGNIFIES THE NUMBER OF SPECIES.  THE COMPUTED DISTANCES
00060 REM     ARE WRITTEN INTO DISK FILE DIS.
00070 PRINT "====== =========== ============= ==================== ============="
00080 FILES RAWD9, DIS
00090 SCRATCH #2
00100 DIM X(3,5), Y(5)
00110 REM
00120 REM---EXPLANATIONS TO ARRAY SYMBOLS:
00130 REM
00140 REM       X - A P*N ARRAY OF DATA
00150 REM       Y - AN N-VALUED VECTOR
00160 REM
00170 REM
00180 REM---READ DATA, NORMALIZE QUADRAT VECTORS IF REQUESTED
00190 PRINT
00200 PRINT "NUMBER OF SPECIES";
00210 INPUT P
00220 PRINT "NUMBER OF QUADRATS";
00230 INPUT N
00240 PRINT "TYPE 1 IF NORMALIZATION IS REQUIRED ELSE TYPE 0";
00250 INPUT Z
00260 MAT Y=ZER
00270 FOR I=1 TO P
00280 FOR J=1 TO N
00290 READ #1, A
00300 LET X(I,J)=A
```

181

```
00310 LET Y(J)=Y(J)+X(I,J)^2
00320 NEXT J
00330 NEXT I
00340 IF Z=1 THEN 360
00350 MAT Y=CON
00360 FOR I=1 TO N
00370 LET Y(I)=SQR(Y(I))
00380 NEXT I
00390 REM
00400 REM---COMPUTE DISTANCES
00410 PRINT "TYPE 1 IF PRINTING OF DISTANCES REQUIRED ELSE TYPE 0";
00420 INPUT V
00430 FOR J=1 TO N-1
00440 FOR K=J+1 TO N
00450 LET S=0
00460 FOR I=1 TO P
00470 LET S=S+(X(I,J)/Y(J)-X(I,K)/Y(K))^2
00480 NEXT I
00490 WRITE #2,SQR(S)
00500 NEXT K
00510 NEXT J
00520 REM
00530 REM
00540 IF V=0 THEN 650
00550 RESTORE #2
00560 PRINT "UPPER HALF OF DISTANCE MATRIX"
00570 FOR J=1 TO N-1
00580 FOR K=J+1 TO N
00590 READ #2,A
00600 PRINT A;
00610 NEXT K
00620 PRINT
00630 PRINT
00640 NEXT J
00650 END


READY
OLD
OLD FILE NAME--RAWD9

READY
LIST
```

```
01000    2
```

```
01010     5
01020     2
01030     1
01040     0
01050     0
01060     1
01070     4
01080     3
01090     1
01100     3
01110     4
0.1120    1
01130     0
01140     0
```

READY
OLD
OLD FILE NAME--EUCD

READY
RUN

EUCD   12:41   9-MAY-74

PROGRAM NAME --- EUCD
======== ============== ============== ============== ========

NUMBER OF SPECIES ?3
NUMBER OF QUADRATS ?5
TYPE I IF NORMALIZATION IS REQUIRED ELSE TYPE 0 ?0
TYPE I IF PRINTING OF DISTANCES REQUIRED ELSE TYPE 0?1
UPPER HALF OF DISTANCE MATRIX
  3.31662 4.47214 4.3589 3.74166

  5.19615 6 6.40312
  1.73205 3.74166
  2.23607

TIME: 0.79 SECS.

READY
RUN

PROGRAM NAME --- EUCD
===
NUMBER OF SPECIES ?3
NUMBER OF QUADRATS ?5
TYPE 1 IF NORMALIZATION IS REQUIRED ELSE TYPE 0 ?1
TYPE 1 IF PRINTING OF DISTANCES REQUIRED ELSE TYPE 0 ?1
UPPER HALF OF DISTANCE MATRIX
 0.342014 1.07363 1.2842 1.41421

0.887591 1.10421 1.30054

0.260416 0.504239

0.320364

TIME: 0.78 SECS.

READY
OLD
OLD FILE NAME--CORRS

READY
LIST

CORRS   12:44   9-MAY-74

00010 PRINT "PROGRAM NAME --- CORRS"
00020 REM---   THIS PROGRAM COMPUTES SCALAR PRODUCS BETWEEN SPECIES
00030 REM   VECTORS (OPTION V=1) OR QUADRAT VECTORS (OPTION V=0).
00040 REM   THE DATA ARE CENTERED WITHIN SPECIES, AN OPTION FOR
00050 REM   NORMALIZATION (Z=1) WITHIN SPECIES IS PROVIDED. THE DAT
00060 REM   ARE STORED IN DISK FILE RAWD9 AS P SETS OF N NUMBERS.
00070 REM   CORRELATION VALUES COMPUTED IN THE PROGRAM ARE WRITTEN
00080 REM   DISK FILE COR.
00090 PRINT "=="
00100 FILES RAWD9, COR
00110 SCRATCH #2
00120 DIM X(3,5), I(5,3), R(3,3), Q(5,5)
00130 REM
00140 REM---EXPLANATIONS TO ARRAY SYMBOLS:
00150 REM
00160 REM   X - A P*N ARRAY OF RAW DATA
00170 REM   I - A TRANSPOSE OF X

```
00180 REM        R - A P*P ARRAY
00190 REM        Q - AN N*N ARRAY
00200 REM
00210 REM
00220 REM--READ DATA, CENTER DATA WITHIN SPECIES, NORMALIZE SPECIES
00230 REM    VECTORS IF REQUIRED
00240 PRINT
00250 PRINT "NUMBER OF SPECIES";
00260 INPUT P
00270 PRINT "NUMBER OF QUADRATS";
00280 INPUT N
00290 PRINT "TYPE 1 TO NORMALIZE SPECIES VECTORS ELSE TYPE 0";
00300 INPUT Z
00310 PRINT "TYPE 1 TO COMPUTE THE SCALAR PRODUCT OF SPECIES VECTORS"
00320 PRINT "ELSE TYPE 0";
00330 INPUT V
00340 PRINT "TYPE 1 IF PRINTING OF VECTOR SCALAR PRODUCTS ARE "
00350 PRINT "REQUIRED ELSE TYPE 0";
00360 INPUT Y
00370 FOR I=1 TO P
00380 LET M=0
00390 LET S=0
00400 FOR J=1 TO N
00410 READ #1,A
00420 LET A=A/SQR(N-1)
00430 LET X(I,J)=A
00440 LET M=M+A
00450 LET S=S+A^2
00460 NEXT J
00470 LET S=SQR(S-M^2/N)
00480 LET M=M/N
00490 IF Z=1 THEN 510
00500 LET S=1
00510 FOR J=1 TO N
00520 LET X(I,J)=(X(I,J)-M)/S
00530 LET I(J,I)=X(I,J)
00540 NEXT J
00550 NEXT I
00560 IF V=0 THEN 680
00570 MAT R=X*I
00580 FOR H=1 TO P
00590 FOR I=H TO P
00600 WRITE #2,R(H,I)
00610 IF Y=0 THEN 630
00620 PRINT R(H,I);
00630 NEXT I
00640 IF Y=0 THEN 660
00650 PRINT
00660 NEXT H
```

185

```
00670 GO TO 750
00680 MAT Q=I*X
00690 FOR J=1 TO N
00700 FOR K=J TO N
00710 WRITE  #2, Q(J,K)
00720 IF Y=0 THEN 740
00730 PRINT Q(J,K);
00740 NEXT K
00750 IF Y=0 THEN 770
00760 PRINT
00770 NEXT J
00780 END
```

```
READY
OLD
OLD FILE NAME--RAWD9

READY
LIST
```

```
01000     2
01010     5
01020     2
01030     1
01040     0
01050     0
01060     1
01070     4
01080     3
01090     1
01100     3
01110     4
0.1120    1
01130     0
01140     0
```

```
READY
OLD
OLD FILE NAME--CORRS

READY
RUN
```

PROGRAM NAME --- CORRS
==

NUMBER OF SPECIES ?3
NUMBER OF QUADRATS ?5
TYPE 1 TO NORMALIZE SPECIES VECTORS ELSE TYPE 0?0
TYPE 1 TO COMPUTE THE SCALAR PRODUCT OF SPECIES VECTORS
ELSE TYPE 0 ?1
TYPE 1 IF PRINTING OF VECTOR SCALAR PRODUCTS ARE
REQUIRED ELSE TYPE 0 ?1
 3.5 -0.5 3.
 2.7 -1.6
 3.3

TIME: 1.02 SECS.

READY RUN

CORRS   12:51   9-MAY-74

PROGRAM NAME --- CORRS
==

NUMBER OF SPECIES ?3
NUMBER OF QUADRATS ?5
TYPE 1 TO NORMALIZE SPECIES VECTORS ELSE TYPE 0?1
TYPE 1 TO COMPUTE THE SCALAR PRODUCT OF SPECIES VECTORS
ELSE TYPE 0 ?1
TYPE 1 IF PRINTING OF VECTOR SCALAR PRODUCTS ARE
REQUIRED ELSE TYPE 0 ?1
 1. -0.16265 0.882735
 1. -0.53602
 1.

TIME: 0.96 SECS.

READY
RUN

187

CORRS   12:52   9-MAY-74

PROGRAM NAME --- CORRS
==

NUMBER OF SPECIES ?3
NUMBER OF QUADRATS ?5
TYPE 1 TO NORMALIZE SPECIES VECTORS ELSE TYPE 0?0
TYPE 1 TO COMPUTE THE SCALAR PRODUCT OF SPECIES VECTORS
ELSE TYPE 0 ?0
TYPE 1 IF PRINTING OF VECTOR SCALAR PRODUCTS ARE
REQUIRED ELSE TYPE 0 ?1
  1.3   1.2 -1.2 -1.1 -0.2
  3.85 -0.8 -1.95 -2.3
  1.3   0.9 -0.2
  1.25 0.9
  1.8

TIME: 0.96 SECS.

READY
RUN

CORRS   12:53   9-MAY-74

PROGRAM NAME --- CORRS
==

NUMBER OF SPECIES ?3
NUMBER OF QUADRATS ?5
TYPE 1 TO NORMALIZE SPECIES VECTORS ELSE TYPE 0?1
TYPE 1 TO COMPUTE THE SCALAR PRODUCT OF SPECIES VECTORS
ELSE TYPE 0 ?0
TYPE 1 IF PRINTING OF VECTOR SCALAR PRODUCTS ARE
REQUIRED ELSE TYPE 0 ?1
  0.44845   0.38789 -0.430303 -0.369697 -3.63636E-2
  1.13848 -0.272054 -0.594084 -0.660221
  0.475421   0.317172 -9.02357E-2
  0.398701   0.247908
  0.538913

TIME: 0.92 SECS.

188

```
READY
OLD
OLD FILE NAME--OBLIK

READY
LIST


OBLIK            12:54          9-MAY-74


00010 PRINT "PROGRAM NAME --- OBLIK"
00020 REM---    THIS PROGRAM COMPUTES EUCLIDEAN DISTANCE BASED ON AN
00030 REM    OBLIQUE REFERENCE SYSTEM.   THE DATA ARE READ FROM DISK
00040 REM    FILE RAWD9 ARRANGED AS P SETS OF N NUMBERS WHERE P INDI-
00050 REM    CATES THE NUMBER OF SPECIES AND N THE NUMBER OF QUADRATS.
00060 REM    THE COMPUTED QUADRAT DISTANCES ARE WRITTEN INTO DISK FILE
00070 REM    DIS.  RUN PROGRAM EUCD WITH OPTION Z=0 AND CORRS WITH
00080 REM    OPTIONS Z=1 AND V=1 BEFORE RUNNING PROGRAM OBLIK.
00090 PRINT "======================================================="
00100 FILES RAWD9, OBD, DIS, COR
00110 SCRATCH #2
00120 DIM X(3,5), R(3,3)
00130 REM
00140 REM---EXPLANATIONS TO ARRAY SYMBOLS:
00150 REM
00160 REM       X - A P*N ARRAY OF DATA
00170 REM       R - A P*P ARRAY
00180 REM
00190 REM
00200 REM---READ DATA, CENTRE DATA WITHIN SPECIES
00210 PRINT
00220 PRINT "NUMBER OF SPECIES";
00230 INPUT P
00240 PRINT "NUMBER OF QUADRATS";
00250 INPUT N
00260 PRINT "TYPE 1 IF PRINTING OF DISTANCES REQUIRED ELSE TYPE 0";
00270 INPUT Z
00280 FOR I=1 TO P
00290 FOR J=1 TO N
00300 READ #1,A
00310 LET X(I,J)=A
00320 NEXT J
00330 NEXT I
00340 REM
00350 REM
00360 REM---READ FILES DIS,COR
00370 FOR H=1 TO P
00380 FOR I=H TO P
00390 READ #4,A
00400 LET R(H,I)=A
00410 NEXT I
00420 NEXT H
00430 REM
```

```
00440 REM
00450 REM---COMPUTE DISTANCE MATRIX
00460 FOR J=1 TO N-1
00470 FOR K=J+1 TO N
00480 LET S=0
00490 FOR H=1 TO P-1
00500 FOR I=H+1 TO P
00510 LET S=S+(X(H,J)-X(H,K))*(X(I,J)-X(I,K))*R(H,I)
00520 NEXT I
00530 NEXT H
00540 READ #3,D
00550 LET A=SQR(D^2+2*S)
00560 WRITE #2,A
00570 NEXT K
00580 NEXT J
00590 REM
00600 REM
00610 REM---PRINT DISTANCE MATRIX IF REQUIRED
00620 IF Z=0 THEN 700
00630 RESTORE #2
00640 PRINT "UPPER HALF OF DISTANCE MATRIX"
00650 FOR J=1 TO N-i
00660 FOR K=J+1 TO N
00670 READ #2,A
00680 PRINT A;
00690 NEXT K
00700 PRINT
00710 PRINT
00720 NEXT J
00730 END


READY
OLD
OLD FILE NAME--RAWD9

READY
LIST
```

```
01000     2
01010     5
01020     2
```

```
01030     1
01040     0
01050     0
01060     1
01070     4
01080     3
01090     1
01100     3
01110     4
01120     1
01130     0
0.1140    0
```

READY
OLD
OLD FILE NAME--EUCD

READY
RUN

EUCD   12:59   9-MAY-74

PROGRAM NAME --- EUCD
===

NUMBER OF SPECIES ?3
NUMBER OF QUADRATS ?5
TYPE 1 IF NORMALIZATION IS REQUIRED ELSE TYPE 0 ?0
TYPE 1 IF PRINTING OF DISTANCES REQUIRED ELSE TYPE 0 ?0

TIME: 0.75 SECS.

READY
OLD
OLD FILE NAME--CORRS

READY
RUN

PROGRAM NAME --- CORRS
==== ============== ===============================

NUMBER OF SPECIES ?3
NUMBER OF QUADRATS ?5
TYPE 1 TO NORMALIZE SPECIES VECTORS   ELSE TYPE 0 ?1
TYPE 1 TO COMPUTE THE SCALAR PRODUCT OF SPECIES VECTORS
ELSE TYPE 0 ?1
TYPE 1 IF PRINTING OF VECTOR SCALAR PRODUCTS ARE
REQUIRED ELSE TYPE 0 ?0

TIME: 1.04 SECS.

READY
OLD
OLD FILE NAME--OBLIK

READY
RUN

OBLIK   13:01   9-MAY-74

PROGRAM NAME --- OBLIK
==== ============== ==================================

NUMBER OF SPECIES ?3
NUMBER OF QUADRATS ?5
TYPE 1 IF PRINTING OF DISTANCES REQUIRED ELSE TYPE 0 ?1
UPPER HALF OF DISTANCE MATRIX
 3.77471   5.34569   5.90937   5.33475

 7.4475   8.68483   8.73552

 1.83525   3.51611

 2.08552

TIME: 1.09 SECS.

READY

```
00010 PRINT "PROGRAM NAME --- GEND"
00020 REM---    THIS PROGRAM COMPUTES THE GENERALIZED DISTANCE OF
00030 REM    EXTERNAL QUADRAT X FROM A GIVEN REFERENCE GROUP SPECIFIED
00040 REM    BY ITS MEAN VECTOR XM AND COVARIANCE MATRIX SM.  THE DATA
00050 REM    FOR GROUP M IS STORED IN DISK FILE RAWD9 AS P SETS OF N
00060 REM    NUMBERS WHERE P INDICATES THE NUMBER OF SPECIES AND N THE
00070 REM    NUMBER OF QUADRATS.  WHEN THERE ARE K EXTERNAL QUADRATS
00080 REM    THEIR VECTORS ARE STORED AS K SETS OF P NUMBERS IN DISK
00090 REM    FILE EXI.  RUN PROGRAM CORRS WITH OPTIONS Z=0 AND V=1
00100 REM    BEFORE RUNNING PROGRAM GEND.
00110 PRINT "=========================================================="
00120 FILES RAWD9, COR, DIS, EXI
00130 SCRATCH #3
00140 DIM M(3), X(3), R(3,3), I(3,3), Q(3), G(3)
00150 REM
00160 REM---EXPLANATIONS TO ARRAY SYMBOLS:
00165 REM
00170 REM          R, I - P*P ARRAYS
00190 REM          M, X, Q, G - P-VALUED VECTORS
00200 REM---READ DATA, COMPUTE GROUP MEAN VECTOR
00210 REM
00220 REM---READ DATA, COMPUTE GROUP MEAN VECTOR.
00225 PRINT
00230 PRINT "NUMBER OF SPECIES";
00240 INPUT P
00250 PRINT "NUMBER OF QUADRATS IN GROUP";
00260 INPUT N
00270 PRINT "NUMBER OF EXTERNAL QUADRATS";
00280 INPUT K
00290 PRINT "TYPE 1 IF PRINTING OF DISTANCES REQUIRED ELSE TYPE 0";
00300 INPUT Z
00310 MAT M=ZER
00320 FOR I=1 TO P
00330 FOR J=1 TO N
00340 READ #1,A
00350 LET G(I)=G(I)+A
00360 NEXT J
00370 LET M(I)=M(I)/N
00380 NEXT I
00390 FOR H=1 TO P
00400 FOR I=H TO P
00410 READ #2, A
00420 LET R(H,I)=A
00430 LET R(I,H)=A
00440 NEXT I
00450 NEXT H
00460 LET C=0
00470 FOR I=1 TO P
00480 READ #4, X(I)
```

```
00490 NEXT I
00500 REM
00510 REM
00520 REM---COMPUTE DISTANCE
00530 MAT I=INV(R)
00540 MAT M=X-G
00550 MAT M=TRN(M)
00560 MAT Q=M*I
00570 LET A=0
00580 FOR I=1 TO P
00590 LET A=A+Q(I)*M(I)
00600 NEXT I
00610 IF Z=0 THEN 640
00620 LET A=SQR(A)
00630 PRINT A
00640 WRITE #3, A
00650 LET C=C+1
00660 IF C<K THEN 470
00670 END


READY
OLD
OLD FILE NAME--RAWD9

READY
LIST
```

```
01000     2
01010     5
01020     2
01030     1
01040     0
01050     0
01060     1
01070     4
01080     3
01090     1
01100     3
01110     4
01120     1
01130     0
01140     0
```

READY
OLD
OLD FILE NAME--EXI

READY
LIST

EXI   13:07   9-MAY-74

01000   5
01010   1
01020   4
01030

READY
OLD
OLD FILE NAME--CORRS

READY
RUN

CORRS   13:09   9-MAY-74

PROGRAM NAME --- CORRS
==

NUMBER OF SPECIES ?3
NUMBER OF QUADRATS ?5
TYPE 1 TO NORMALIZE SPECIES VECTORS ELSE TYPE 0 ?0
TYPE 1 TO COMPUTE THE SCALAR PRODUCT OF SPECIES VECTORS
ELSE TYPE 0 ?1
TYPE 1 IF PRINTING OF VECTOR SCALAR PRODUCTS ARE
REQUIRED ELSE TYPE 0 ?0

TIME: 1.46 SECS.

READY
OLD
OLD FILE NAME--GEND

READY
RUN

PROGRAM NAME --- GEND
==== ============== ================== ============== ================ ===

NUMBER OF SPECIES ?3
NUMBER OF QUADRATS IN GROUP ?5
NUMBER OF EXTERNAL QUADRATS ?1
TYPE 1 IF PRINTING OF DISTANCES REQUIRED ELSE TYPE 0 ?1
 9.93532

TIME: 1.35 SECS.

READY
OLD
OLD FILE NAME--PINDEX

READY
LIST

PINDEX   13:12   9-MAY-74


```
00010 PRINT "PROGRAM NAME --- PINDEX"
00020 REM---    THIS PROGRAM COMPUTES ONE VERSION OF GOODALL'S
00030 REM    SIMILARITY INDEX FOR THE COLUMNS OF A DATA MATRIX.   THE
00040 REM    INPUT DATA ARE READ FROM DISK FILE RAWD ARRANGED AS P
00050 REM    SETS OF N NUMBERS.   THE COMPUTED VALUES OF CHI SQUARE A
00060 REM    WRITTEN INTO DISK FILE COR.
00070 PRINT "========== ============== ================== ================ ==="
00080 FILES RAWD, COR
00090 SCRATCH #2
00100 DIM X(5,10), D(5,45), P(5)
00110 REM---EXPLANATIONS TO ARRAY SYMBOLS:
00120 REM
00130 REM        X - A P*N ARRAY OF DATA
00140 REM        D - A P*N(N-1)/2 ARRAY
00150 REM        P - A P-VALUED VECTOR
00160 REM
00170 REM
00180 REM---READ DATA
00190 PRINT
00200 PRINT "NUMBER OF ROWS";
00210 INPUT P
```

```
00220 PRINT "NUMBER OF COLUMNS";
00230 INPUT N
00240 FOR H=1 TO P
00250 FOR J=1 TO N
00260 READ #1,X(H,J)
00270 NEXT J
00280 NEXT H
00290 REM
00300 REM
00310 REM---COMPUTE DIFFERENCES
00320 FOR H=1 TO P
00330 LET A=0
00340 FOR J=1 TO N-1
00350 FOR K=J+1 TO N
00360 LET A=A+1
00370 LET D(H,A)=ABS(X(H,J)-X(H,K))
00380 NEXT K
00390 NEXT J
00400 NEXT H
00410 REM
00420 REM
00430 REM---DETERMINE PROPORTIONS AND COMPUTE CHI SQUARES
00440 PRINT "CHI SQUARE VALUES"
00450 FOR J=1 TO N-1
00460 FOR K=J+1 TO N
00470 LET Q=0
00480 FOR H=1 TO P
00490 LET C=0
00500 LET D=ABS(X(H,J)-X(H,K))
00510 FOR I=1 TO A
00520 IF D(H,I)>D THEN 540
00530 LET C=C+1
00540 NEXT I
00570 LET B=C/A
00580 LET Q=Q-2*LOG(B)
00590 NEXT H
00600 WRITE #2,Q
00610 PRINT Q;
00620 NEXT K
00630 PRINT
00640 NEXT J
00670 END


READY
```

```
OLD
OLD FILE NAME--RAWD

READY
LIST


RAWD              13:15             9-MAY-74



01000    45,2,9,26,3,5,2,90,31,16,18,92,32,48,73,80,95,13,92,78
01010    3,40,5,83,68,27,2,17,1,23,10,61,11,3,32,2,39,2,8,6
01020    9,53,99,21,49,81,72,6,90,62


READY
OLD
OLD FILE NAME--PINDEX

READY
RUN


PINDEX            13:17             9-MAY-74



PROGRAM NAME --- PINDEX
===============================================================

NUMBER OF ROWS ?5
NUMBER OF COLUMNS ?10
CHI SQUARE VALUES
 2.76587   13.0518   8.44779   4.0769   4.317   8.00294   16.3   11.0273
 6.51841
 5.33273   4.41584   15.3182   11.7907   16.8436   2.28712   10.6981
 10.712
 5.9031   6.87363   10.1315   10.4465   6.45816   13.0507   9.36509
 7.68409   8.61957   3.14895   9.62788   7.29767   8.91253
 11.4522   11.5202   2.79612   5.16194   11.0879
 12.1384   11.492   11.6431   17.4365
 3.06485   15.0172   9.97839
 4.86847   7.4063
 11.6465

TIME: 4.66 SECS.

READY
OLD
OLD FILE NAME--INFC
```

198

```
00010 PRINT "PROGRAM NAME --- INFC"
00020 REM---   THIS PROGRAM FORMS TWO-DIMENSIONAL TABLES OF JOINT
00030 REM   FREQUENCIES BETWEEN THE ROWS OF THE INPUT DATA MATRIX.
00040 REM   THE RAW DATA ARE INPUT FROM DISK FILE RAWD8 ARRANGED
00050 REM   AS P SETS OF N NUMBERS.   P SIGNIFIES THE NUMBER OF ROWS
00060 REM   AND N THE NUMBER OF COLUMNS.  THE FOLLOWING QUANTITIES
00070 REM   ARE COMPUTED:
00080 REM              1.  MULTIPLE OF ENTROPY OF ORDER ONE
00090 REM              2.  JOINT INFORMATION
00100 REM              3.  MUTUAL INFORMATION
00110 REM              4.  EQUIVOCATION INFORMATION
00120 REM              5.  RAJSKI'S METRIC
00130 REM              6.  COHERENCE COEFFICIENT
00140 REM   THE VALUES OF RAJSKI'S METRIC ARE WRITTEN INTO DISK FILE
00150 REM   DIS.  IT IS ASSUMED THAT THE DATA REPRESENT DISCRETE CLASS
00160 REM   SYMBOLS GIVEN AS INTEGER NUMBERS.
00170 PRINT "===================================================="
00180 PRINT
00190 FILES RAWD8, DIS
00200 SCRATCH #2
00210 DIM X(2,25),I(2),J(2,2),C(25),K(25),F(25)
00220 REM
00230 REM
00240 REM---EXPLANATIONS TO ARRAY SYMBOLS:
00250 REM
00260 REM         X - A P*N ARRAY OF DATA
00270 REM         I - A P-VALUED VECTOR
00280 REM         C, K, F - N-VALUED VECTORS
00290 REM         J A P*P ARRAY
00300 REM
00310 REM
00320 REM---READ DATA
00330 PRINT
00340 PRINT "NUMBER OF ROWS";
00350 INPUT P
00360 PRINT "NUMBER OF COLUMNS";
00370 INPUT N
00380 PRINT "SPECIFY THE INFORMATION TO BE COMPUTED ; TYPE A NUMBER"
00390 PRINT "BETWEEN 1 AND 6";
00400 INPUT Z
00410 FOR H = 1 TO P
00420 FOR J = 1 TO N
00430 READ #1, A
```

199

```
00440 LET X(H,J) = A
00450 NEXT J
00460 NEXT H
00470 REM
00480 REM
00490 REM---COUNT FREQUENCIES AND COMPUTE INFORMATION
00500 FOR H = 1 TO P
00510 FOR I = H TO P
00520 LET C(I) = X(H,I)
00530 LET K(I) = X(I,I)
00540 MAT F = CON
00550 LET Q = 1
00560 FOR J = 2 TO N
00570 LET A = X(H,J)
00580 LET B = X(I,J)
00590 FOR L = 1 TO Q
00600 IF C(L) <>A THEN 640
00610 IF K(L) <>B THEN 640
00620 LET F(L) = F(L) + 1
00630 GO TO 680
00640 NEXT L
00650 LET Q = Q + 1
00660 LET C(Q)= A
00670 LET K(Q)= B
00680 NEXT J
00690 REM---AT THIS POINT VECTORS C AND K HOLD THE REALIZED JOINT
00700 REM   CLASS SYMBOLS AND VECTOR F THE JOINT FREQUENCIES FOR
00710 REM   ROWS H AND I
00720 LET S = 0
00730 FOR J = 1 TO Q
00740 LET A = F(J)
00750 LET S = S + A * LOG(A)
00760 NEXT J
00770 LET J(H,I) = N * LOG(N)-S
00780 NEXT I
00790 REM---THE H,I ELEMENT IN MATRIX J HOLDS THE JOINT INFORMATION
00800 REM   OF ROW H AND I
00810 MAT F = CON
00820 LET C(I) = X(H,I)
00830 LET Q=1
00840 FOR J = 2 TO N
00850 LET A = X(H,J)
00860 FOR L = 1 TO Q
00870 IF C(L) <> A THEN 900
00880 LET F(L) = F(L) + 1
00890 GO TO 930
00900 NEXT L
00910 LET Q = Q + 1
00920 LET C(Q)=A
00930 NEXT J
```

```
00940 REM---AT THIS POINT VECTOR C HOLDS THE CLASS SYMBOLS AND VECTOR F
00950 REM   THE CLASS FREQUENCIES FOR ROW H.
00960 LET S = 0
00970 FOR J = 1 TO Q
00980 LET A = F(J)
00990 LET S = S + A * LOG(A)
01000 NEXT J
01010 LET I(H) = N * LOG(N) - S
01020 NEXT H
01030 REM---AT THIS POINT THE HTH ELEMENT OF VECTOR H HOLDS THE
01040 REM   N-MULTIPLE OF ENTROPY IN ROW H.
01050 IF Z = 1 THEN 1110
01060 IF Z = 2 THEN 1140
01070 IF Z = 3 THEN 1220
01080 IF Z = 4 THEN 1310
01090 IF Z = 5 THEN 1390
01100 IF Z = 6 THEN 1500
01110 PRINT "MULTIPLE OF ENTROPY OF ORDER ONE"
01120 MAT PRINT I:
01130 GO TO 1390
01140 PRINT "JOINT INFORMATION"
01150 FOR H=1 TO P-1
01160 FOR I=H+1 TO P
01170 PRINT J(H,I):
01180 NEXT I
01190 PRINT
01200 NEXT H
01210 GOTO 1390
01220 PRINT "MUTUAL INFORMATION"
01230 FOR H=1 TO P-1
01240 FOR I=H+1 TO P
01250 PRINT I(H) + I(I) - J(H,I):
01260 NEXT I
01270 PRINT
01280 PRINT
01290 NEXT H
01300 GO TO 1390
01310 PRINT "EQUIVOCATION INFORMATION"
01320 FOR H = 1 TO P
01330 FOR I = H TO P
01340 PRINT 2*J(H,I) - I(H)-I(I):
01350 NEXT I
01360 PRINT
01370 PRINT
01380 NEXT H
01390 PRINT "RAJSKI'S METRIC"
01400 FOR H = 1 TO P
01410 FOR I = H TO P
01420 LET M=2 -(I(H) + I(I))/J(H,I)
01430 WRITE #2, M
01440 PRINT M:
```

```
01450 NEXT I
01460 PRINT
01470 PRINT
01480 NEXT H
01490 GO TO 1600
01500 PRINT "COHERENCE COEFFICIENT"
01510 FOR H=1 TO P
01520 FOR I=H TO P
01530 LET M = 2 - (I(H) + I (I))/J(H,I)
01540 PRINT SQR(1-M^2);
01550 NEXT I
01560 PRINT
01570 PRINT
01580 NEXT H
01590 GO TO 1390
01600 END


READY
OLD
OLD FILE NAME--RAWD8

READY
LIST


RAWD8          13:21          9-MAY-74

01000    1,1,5
01010    5,1,5
01020    5,5,0
01030    6,5,5
01040    1,5,1
01050    4,1,4
01060    3,2,1
01070    1,3,1
01080    3,3,4
01090    3,3,1
01100    3,5,4
01110    6,2,5
01120    5,5,1
01130    5,1,5
01140    0,0,1
01450    1,2,0
01460    1,5
```

READY
OLD
OLD FILE NAME--INFC

READY
RUN

INFC   13:24   9-MAY-74

PROGRAM NAME --- INFC
===

NUMBER OF ROWS ?2
NUMBER OF COLUMNS ?25
SPECIFY THE INFORMATION TO BE COMPUTED ; TYPE A NUMBER
BETWEEN 1 AND 6 ?1
MULTIPLE OF ENTROPY OF ORDER ONE

 39.3792   44.4864
RAJSKI'S METRIC
 0   0.727425

 0

TIME: 2.29 SECS.

READY
RUN

INFC   13:26   9-MAY-74

PROGRAM NAME --- INFC
===

NUMBER OF ROWS ?2
NUMBER OF COLUMNS ?25
SPECIFY THE INFORMATION TO BE COMPUTED ; TYPE A NUMBER
BETWEEN 1 AND 6 ?2
JOINT INFORMATION
 65.9023
RAJSKI'S METRIC
 0   0.727425

 0

TIME: 1.80 SECS.

203

READY
RUN

INFC   13:28   9-MAY-74

PROGRAM NAME --- INFC
==

NUMBER OF ROWS ?2
NUMBER OF COLUMNS ?25
SPECIFY THE INFORMATION TO BE COMPUTED : TYPE A NUMBER
BETWEEN 1 AND 6 ?3
MUTUAL INFORMATION
 17.9633
RAJSKI'S METRIC
 0 0.727425

 0

TIME: 1.83 SECS.

READY
RUN

INFC   13:30   9-MAY-74

PROGRAM NAME --- INFC
==

NUMBER OF ROWS ?2
NUMBER OF COLUMNS ?25
SPECIFY THE INFORMATION TO BE COMPUTED : TYPE A NUMBER
BETWEEN 1 AND 6 ?4
EQUIVOCATION INFORMATION
 0   47.9389
 0
RAJSKI'S METRIC
 0 0.727425

 0

TIME: 1.96 SECS.

READY

204

RUN

PROGRAM NAME --- INFC
==

NUMBER OF ROWS ?2
NUMBER OF COLUMNS ?25
SPECIFY THE INFORMATION TO BE COMPUTED : TYPE A NUMBER
BETWEEN 1 AND 6 ?5
RAJSKI'S METRIC
  0 0.727425

  0

TIME: 1.70 SECS.

READY
RUN

INFC   13:34   9-MAY-74

PROGRAM NAME --- INFC
==

NUMBER OF ROWS ?2
NUMBER OF COLUMNS ?25
SPECIFY THE INFORMATION TO BE COMPUTED : TYPE A NUMBER
BETWEEN 1 AND 6 ?6
COHERENCE COEFFICIENT
  1 0.686187

  1
RAJSKI'S METRIC
  0 0.727425

  0

TIME: 1.97 SECS.

READY
OLD
OLD FILE NAME--PCAR

PCAR   13:36   9-MAY-74

```
00010 PRINT "PROGRAM NAME --- PCAR"
00020 REM---    THIS PROGRAM COMPUTES COMPONENT COEFFICIENTS FOR
00030 REM   SPECIES AND COMPONENT SCORES FOR QUADRATS.  THE INPUT
00040 REM   DATA ARE READ FROM DISK FILE RAWD2.  IN THIS FILE
00050 REM   THE DATA ARE ARRANGED AS R SETS OF C NUMBERS WHERE
00060 REM   R REPRESENTS THE NUMBER OF SPECIES AND C THE NUMBER OF
00070 REM   QUADRATS.  COMPONENT SCORES ARE WRITTEN INTO DISK FILE
00080 REM   DOMS.
00090 PRINT "=================================================="
00100 FILES RAWD2, DOMS
00110 SCRATCH #2
00120 DIM X(2,5),R(2,2),B(2,2),T(5,2),Q(2),C(5,2)
00130 REM---EXPLANATIONS TO ARRAY SYMBOLS:
00140 REM
00150 REM       X - A R*C ARRAY OF RAW DATA
00160 REM       T, C - C*R ARRAYS
00170 REM       R, B - R*R ARRAYS
00180 REM       Q - A R-VALUED VECTOR
00190 REM
00200 REM
00210 REM---READ DATA.
00220 PRINT
00230 PRINT "NUMBER OF SPECIES";
00240 INPUT R
00250 PRINT "NUMBER OF QUADRATS";
00260 INPUT C
00270 PRINT "TYPE 1 FOR COVARIANCE, 0 FOR CORRELATION";
00280 INPUT Z1
00290 PRINT "TYPE 1 IF PRINTING OF SCALAR PRODUCTS REQUIRED,"
00300 PRINT "ELSE TYPE 0";
00310 INPUT Z2
00320 LET L=C
00330 LET N=R
00360 MAT B=IDN
00370 FOR I=1 TO R
00380 LET A=0
00390 LET B=0
00400 FOR J=1 TO C
00410 READ #1,Q
00420 LET X(I,J)=Q
00430 LET A=A+Q
00440 LET B=B+Q^2
```

```
00450 NEXT J
00460 LET B=SQR(ABS(B-A^2/C))
00470 LET A=A/C
00480 FOR J=1 TO C
00490 IF Z1=0 THEN 510
00500 LET B=SQR(C-1)
00510 LET X(I,J)=(X(I,J)-A)/B
00520 NEXT J
00530 NEXT I
00540 MAT T=TRN(X)
00550 MAT R=X*T
00560 IF Z2=0 THEN 600
00570 PRINT
00580 PRINT "SCALAR PRODUCTS"
00590 MAT PRINT R:
00600 REM
00610 REM
00620 REM---EIGENVALUE AND VECTOR PROCEDURE
00630 LET A=0.00000001
00640 LET C=0
00650 FOR I=2 TO N
00660 FOR J=1 TO I-1
00670 LET C=C+2*(R(I,J)^2)
00680 NEXT J
00690 NEXT I
00700 LET Y=SQR(C)
00710 LET O=(A/N)*Y
00720 LET T=Y
00730 LET D=0
00740 LET T=T/N
00750 FOR Q=2 TO N
00760 FOR P=1 TO Q-1
00770 IF ABS(R(P,Q))< T THEN 1080
00780 LET D=1
00790 LET V=R(P,P)
00800 LET Z=R(P,Q)
00810 LET E=R(Q,Q)
00820 LET F=.5*(V-E)
00830 IF F=0 THEN 860
00840 LET G=-(SGN(F))
00850 GO TO 870
00860 LET G=-1
00870 LET G=G*Z/(SQR(Z^2+F^2))
00880 LET H=G/(SQR(2*(1+SQR(1-G^2))))
00890 LET K=SQR(1-H^2)
00900 FOR I=1 TO N
00910 IF I=P THEN 990
00920 IF I=Q THEN 990
00930 LET C=R(I,P)
00940 LET F=R(I,Q)
```

```
00950 LET R(Q,I)=C*H+F*K
00960 LET R(I,Q)=R(Q,I)
00970 LET R(P,I)=C*K -F*H
00980 LET R(I,P)=R(P,I)
00990 LET C=B(I,P)
01000 LET F=B(I,Q)
01010 LET B(I,Q)=C*H+F*K
01020 LET B(I,P)=C*K-F*H
01030 NEXT I
01040 LET R(P,P)=V*K^2+E*H^2-2*Z*H*K
01050 LET R(Q,Q)=V*H^2+E*K^2+2*Z*H*K
01060 LET R(P,Q)=(V-E)*H*K+Z*(K^2-H^2)
01070 LET R(Q,P)=R(P,Q)
01080 NEXT P
01090 NEXT Q
01100 IF D<>1 THEN .1130
01110 LET D=0
01120 GOTO 750
01130 IF T>0 THEN 740
01140 FOR I=1 TO N
01150 LET Q(I)=I
01160 NEXT I
01170 LET J=0
01180 LET V1=0
01190 LET J=J+1
01200 FOR I=1 TO N-J
01210 IF R(I,I)>=R(I+1,I+1) THEN 1290
01220 LET V1=1.0
01230 LET V2=R(I,I)
01240 LET R(I,I)=R(I+1,I+1)
01250 LET R(I+1,I+1)=V2
01260 LET P=Q(I)
01270 LET Q(I)=Q(I+1)
01280 LET Q(I+1)=P
01290 NEXT I
01300 IF V1<>0 THEN 1180
01310 FOR J=1 TO N
01320 PRINT
01330 LET K=Q(J)
01340 PRINT "ROOT"; J; "="; R(J,J)
01350 PRINT "VECTOR";J
01360 LET V=0
01370 FOR I=1 TO N
01380 LET V=V+B(I,K)^2
01390 NEXT I
01400 FOR I=1 TO N
01410 LET B(I,K)=B(I,K)*SQR(1/V)
01420 PRINT B(I,K);
01430 NEXT I
```

208

```
01440 PRINT
01450 PRINT
01460 NEXT J
01470 LET C=L
01480 MAT C=T*B
01490 FOR J=1 TO R
01500 PRINT "COMPONENT";J
01510 PRINT "COMPONENT SCORES OF INDIVIDUALS"
01520 LET K=Q(J)
01530 FOR I=1 TO C
01540 LET Q=C(I,K)
01550 WRITE #2,Q
01560 PRINT Q;
01570 NEXT I
01580 PRINT
01590 PRINT
01600 NEXT J
01610 END


READY
OLD
OLD FILE NAME--RAWD2

READY
LIST


01000      2
01010      5
01020      2
01030      1
01040      0
01050      0
01060      1
01070      4
01080      3
01090      1
01100


READY
OLD
OLD FILE NAME--PCAR
```

READY
RUN

PCAR   13:39   9-MAY-74

PROGRAM NAME -- PCAR
====== ============= ================= ============= =====

NUMBER OF SPECIES ?2
NUMBER OF QUADRATS ?5
TYPE 1 FOR COVARIANCE, 0 FOR CORRELATION ?1
TYPE 1 IF PRINTING OF SCALAR PRODUCTS REQUIRED,
ELSE TYPE 0 ?1

SCALAR PRODUCTS

 3.5 -0.5

-0.5 2.7

ROOT 1 = 3.74031
VECTOR 1
 0.901303 -0.433189

ROOT 2 = 2.45969
VECTOR 2
 0.433189 0.901303

COMPONENT 1
COMPONENT SCORES OF INDIVIDUALS
 0.38987 1.52523 -0.476508 -0.710565 -0.728028

COMPONENT 2
COMPONENT SCORES OF INDIVIDUALS
-0.811173 0.289262 0.991434 0.324188 -0.79371

TIME: 1.61 SECS.

READY
RUN

PCAR   13:40   9-MAY-74

PROGRAM NAME --- PCAR
== ============== ============== ============== ============== ===

NUMBER OF SPECIES ?2
NUMBER OF QUADRATS ?5

210

```
TYPE I FOR COVARIANCE, O FOR CORRELATION ?0
TYPE I IF PRINTING OF SCALAR PRODUCTS REQUIRED,
ELSE TYPE O ?I

SCALAR PRODUCTS

  I. -0.16265
-0.16265  I.

ROOT I = 1.16265
VECTOR I
 0.707107 -0.707107

ROOT2 = 0.83735
VECTOR 2
 0.707107  0.707107

COMPONENT I
COMPONENT SCORES OF INDIVIDUALS
 0.387298  0.739079 -0.473365 -0.447181 -0.205832

COMPONENT 2
COMPONENT SCORES OF INDIVIDUALS
-0.387298  0.394814  0 .473365  6.92167E-2 -0.550097

TIME:  1.47 SECS.


READY
OLD
OLD FILE NAME--PCAD

READY
LIST


PCAD              13:40        . 9-MAY-74


00010 PRINT "PROGRAM NAME --- PCAD"
00020 REM---   COMPONENT SCORES ARE COMPUTED FOR N INDIVIDUALS
00030 REM   BASED ON THE D-ALGORITHM OF COMPONENT ANALYSIS.  THE
00040 REM   INPUT DATA CONTAIN THE UPPER HALF OF A EUCLIDEAN DISTANCE
00050 REM   MATRIX, INCLUDING ZEROS IN THE PRINCIPAL DIAGONAL, STORED
00060 REM   IN DISK FILE DIST3.  THE COMPUTED COMPONENT SCORES ARE
```

```
00070 REM    IN DISK FILE COMS.  TO COMPUTE THE Q-ALGORITHM OF COMPO
00080 REM    ANALYSIS REPLACE STATEMENTS 130, 380 , 390 BY THE FOLLOW
00090 REM         130 FILES COR, COMS
00100 REM         380 LET R(I,J)=A
00110 REM         390 LET R(I,J)=A
00120 PRINT "===== ============== ================ ================== ==========
00130 FILES DIST3, COMS
00140 SCRATCH #2
00150 DIM R(5,5), B(5,5), Q(5)
00160 REM
00170 REM---EXPLANATIONS TO ARRAY SYMBOLS:
00180 REM
00190 REM       R, B - N*N ARRAS
00200 REM       Q - AN N-VALUED VECTOR
00210 REM
00220 REM
00230 REM---READ DATA
00240 PRINT
00250 PRINT "SPECIFY NUMBER OF INDIVIDUALS ";
00260 INPUT N
00270 PRINT "TO DIVIDE DATA BY SQR(N-1) TYPE 1"
00280 PRINT "ELSE TYPE A NUMBER OTHER THAN 1";
00290 INPUT I
00300 IF I<>1 THEN 330
00310 LET P=N-1
00320 GO TO 340
00330 LET P=1
00340 FOR I=1 TO N
00350 FOR J=1 TO N
00360 READ #1, A
00370 LET A=A/SQR(P)
00380 LET R(I,J)= -0.5*A^2
00390 LET R(J,I)= -0.5*A^2
00400 NEXT J
00410 NEXT I
00420 MAT B=IDN
00430 REM
00440 REM
00450 REM---EIGENVALUE AND VECTOR PROCEDURE
00460 LET A=0.00000001
00470 LET C=0
00480 FOR I=2 TO N
00490 FOR J=1 TO I-1
```

```
00500 LET C=C+2*(R(I,J)^2)
00510 NEXT J
00520 NEXT I
00530 LET Y=SQR(C)
00540 LET O=(A/N)*Y
00550 LET T=Y
00560 LET D=0
00570 LET T=T/N
00580 FOR Q=2 TO N
00590 FOR P=1 TO Q-1
00600 IF ABS(R(P,Q))< T THEN 910
00610 LET D=1
00620 LET V=R(P,P)
00630 LET Z=R(P,Q)
00640 LET E=R(Q,Q)
00650 LET F=.5*(V-E)
00660 IF F=0 THEN 690
00670 LET G=-(SGN(F))
00680 GO TO 700
00690 LET G=-1
00700 LET G=G*Z/(SQR(Z^2+F^2))
00710 LET H=G/(SQR(2*(1+SQR(1-G^2))))
00720 LET K=SQR(1-H^2)
00730 FOR I=1 TO N
00740 IF I=P THEN 820
00750 IF I=Q THEN 820
00760 LET C=R(I,P)
00770 LET F=R(I,Q)
00780 LET R(Q,I)=C*H+F*K
00790 LET R(I,Q)=R(Q,I)
00800 LET R(P,I)=C*K -F*H
00810 LET R(I,P)=R(P,I)
00820 LET C=B(I,P)
00830 LET F=B(I,Q)
00840 LET B(I,Q)=C*H+F*K
00850 LET B(I,P)=C*K-F*H
00860 NEXT I
00870 LET R(P,P)=V*K^2+E*H^2-2*Z*H*K
00880 LET R(Q,Q)=V*H^2+E*K^2+2*Z*H*K
00890 LET R(P,Q)=(V-E)*H*K+Z*(K^2-H^2)
00900 LET R(Q,P)=R(P,Q)
00910 NEXT P
00920 NEXT Q
00930 IF D<>1 THEN 960
00940 LET D=0
00950 GOTO 580
00960 IF T>0 THEN 570
00970 FOR I=1 TO N
00980 LET Q(I)=I
```

```
00990 NEXT I
01000 LET J=0
01010 LET VI=0
01020 LET J=J+1
01030 FOR I=1 TO N-J
01040 IF R(I,I)>=R(I+1,I+1) THEN 1120
01050 LET VI=1.0
01060 LET V2=R(I,I)
01070 LET R(I,I)=R(I+1,I+1)
01080 LET R(I+1,I+1)=V2
01090 LET P=Q(I)
01100 LET Q(I)=Q(I+1)
01110 LET Q(I+1)=P
0.1120 NEXT I
01130 IF VI<>0 THEN 1010
01140 FOR J=1 TO N
01150 IF R(J,J)<0 THEN 1310
01160 PRINT
01170 LET K=Q(J)
01180 PRINT "ROOT"; J; "="; R(J,J)
01190 PRINT "COMPONENT SCORES OF INDIVIDUALS"
01200 LET V=0
01210 FOR I=1 TO N
01220 LET V=V+B(I,K)^2
01230 NEXT I
01240 FOR I=1 TO N
01250 LET A=B(I,K) * SQR(R(J,J)/V)
01260 PRINT A;
01270 WRITE #2, A
01280 NEXT I
01290 PRINT
01300 PRINT
01310 NEXT J
01320 END


READY
OLD
OLD FILE NAME--DIST3

READY
LIST
```

```
01000    0
01010    3.16228
```

```
01020     4
01030     3.16228
01040     2.23607
01050     0
01060     4.24264
01070     4.47214
01080     5
01090     0
01100     1.41421
01110     3.60555
01120     0
01130     2.23607
01140     0
```

READY
OLD
OLD FILE NAME--PCAD   .

READY
RUN

PCAD   13:47   9-MAY-74

PROGRAM NAME -- PCAD
==== ============== =============== =============== ==============

SPECIFY NUMBER OF INSIVIDUALS ?5
TO DIVIDE DATA TY SQR (N-1) TYPE 1
ELSE TYPE A NUMBER OTHER THAN 1 ?1

ROOT 1 = 3.89606
COMPONENT SCORES OF INDIVIDUALS
   0.217252   1.46121 -0.549978 -0.836761 -0.843256

ROOT 2 = 2.47388
COMPONENT SCORES OF INDIVIDUALS
   0.864404 -0.222543 -0.981171 -0.311261   0.785864

ROOT 3 = 0.115608
COMPONENT SCORED OF INDIVIDUALS
-0.223998   6.82844E-2 -5.89026E-3 -0.139667   0.203048

TIME: 1.91 SECS.

READY

```
OLD
OLD FILE NAME--PVO

READY
LIST


PVO                13:49          9-MAY-74


00010 PRINT "PROGRAM NAME --- PVO"
00020 REM---     THIS PROGRAMS COMPUTES METRIC CO-ORDINATES FOR N
00030 REM    INDIVIDUALS"BASED ON POSITION VECTORS ORDINATION.  THE
00040 REM    INPUT DATA CONTAIN THE UPPER HALF OF A SCALAR PRODUCT
00050 REM    MATRIX, INCLUDING ELEMENTS OF THE PRICIPAL DIAGONAL,
00060 REM    FROM DISK FILE COR3.  THE METRIC CO-ORDINATES ARE
00070 REM    STORED IN DISK FILE COMS.
00080 PRINT "===== ============ ============== ================ ============
00090 FILES COR3, COMS
00100 SCRATCH #2
00110 DIM X(6,6), K(6)
00120 REM
00130 REM---EXPLANATIONS TO ARRAY SYMBOLS:
00140 REM
00150 REM      X - AN N*N ARRAY
00160 REM      K - A K-VALUED VECTOR
00170 REM
00180 REM
00190 REM---READ DATA
00200 REM
00210 PRINT "SPECIFY NUMBER OF INDIVIDUALS";
00220 INPUT N
00230 LET Q=0
00240 FOR H=1 TO N
00250 FOR J=H TO N
00260 READ #1, A
00270 LET X(H,J)=A
00280 LET X(J,H)=A
00290 NEXT J
00300 LET Q=Q+X(H,H)
00310 NEXT H
00320 LET W=0
00330 LET S=0
00340 FOR H=1 TO N
00350 FOR J=1 TO N
00360 LET S=S+X(H,J)^2
00370 NEXT J
00380 IF X(H,H)<=0 THEN 410
00390 LET C=S/X(H,H)
00400 GO TO 420
00410 LET C=0
00420 IF C<W THEN 450
00430 LET W=C
00440 LET Z=H
00450 LET S=0
00460 NEXT H
```

216

PVO   13:51   9-MAY-74

```
00470 IF W=0 THEN 780
00480 PRINT
00490 PRINT
00500 PRINT "VECTOR ";
00510 PRINT Z
00520 PRINT
00530 PRINT "SUM OF SQUARES ";
00540 PRINT W;Q;W/Q
00550 PRINT
00560 PRINT "CO-ORDINATES"
00570 FOR J=1 TO N
00580 IF X(Z,Z)<=0 THEN 600
00590 GO TO 620
00600 LET W=0
00610 GO TO 630
00620 LET W=X(Z,J)/SQR(X(Z,Z))
00630 LET K(J)=W
00640 PRINT W;
00650 WRITE #2,W
00660 NEXT J
00670 PRINT
00680 FOR H=1 TO N
00690 FOR J=H TO N
00700 LET W=X(H,J)-K(H)*K(J)
00710 LET X(H,J)=W
00720 LET X(J,H)=W
00730 NEXT J
00740 LET X(Z,H)=0
00750 LET X(H,Z)=0
00760 NEXT H
00770 GO TO 320
00780 END
```

```
READY
OLD
OLD FILE NAME--COR3

READY
LIST
```

COR3   13:53   9-MAY-74

```
01000    0.722222
01010   -0.444444
```

```
01020    -0.444444
01030    -0.111111
01040     0.722222
01050    -0.444444
01060     0.388889
01070     0.388889
01080    -0.277778
01090    -0.444444
01100     0.388889
01110     0.388889
0.1120   -0.277778
01130    -0.444444
01140     0.388889
01150     1.05556
01160    -0.111111
01170    -0.277778
01180     0.722222
01190    -0.444444
01200     0.388889
```

```
READY
OLD
OLD FILE NAME--PVO

READY
RUN


PVO              13:54        9-MAY-74


PROGRAM NAME --- PVO
=== ============= ============= =============== =============== ====
SPECIFY NUMBER OF INDIVIDUALS ?6


VECTOR 6

SUM OF SQUARES  2.38095  3.66667  0.649349

CO-ORDINATED
-0.712696  0.62361  0.62361  -0.445436  -0.712696  0.62361


VECTOR 4

SUM OF SQUARES  1.28572  3.66667  0.350649
```

218

CO-ORDINATES
-0.462909 0 0 0.925822 -0.462902 0

VECTOR 5

SUM OF SQUARES 4.50388E-6 3.66667 1.22833E-6

CO-ORDINATES
1.50065E-3 0 0 0 1.50065E-3 0

TIME: 0.92 SECS.

READY
OLD
OLD FILE NAME--RQT

READY
LIST

RQT   13:55   9-MAY-74


```
00010 PRINT "PROGRAM NAME --- RQT"
00020 REM---    THIS PROGRAM COMPUTES THE RQ-ALGORITHM FOR GRADIENT
00030 REM     ANALYSIS.  THE DATA ARE INPUT FROM DISK FILE RAWD
00040 REM     ARRANGED AS R SETS OF C NUMBERS.  R INDICATES THE NUMBER
00050 REM     OF SPECIES AND C THE NUMBER OF QUADRATS.  SPECIES SCORES
00060 REM     ARE WRITTEN INTO DISK FILE SOMS AND THE QUADRAT SCORES INTO
00070 REM     DISK FILE COMS.
00080 PRINT "=== ========================================= ==============="
00090 FILES RAWD, SOMS, COMS
00100 SCRATCH #2,3
00110 DIM X(5,10), R(5,5), B(5,5), T(10,5), Q(5), C(10,5)
00120 DIM S(5), Q(10), D(5,10)
00130 MAT S=ZER
00140 MAT Q=ZER
00150 REM
00160 REM---EXPLANATIONS TO ARRAY SYMBOLS:
00170 REM
00180 REM      X, D - R*C ARRAYS OF DATA
00190 REM      T, C - C*R ARRAYS
00200 REM      R, B - R*R ARRAYS
00210 REM      Q, S - R-VALUED VECTORS
```

```
00220 REM        O - A C-VALUED ARRAY
00230 REM
00240 REM
00250 REM---READ DATA.
00260 PRINT
00270 PRINT "NUMBER OF SPECIES";
00280 INPUT R
00290 PRINT "NUMBER OF QUADRATS";
00300 INPUT C
00310 PRINT "TYPE 1 IF PRINTING OF SCALAR PRODUCTS REQUIRED,"
00320 PRINT "ELSE TYPE 0";
00330 INPUT Z2
00340 LET L=C
00350 LET N=R
00360 MAT B=IDN
00370 LET A=0
00380 FOR I=1 TO R
00390 FOR J=1 TO C
00400 READ #1,Q
00410 LET X(I,J)=Q
00420 LET D(I,J)=Q
00430 LET S(I)=S(I)+Q
00440 LET O(J)=O(J)+Q
00450 NEXT J
00460 LET A=A+S(I)
00470 NEXT I
00480 FOR I=1 TO R
00490 FOR J=1 TO C
00500 LET X(I,J)=X(I,J)/SQR(S(I)*O(J))
00510 LET X(I,J)=X(I,J)- SQR(S(I)*O(J))/A
00520 NEXT J
00530 NEXT I
00540 MAT T=TRN(X)
00550 MAT R=X*T
00560 IF Z2=0 THEN 600
00570 PRINT
00580 PRINT "SCALAR PRODUCTS"
00590 MAT PRINT R;
00600 REM
00610 REM
00620 REM---EIGENVALUE AND VECTOR PROCEDURE
00630 LET A=0.00000001
00640 LET C=0
00650 FOR I=2 TO N
00660 FOR J=1 TO I-1
00670 LET C=C+2*(R(I,J)^2)
00680 NEXT J
00690 NEXT I
00700 LET Y=SQR(C)
```

```
00710 LET O=(A/N)*Y
00720 LET T=Y
00730 LET D=0
00740 LET T=T/N
00750 FOR Q=2 TO N
00760 FOR P=1 TO Q-1
00770 IF ABS(R(P,Q))< T THEN 1080
00780 LET D=1
00790 LET V=R(P,P)
00800 LET Z=R(P,Q)
00810 LET E=R(Q,Q)
00820 LET F=.5*(V-E)
00830 IF F=0 THEN 860
00840 LET G=-(SGN(F))
00850 GO TO 870
00860 LET G=-1
00870 LET G=G*Z/(SQR(Z^2+F^2))
00880 LET H=G/(SQR(2*(1+SQR(1-G^2))))
00890 LET K=SQR(1-H^2)
00900 FOR I=1 TO N
00910 IF I=P THEN 990
00920 IF I=Q THEN 990
00930 LET C=R(I,P)
00940 LET F=R(I,Q)
00950 LET R(Q,I)=C*H+F*K
00960 LET R(I,Q)=R(Q,I)
00970 LET R(P,I)=C*K -F*H
00980 LET R(I,P)=R(P,I)
00990 LET C=B(I,P)
01000 LET F=B(I,Q)
01010 LET B(I,Q)=C*H+F*K
01020 LET B(I,P)=C*K-F*H
01030 NEXT I
01040 LET R(P,P)=V*K^2+E*H^2-2*Z*H*K
01050 LET R(Q,Q)=V*H^2+E*K^2+2*Z*H*K
01060 LET R(P,Q)=(V-E)*H*K+Z*(K^2-H^2)
01070 LET R(Q,P)=R(P,Q)
01080 NEXT P
01090 NEXT Q
01100 IF D<>1 THEN 1130
01110 LET D=0
01120 GOTO 750
01130 IF T>0 THEN 740
01140 FOR I=1 TO N
01150 LET Q(I)=I
01160 NEXT I
01170 LET J=0
01180 LET V1=0
01190 LET J=J+1
```

```
01200 FOR I=1 TO N-J
01210 IF R(I,I)>=R(I+1,I+1) THEN 1290
01220 LET V1=1.0
01230 LET V2=R(I,I)
01240 LET R(I,I)=R(I+1,I+1)
01250 LET R(I+1,I+1)=V2
01260 LET P=Q(I)
01270 LET Q(I)=Q(I+1)
01280 LET Q(I+1)=P
01290 NEXT I
01300 IF V1<>0 THEN 1180
01310 FOR J=1 TO N
01320 IF R(J,J)<0 THEN 1420
01330 LET K=Q(J)
01340 PRINT "SQUARED CORRELATION";R(J,J)
01350 PRINT "SET"J"OF SPECIES SCORES"
01360 FOR I=1 TO N
01370 PRINT B(I,K);
01380 WRITE #2,B(I,K)
01390 NEXT I
01400 PRINT
01410 PRINT
01420 NEXT J
01430 LET C=L
01440 MAT T=TRN(D)
01450 MAT C=T*B
01460 FOR J=1 TO R
01470 IF R(J,J)<0 THEN 1580
01480 PRINT "SET "J" OF QUADRAT SCORES"
01490 LET K=Q(J)
01500 FOR I=1 TO C
01510 LET Q=C(I,K)/(O(I)*SQR(R(J,J)))
01520 WRITE #3,Q
01530 PRINT Q;
01540 NEXT I
01550 PRINT
01560 PRINT
01570 NEXT J
01580 END


READY
OLD
OLD FILE NAME--RAWD

READY
LIST
```

```
01000    45,2,9,26,3,5,2,90,31,16,18,92,32,48,73,80,95;13,92,78
01010    3,40,5,83,68,27,2,17,1,23,10,61,11,3,32,2,39,2,8,6
01020    9,53,99,21,49,81,72,6,90,62
```

```
READY
OLD
OLD FILE NAME--RQT

READY
RUN


RQT                14:04            9-MAY-74



PROGRAM NAME --- RQT
============= ============= ============= ============= =====

NUMBER OF SPECIES ?5
NUMBER OF QUADRATS ?10
TYPE I IF PRINTING OF SCALAR PRODUCTS REQUIRED,
ELSE TYPE 0 ?1
SCALAR PRODUCTS
 0.299985 -6.84761E-2 -1.51015E-2 -5.49618E-2 -7.99155E-2
-6.84761E-2  3.04182E-2 -1.62509E-2  1.15827E-2  1.68363E-2

-1.51015E-2 -1.62509E-2  0.129276 -1.02631E-2 -5.80477E-2

-5.49618E-2  1.15827E-2 -1.02631E-2  7.37661E-2 -1.12381E-2

-7.99155E-2  1.68363E-2 -5.80477E-2 -1.12381E-2  8.11857E-2
SQUARED CORRELATION 0.351403
SET I OF SPECIES SCORES
 0.915144 -0.218502  3.64655E-2 -0.180108 -0.284606
SQUARED CORRELATION 0.163559

SET 2 OF SPECIES SCORES
-0.180458 -6.54975E-2  0.866385  6.01864E-2 -0.457055

SQUARED CORRELATION 7.87536E-2
SET 3 OF SPECIES SCORES
 6.64177E-2  5.74633E-2 -0.260173  0.8682 -0.413311

SQUARED CORRELATION  2.09145E-2
SET 4 OF SPECIES SCORES
 2.72056E-2 -0.778619  0.183748  0.339625  0.493868

SET I OF QUADRAT SCORES
 0.654832 -0.291703 -0.310683  9.14783E-2 -0.228183 -0.305665
-0.372493  1.02895 -0.14249 -0.185001

SET 2 OF QUADRAT SCORES
-0.297069  7.69326E-2 -0.697011  0.746665  0.363993 -0.249177
-0.416949 -9.63201E-2 -0.572575 -0.21446

SET 3 OF QUADRAT SCORES
 0.343966  0.374549 -0.690565 -0.456435 -9.13426E-2 -0.618338
 0.155652  4.33790E-2 -0.371861 -0.401706

SET 4 OF QUADRAT SCORES
-0.357822 -0.483372  1.27997 -0.382989 -0.282584 -0.585433 -0.814716
-4.90161E-2 -0.730114 -0.87511


TIME: 3.32 SECS.

READY
```

223

```
00010 PRINT "PROGRAM NAME --- ALC"
00020 REM---    THIS PROGRAM COMPUTES A HIERARCHICAL CLASSIFICATION O
00030 REM    N INDIVIDUALS BASED ON AN N*N SIMILARITY MATRIX.  THE
00040 REM    METHOD USED IS AVERAGE LINKAGE CLUSTERING.  THE INPUT
00050 REM    DATA ARE READ FROM DISK FILE COR2 CONTAINING THE
00060 REM    UPPER HALF OF THE SIMILARITY MATRIX INCLUDING ELEMENTS
00070 REM    IN THE PRINCIPAL DIAGONAL.
00080 PRINT " ==================================================== ====
00090 FILES COR2
00100 DIM S(5,5),R(5,5),N(5),Q(5)
00110 REM
00120 REM---EXPLANATIONS TO ARRAY SYMBOLS:
00130 REM
00140 REM        S - AN N*N ARRAY OF SIMILARITY VALUES
00150 REM        R - AN N*N ARRAY
00160 REM        N, Q - N-VALUED ARRAYS
00170 REM
00180 REM
00190 REM---READ DATA
00200 PRINT
00210 PRINT "NUMBER OF INDIVIDUALS";
00220 INPUT N
00230 FOR L=1 TO N
00240 FOR M=L TO N
00250 READ #1,A
00260 LET S(L,M)=A
00270 LET S(M,L)=A
00280 NEXT M
00290 NEXT L
00300 MAT N=CON
00310 MAT R=ZER
00320 FOR L=1 TO N
00330 LET R(L,1)=L
00340 NEXT L
00350 REM
00360 REM
00370 REM---FIND VALID FUSIONS
00380 LET Q=0
00390 FOR I=1 TO N-1
00400 FOR J=I +1 TO N
00410 IF S(I,J)<=Q THEN 450
00420 LET Q=S(I,J)
00430 LET L=I
00440 LET M=J
00450 NEXT J
00460 NEXT I
00470 IF Q=0 THEN 990
00480 LET C=0
00490 REM
```

```
00500 REM
00510 REM---UPDATE GROUP REGISTERS
00520 FOR I=N(L)+1 TO N(L)+N(M)
00530 LET C=C+1
00540 LET R(L,I)=R(M,C)
00550 LET R(M,C)=0
00560 NEXT I
00570 LET N1=N(L)
00580 LET N2=N(M)
00590 LET N3=N1+N2
00600 LET C=0
00610 LET N(L)=N(L)+N(M)
00620 LET Q(L)=Q
00630 LET N(M)=0
00640 REM
00650 REM
00660 REM---PRINT FUSION STATISTICS
00670 FOR I=1 TO N
00680 IF R(I,1)=0 THEN 810
00690 LET C=C+1
00700 PRINT
00710 PRINT
00720 PRINT "GROUP"C
00730 PRINT "NUMBER OF INDIVIDUALS"N(I)
00740 PRINT "AVERAGE SIMILARITY"Q(I)
00750 PRINT "INDIVIDUALS:"
00760 FOR J=1 TO N
00770 IF R(I,J)=0 THEN 810
00780 PRINT R(I,J);
00790 NEXT J
00800 PRINT
00810 NEXT I
00820 REM
00830 REM
00840 REM---COMPUTE AVERAGE SIMILARITIES.
00850 FOR J=1 TO N
00860 IF S(L,J)=-1000 THEN 930
00870 IF J=L THEN 930
00880 LET A=(N1/N3)*S(L,J)
00890 LET B=(N2/N3)*S(M,J)
00900 LET D=((N1*N2)/(N3^2))*(1-S(L,M))
00910 LET S(L,J)=A+B+D
00920 LET S(J,L)=A+B+D
00930 NEXT J
00940 FOR J=1 TO N
00950 LET S(M,J)=-1000
00960 LET S(J,M)=-1000
00970 NEXT J
00980 GO TO 370
00990 END
```

225

```
READY
OLD
OLD FILE NAME--COR2

READY
LIST


COR2              14:10              9-MAY-74


01000    1,.94,.42,.13,0,1,.61,.39,.15,1,.97,.87,1,.95,1

READY
OLD
OLD FILE NAME--ALC

READY
RUN


ALC               14:12              9-MAY-74


PROGRAM NAME -- ALC
========== ============= ============== ============== ========

NUMBER OF INDIVIDUALS ?5

GROUP 1
NUMBER OF INDIVIDUALS 1
AVERAGE SIMILARITY 0
INDIVIDUALS:
 1

GROUP 2
NUMBER OF INDIVIDUALS 1
AVERAGE SIMILARITY 0
INDIVIDUALS:
 2

GROUP 3
NUMBER OF INDIVIDUALS 2
AVERAGE SIMILARITY 0.97
INDIVIDUALS:
 3  4

GROUP 4
NUMBER OF INDIVIDUALS 1
AVERAGE SIMILARITY 0
INDIVIDUALS:
 5
```

GROUP 1
NUMBER OF INDIVIDUALS 2
AVERAGE SIMILARITY 0.94
INDIVIDUALS:
  1 2

GROUP 2
NUMBER OF INDIVIDUALS 2
AVERAGE SIMILARITY 0.97
INDIVIDUALS:
  3 4

GROUP 3
NUMBER OF INDIVIDUALS 1
AVERAGE SIMILARITY 0
INDIVIDUALS:
  5

GROUP 1
NUMBER OF INDIVIDUALS 2
AVERAGE SIMILARITY 0.94
INDIVIDUALS:
  1 2

GROUP 2
NUMBER OF INDIVIDUALS 3
AVERAGE SIMILARITY 0.911875
INDIVIDUALS:
  3 4 5

GROUP 1
NUMBER OF INDIVIDUALS 5
AVERAGE SIMILARITY 0.32
INDIVIDUALS:
  1 2 3 4 5

TIME: 1.48 SECS.

READY
OLD
OLD FILE NAME--SSA

READY
LIST

SSA   14:14   9-MAY-74

00010 PRINT "PROGRAM NAME --- SSA"
00020 REM---   THIS PROGRAM COMPUTES A HIERARCHICAL CLASSIFICATION

```
00030 REM     FOR N INDIVIDUALS BASED ON AN N*N MATRIX OF EUCLIDEAN
00040 REM     DISTANCES.  THE DISTANCES ARE READ FROM DISK FILE DIS2
00050 REM     CONTAINING THE UPPER HALF OF THE DISTANCE MATRIX INC-
00060 REM     LUDING ALSO THE ELEMENTS IN THE PRINCIPAL DIAGONAL.
00070 PRINT "==============================================="
00080 FILES DIS2
00090 DIM D(5,5),R(5,5),N(5),Q(5),A(5,5),X(5)
00100 REM
00110 REM---EXPLANATIONS TO ARRAY SYMBOLS:
00120 REM
00130 REM       D, R, A - N*N ARRAYS
00140 REM       N, Q, X - N-VALUED ARRAYS
00150 REM
00160 REM
00170 REM---READ DATA
00180 PRINT
00190 PRINT "NUMBER OF INDIVIDUALS";
00200 INPUT N
00210 FOR J=1 TO N
00220 FOR K=J TO N
00230 READ #1, A
00240 LET D(J,K)=A*A/2
00250 LET D(K,J)=A*A/2
00260 LET A(J,K)=A*A
00270 LET A(K,J)=A*A
00280 NEXT K
00290 NEXT J
00300 REM
00310 REM
00320 REM---AT THIS POINT MATRIX D CONTAINS THE WITHIN GROUP SUM OF
00330 REM     SQUARES FOR ALL POTENTIAL FUSIONS.
00340 LET D=0
00350 MAT N=CON
00360 MAT R=ZER
00370 MAT Q=ZER
00380 FOR I=1 TO N
00390 LET R(I,1)=I
00400 NEXT I
00410 REM
00420 REM
00430 REM---SEARCH FOR VALID FUSIONS
00440 LET D=D+1
00450 LET Q=10^10
00460 FOR J=1 TO N-1
00470 IF R(J,1)=0 THEN 560
00480 FOR K=J+1 TO N
00490 IF R(K,1)=0 THEN 550
00500 LET W=D(J,K)-Q(J)-Q(K)
00510 IF W>=Q THEN 550
```

```
00520 LET Q=W
00530 LET L=J
00540 LET M=K
00550 NEXT K
00560 NEXT J
00570 LET C=0
00580 FOR I=N(L)+1 TO N(L)+N(M)
00590 LET C=C+1
00600 LET R(L,I)=R(M,C)
00610 LET R(M,C)=0
00620 NEXT I
00630 PRINT
00640 PRINT
00650 PRINT "CLUSTERING PASS"D
00660 LET N(L)=N(L)+N(M)
00670 LET N(M)=0
00680 LET Q(L)=D(L,M)
00690 LET Q(M)=0
00700 FOR I=1 TO N
00710 LET D(M,I)=0
00720 LET D(I,M)=0
00730 NEXT I
00740 PRINT "GROUPS IN FUSION("L"+"M")"
00750 PRINT "NUMBER OF INDIVIDUALS IN GROUP"N(L)
00760 PRINT "SUM OF SQUARES"Q(L)
00770 PRINT "INDIVIDUALS"
00780 FOR J=1 TO N(L)
00790 PRINT R(L,J);
00800 NEXT J
00810 REM
00820 REM
00830 REM---GENERATE NEW D MATRIX
00840 FOR I=1 TO N
00850 LET S=0
00860 IF R(I,1)=0 THEN 1040
00870 IF I=L THEN 1040
00880 FOR J=1 TO N(I)
00890 LET X(J)=R(I,J)
00900 NEXT J
00910 FOR H=1 TO N(L)
00920 LET J=J+1
00930 LET X(J)=R(L,H)
00940 NEXT H
00950 FOR J=1 TO N(I)+N(L)-1
00960 LET A=X(J)
00970 FOR H=J+1 TO N(I)+N(L)
00980 LET B=X(H)
00990 LET S=S+A(A,B)
01000 NEXT H
```

```
01010 NEXT J
01020 LET D(I,L)=S/(N(I)+N(L))
01030 LET D(L,I)=D(I,L)
01040 NEXT I
01050 IF D=N-1 THEN 1070
01060 GO TO 440
01070 END
```

READY
OLD
OLD FILE NAME--DIS2

READY
LIST

DIS2   14:20   9-MAY-74

```
01000    0,.34641,1.07703,1.28062,1.41421,0
01010    0.883176,1.10454,1.30384,0,0.244949
01020    0.509902,0,0.316228,0
```

READY
OLD
OLD FILE NAME--SSA

READY
RUN

SSA   14:21   9-MAY-74

PROGRAM NAME -- SSA
======= ============= ======================= ==========

NUMBER OF INDIVIDUALS ?5

CLUSTERING PASS 1
GROUPS IN FUSION (3 + 4)
NUMBER OF INDIVIDUALS IN GROUP 2
SUM OF SQUARES 0.03
INDIVIDUALS
 3 4

```
CLUSTERING PASS 2
GROUPS IN FUSION( 1 + 2 )
NUMBER OF INDIVIDUALS IN GROUP 2
SUM OF SQUARES 5.99999E-2
INDIVIDUALS
 1  2


CLUSTERING PASS 3
GROUPS IN FUSION( 3 + 5 )
NUMBER OF INDIVIDUALS IN GROUP 3
SUM OF SQUARES 0.14
INDIVIDUALS
 3  4  5
CLUSTERING PASS 4
GROUPS IN FUSION( 1 + 3 )
NUMBER OF INDIVIDUALS IN GROUP 5
SUM OF SQUARES 1.808
INDIVIDUALS
 1  2  3  4  5

TIME:  0.96 SECS.

READY
OLD
OLD FILE NAME--TRGRUP

READY
LIST


TRGRUP          17:13         15-JUL-74



10 PRINT "PROGRAM NAME -- TRGRUP"
20 REM---    THIS PROGRAM, BASED ON THE JANCEY CLUSTERING ALGORITHM
30 REM     USING A SINGLE LINKAGE CRITERION, TESTS THE HYPOTHESIS THAT
40 REM     THE SAMPLE DIVIDES INTO R NATURAL CLASSES.  IF
50 REM     NO SOLUTION IS FOUND UNDER THE HYPOTHESIS THE ANALYSIS
60 REM     IS CONTINUED AT THE NEXT SMALLER VALUE OF R.  THE DATA INPUT
70 REM     IS FROM DISK FILE RAWD7  ARRANGED AS P SETS OF N NUMBERS.
80 REM     THE SYMBOL P INDICATES THE NUMBER OF ATTRIBUTES, AND N
90 REM     THE NUMBER OF OBJECTS.
100        PRINT"=============== =========== ==========="
110        FILES RAWD4
120        DIM D(2,85), A(85,85), N(85), M(2,85), P(85),O(85)
130        DIM S(85,85), B(85,85), X(85), Y(85,85), Z(85,85), W(85)
140        REM
150        REM---EXPLANATIONS TO ARRAY SYMBOLS:
160        REM
170        REM     D, M - P*N ARRAYS
180        REM     A, S, B, Z, Y - N*N ARRAYS
```

231

```
190        REM        N, P, O, X, N - N-VALUED VECTORS
200        REM
210        PRINT "NUMBER OF ATTRIBUTES";
220        INPUT P
230        PRINT "NUMBER OF OBJECTS";
240        INPUT N
250        PRINT "MINIMUM GROUP SIZE REQUIRED";
260        INPUT S
270        PRINT "NUMBER OF GROUPS REQUIRED";
280        INPUT R
290        REM
300        REM     READ DATA, GENERATE DISTANCE MATRIX
310        MAT A=ZER
320        FOR I=1 TO P
330        FOR K=1 TO N
340        READ #1,D(I,K)
350        NEXT K
360        NEXT I
370        LET L=10^10
380        FOR K=1 TO N-1
390        FOR J=K+1 TO N
400        FOR I=1 TO P
410        LET A(J,K)=A(J,K)+(D(I,K)-D(I,J))^2
420        NEXT I
430        LET A(K,J)=A(J,K)
440        IF A(J,K)>=L THEN 470
450        LET D=L
460        LET L=A(J,K)
470        NEXT J
480        NEXT K
490        LET C=L
500        LET D=D-L
510        PRINT "INITIAL VALUE OF LINKAGE PARAMETER ="C
520        PRINT "CONFIRM BY TYPING "C"ELSE TYPE DESIRED VALUE";
530        INPUT C
540        PRINT "INCREMENT IN LINKAGE PARAMETER ="D
550        PRINT "CONFIRM BY TYPING "D"ELSE TYPE DESIRED VALUE";
560        INPUT D
570        LET O1=C
580        MAT B=ZER
590        MAT N=CON
600        LET N2=0
610        LET N3=0
620        FOR J=1 TO N
630        LET B(J,1)=J
640        NEXT J
650        MAT W=N
660        LET U=N3
670        MAT Z=B
```

232

```
680        LET O2=N2
690        FOR J=1 TO N-1
700        FOR K=J+1 TO N
710        IF A(J,K)>C THEN 1090
720        REM     SEARCH ARRAY B FOR LABEL J
730        FOR H=1 TO N
740        FOR I=1 TO N
750        IF B(H,I)=0 THEN 800
760        IF B(H,I)<>J THEN 790
770        LET R1=H
780        GO TO 820
790        NEXT I
800        NEXT H
810        REM     SEARCH ARRAY B FOR LABEL K
820        FOR H=1 TO N
830        FOR I=1 TO N
840        IF B(H,I)=0 THEN 890
850        IF B(H,I)<>K THEN 880
860        LET R2=H
870        GO TO 900
880        NEXT I
890        NEXT H
900        IF R1=R2 THEN 1090
910        IF R1>R2 THEN 1010
920        LET N2=0
930        FOR I=N(R1)+1 TO N(R1)+N(R2)
940        LET N2=N2+1
950        LET B(R1,I)=B(R2,N2)
960        LET B(R2,N2)=0
970        NEXT I
980        LET N(R1)=N(R1)+N(R2)
990        LET N(R2)=0
1000       GO TO 1090
1010       LET N2=0
1020       FOR I=N(R2)+1 TO N(R1)+N(R2)
1030       LET N2=N2+1
1040       LET B(R2,I)=B(R1,N2)
1050       LET B(R1,N2)=0
1060       NEXT I
1070       LET N(R2)=N(R1)+N(R2)
1080       LET N(R1)=0
1090       NEXT K
1100       NEXT J
1110       LET N2=0
1120       LET N3=0
1130       FOR I=1 TO N
1140       IF N(I)=0 THEN 1180
1150       LET N3=N3+1
1160       IF N(I)<S THEN 1180
```

```
1170    LET N2=N2+1
1180    NEXT I
1190    LET N9=N8
1200    LET N8=C
1210    LET C=C+D
1220    IF N2<R THEN 1270
1230    IF N2>R THEN 1270
1240    IF N3<R THEN 1270
1250    IF N3>R THEN 1270
1260    GO TO 1720
1270    IF O2<R THEN 1320
1280    IF N2>R THEN 1320
1290    IF N2=R THEN 1320
1300    IF O2=R THEN 1550
1310    GO TO 1540
1320    IF N3>R THEN 1390
1330    IF N3=R THEN 1390
1340    IF N2>R THEN 1390
1350    IF N2=R THEN 1390
1360    IF O2>R THEN 1390
1370    IF O2=R THEN 1390
1380    GO TO 1440
1390    IF N2<R THEN 650
1400    IF N2>R THEN 650
1410    IF O2<N2 THEN 650
1420    IF N3>O2 THEN 650
1430    GO TO 1720
1440    PRINT "NO SOLUTION AT R="R"-- R REDUCED TO "R-1
1450    LET R=R-1
1460    LET C=O1
1470    IF R>1 THEN 580
1480    PRINT"ONLY ONE GROUP FOUND, ANALYSIS TERMINATED"
1490    STOP
1500    REM
1510    REM    AT THIS POINT ARRAY B HOLDS
1520    REM    IMFORMATION ABOUT GROUP CONTENTS.
1530    REM    VECTOR N CONTAINS GROUP SIZES.
1540    PRINT "NUMBER OF GROUPS FOUND:"O2"OR"N2
1550    MAT Y=B
1560    MAT O=N
1570    MAT B=Z
1580    MAT N=W
1590    PRINT O2"--GROUPS"
1600    LET J2=R
1610    LET R=O2
1620    LET N4=N2
1630    PRINT "MAXIMUM NEAREST NEIGHBOUR DISTNACE"N9
1640    GO SUB 1770
1650    IF O2<>J2 THEN 1670
```

```
1660     STOP
1670     MAT B=Y
1680     MAT N=0
1690     PRINT N4"--GROUPS"
1700     LET R=N4
1710     GO TO 1730
1720     PRINT N2"--GROUPS"
1730     PRINT "MAXIMUM NEAREST NEIGHBOUR DISTANCE"N8
1740     GO SUB 1760
1750     STOP
1760     LET U=N3
1770     LET N2=0
1780     MAT M=ZER
1790     MAT W=ZER
1800     FOR H=1 TO N
1810     IF N(H)=0 THEN 1890
1820     LET N2=N2+1
1830     FOR I=1 TO P
1840     FOR K=1 TO N(H)
1850     LET A1=B(H,K)
1860     LET M(I,N2)=M(I,N2)+D(I,A1)
1870     NEXT K
1880     NEXT I
1890     NEXT H
1900     REM
1910     REM      AT THIS POINT ARRAY M HOLDS
1920     REM      THE GROUP MEAN VECTORS.
1930     MAT S=ZER
1940     FOR J=1 TO U-1
1950     FOR K=J+1 TO U
1960     FOR I=1 TO P
1970     LET S(J,K)=S(J,K)+(M(I,J)-M(I,K))^2
1980     NEXT I
1990     LET S(K,J)=S(J,K)
2000     NEXT K
2010     NEXT J
2020     MAT P=ZER
2030     FOR J=1 TO U
2040     FOR K=1 TO U
2050     LET P(J)=P(J)+S(K,J)
2060     NEXT K
2070     NEXT J
2080     REM
2090     REM      AT THIS POINT ARRAY P HOLDS
2100     REM      THE SUM OF SQUARED CENTROID
2110     REM      DISTANCES AND ARRAY S THE CENTROID
2120     REM      DISTANCES.
2130     LET N2=0
2140     FOR I=1 TO N
```

```
2150        IF N(I)=0 THEN 2250
2160        LET N2=N2+1
2170        FOR H=1 TO N(I)
2180        LET B(N2,H)=B(I,H)
2190        IF N2=I THEN 2210
2200        LET B(I,H)=0
2210        NEXT H
2220        LET N(N2)=N(I)
2230        IF N2=I THEN 2250
2240        LET N(I)=0
2250        NEXT I
2260        MAT S=ZER
2270        REM        AT THIS POINT ALL LABELS
2280        REM        ARE IN THE FIRST U ROWS OF B.
2290        REM
2300        REM        NOW ORDER THE GROUPS ACCORDING
2310        REM        TO THE RANK ORDER OF ELEMENTS IN N.
2320        FOR H=1 TO U
2330        LET L=0
2340        FOR I=1 TO U
2350        IF N(I)<=L THEN 2380
2360        LET L=N(I)
2370        LET M=I
2380        NEXT I
2390        FOR I=1 TO N(M)
2400        LET S(H,I)=B(M,I)
2410        NEXT I
2420        LET X(H)=N(M)
2430        LET N(M)=-N(M)
2440        LET W(H)=P(M)
2450        NEXT H
2460        MAT N=X
2470        MAT B=S
2480        REM        NOW ORDER THE FIRST U GROUPS ACCORDING TO
2490        REM        THE RANK ORDER OF ELEMENTS IN W.
2500        LET N2=0
2510        FOR I=1 TO U
2520        IF X(I)<S THEN 2540
2530        LET N2=N2+1
2540        NEXT I
2550        FOR H=1 TO N2
2560        LET L=0
2570        FOR I=1 TO N2
2580        IF W(I)<=L THEN 2610
2590        LET L=W(I)
2600        LET M=I
2610        NEXT I
2620        LET W(M)=-W(M)
2630        FOR I=1 TO X(M)
```

236

```
2640      LET S(H,I)=B(M,I)
2650      NEXT I
2660      LET N(H)=X(M)
2670      NEXT H
2680      MAT B=S
2690      MAT X=N
2700      REM     AT THIS POINT ARRAY B HOLDS
2710      REM     THE REARRANGED GROUPS, ARRAY X THE
2720      REM     GROUP SIZES
2730      IF R=U THEN 2980
2740      GO SUB 2990
2750      REM     ASSIGN GROUPS OF THE U-R
2760      REM     LOWEST RANKS TO THE FIRST R
2770      REM     GROUPS.
2780      FOR I=R+1 TO U
2790      FOR J=1 TO X(I)
2800      LET T=B(I,J)
2810      LET Q=10^10
2820      FOR K=1 TO R
2830      FOR L=1 TO X(K)
2840      LET V=B(K,L)
2850      IF A(T,V)>=Q THEN 2880
2860      LET Q=A(T,V)
2870      LET H=K
2880      NEXT L
2890      NEXT K
2900      LET M=X(H)+1
2910      IF X.(K)>N THEN 2950
2920      LET B<H,M)=T
2930      LET X(H)=M
2940      NEXT J
2950      NEXT I
2960      PRINT "GROUPS WITH FLOATING INDIVIDUALS ASSIGNED"
2970      GO TO 2990
2980      PRINT "NO FLOATING INDIVIDUALS"
2990      FOR I=1 TO R
3000      PRINT
3010      PRINT "GROUP" I
3020      PRINT
3030      FOR K=1 TO X(I)
3040      PRINT B(I,K);
3050      NEXT K
3060      PRINT
3070      NEXT I
3080      RETURN
3090      END
```

READY
RUN

PROGRAM NAME -- TRGRUP
===== ============= ============ ======
NUMBER OF ATTRIBUTES ?2

```
NUMBER OF OBJECTS ?85
MINIMUM GROUP SIZE REQUIRED ?4
NUMBER OF GROUPS REQUIRED ?4
INITIAL VALUE OF LINKAGE PARAMETER = 3.25000E-2
CONFIRM BY TYPING 3.25000E-2 ELSE TYPE DESIRED VALUE ?3.25000E-2
INCREMENT IN LINKAGE PARAMETER = 5.75000E-2
CONFIRM BY TYPING 5.75000E-2 ELSE TYPE DESIRED VALUE ?5.75000E-2
   4 --GROUPS
MAXIMUM NEAREST NEIGHBOUR DISTANCE 0.6075
NO FLOATING INDIVIDUALS

GROUP 1

 1   6   9  18   5   8  15  16  17  22  23  21   2   7  10  11  28   3   4
12  13  14  19  24  29  25  20  27  30  26  31  36  37  33  38  34
45  32  42  43  44  49  48  35  39  40  41  47  51  52  50  57  46
54  55  56  53  58

GROUP 2

82  84  83  85

GROUP 3

59  60  62  64  61  65  63  66

GROUP 4

67  68  69  70  71  72  74  75  73  76  78  77  79  80  81

TIME: 52.83 SECS.

READY
OLD
OLD FILE NAME--EMV

READY
LIST


EMV                  14:41              9-MAY-74


00010 PRINT "PROGRAM NAME --- EMV"
00020 REM---    THIS PROGRAM COMPUTES QUANTITIES BASED ON WHICH
00030 REM    THE EQUALITY OF K GROUP MEAN VECTORS CAN BE TESTED.    THE
00040 REM    INPUT DATA ARE STORED IN DISK FILE RAWD3 AS N SETS OF P
00050 REM    NUMBERS WHERE N REPRESENTS THE TOTAL NUMBER OF INDIVI-
00060 REM    DUALS AND P THE NUMBER OF VARIATES.  THE FOLLOWING
00070 REM    ASSUMPTIONS MUST BE MET:
```

```
00080 REM        (1)   THE INDIVIDUALS ARE ASSIGNED TO GROUPS
00090 REM              BASED ON CRITERIA INDEPENDENT FROM THE VARIATES
00100 REM              USED IN THE ANALYSIS.
00110 REM        (2)   THE UNDERLYING DISTRIBUTION IS MULTIVARIATE
00120 REM              NORMAL.
00130 REM        (3)   THE OBSERVATIONS ARE COMMENSURABLE.
00140 REM        (4)   THE POPULATION COVARIANCE MATRICES ARE EQUAL.
00150 PRINT "=========================================================="
00160 FILES RAWD3
00170 DIM X(27,3),T(3,3),Y(27),C(3),G(3),N(3),Z(27)
00180 DIM H(3,3), E(3,3), R(3,3), B(3,3), Q(3)
00190 REM
00200 REM---EXPLANATIONS TO ARRAY SYMBOLS:
00210 REM
00220 REM        X - AN N*P ARRAY OF DATA
00230 REM        T - A K*P ARRAY OF GROUP TOTALS FOR VARIATES
00240 REM        Y - AN N-VALUED VECTOR OF INDIVIDUAL TOTALS
00250 REM        C - A K-VALUED VECTOR OF GROUP TOTALS
00260 REM        G - A P-VALUED VECTOR OF VARIATE TOTALS
00270 REM        N - A K-VALUED VECTOR OF GROUP SIZES
00280 REM        H,E,R,B - P*P ARRAYS
00290 REM        Q - A P-VALUED VECTOR
00300 REM
00310 REM
00320 REM---READ DATA, PERFORM ARCSIN TRANSFORMATION IF REQUIRED,
00330 REM    COMPUTE MARGINAL TOTALS
00340 REM
00350 PRINT "TOTAL NUMBER OF INDIVIDUALS";
00360 INPUT N
00370 PRINT "NUMBER OF VARIATES";
00380 INPUT P
00390 PRINT "NUMBER OF GROUPS K=";
00400 INPUT K
00410 PRINT "K-VALUED VECTOR OF GROUP SIZES";
00420 MAT INPUT N
00430 PRINT "SET Z1 AT 1 IF ARCSIN TRANSFORMATION REQUIRED";
00440 INPUT Z1
00450 PRINT "IF Z1=1 THEN SPECIFY NUMBER OF RANDOM TRIALS ELSE"
00460 PRINT "TYPE ANY NUMBER";
00470 INPUT Z2
00480 MAT Y= ZER
00490 FOR I=1 TO N
00500 FOR H=1 TO P
00510 READ #1,W
00520 IF Z1<>1 THEN 590
00530 IF W<Z2 THEN 550
00540 LET W=W-0.00001
00550 LET W=(W/Z2)^.5
00560 LET W=N/((1-W^2)^.5)
```

```
00570 LET X(I,H)=ATN(W)*(180/3.14159)
00580 GO TO 600
00590 LET X(I,H)=W
00600 LET Y(I)=Y(I)+X(I,H)
00610 NEXT H
00620 NEXT I
00630 MAT Z=Y
00640 MAT C=ZER
00650 MAT G=ZER
00660 LET G=0
00670 FOR H=1 TO P
00680 LET U=0
00690 FOR J=1 TO K
00700 LET T(J,H)=0
00710 FOR I=1 TO N(J)
00720 LET U=U+1
00730 LET T(J,H)=T(J,H)+X(U,H)
00740 NEXT I
00750 LET C(J)=C(J)+T(J,H)
00760 LET G(H)=G(H)+T(J,H)
00770 NEXT J
00780 LET G=G+G(H)
00790 NEXT H
00800 REM
00810 REM
00820 REM---COMPUTE MEAN VECTORS
00830 PRINT
00840 PRINT "PROFILE DATA"
00850 LET U=0
00860 FOR J=1 TO K
00870 PRINT
00880 PRINT
00890 PRINT "MEAN VECTOR OF GROUP";J
00900 FOR H=1 TO P
00910 PRINT T(J,H)/N(J);
00920 NEXT H
00930 NEXT J
00940 PRINT
00950 PRINT
00960 PRINT "SAMPLE MEAN VECTOR"
00970 FOR H=1 TO P
00980 PRINT G(H)/N;
00990 NEXT H
01000 PRINT
01010 PRINT
01020 PRINT "SAMPLE MEAN ";G/N
01030 PRINT
01040 REM
01050 REM
```

```
01060 REM-- COMPUTE BETWEEN GROUPS SUMS OF SQUARES AND CROSS
01070 REM    PRODUCTS (MATRIX H)
01080 MAT H=ZER
01090 FOR R=1 TO P
01100 FOR S=R TO P
01110 FOR J=1 TO K
01120 LET H(R,S)=H(R,S)+(T(J,R)*T(J,S))/N(J)
01130 NEXT J
01140 LET H(R,S)=H(R,S)-(G(R)*G(S))/N
01150 LET H(S,R)=H(R,S)
01160 NEXT S
01170 NEXT R
01180 PRINT
01190 PRINT "H-MATRIX"
01200 MAT PRINT H;
01210 MAT E=ZER
01220 REM
01230 REM
01240 REM---COMPUTE WITHIN GROUP SUMS OF SQUARES AND CROSS
01250 REM    PRODUSTS (MATRIX E)
01260 FOR R=1 TO P
01270 FOR S=R TO P
01280 FOR I=1 TO N
01290 LET E(R,S)=E(R,S)+X(I,R)*X(I,S)
01300 NEXT I
01310 LET Y=0
01320 FOR J=1 TO K
01330 LET Y=Y+T(J,R)*T(J,S)/N(J)
01340 NEXT J
01350 LET E(R,S)=E(R,S)-Y
01360 LET E(S,R)=E(R,S)
01370 NEXT S
01380 NEXT R
01390 PRINT "E-MATRIX"
01400 MAT PRINT E;
01410 MAT R=H
01420 MAT H=INV(E)
01430 MAT E=R*H
01440 MAT R=E
01450 PRINT "INV(E)"
01460 MAT PRINT H;
01470 PRINT "H*INV(E)"
01480 MAT PRINT R;
01490 LET N1=N
01500 LET N=P
01510 LET K1=K
01520 REM
01530 REM
01540 REM -- EIGENVECTORS PROCEDURE
```

241

```
01550 MAT B=IDN
01560 LET A=0.00000001
01570 LET C=0
01580 FOR I=2 TO N
01590 FOR J=1 TO I-1
01600 LET C=C+2*(R(I,J)^2)
01610 NEXT J
01620 NEXT I
01630 LET Y=SQR(C)
01640 LET O=(A/N)*Y
01650 LET T=Y
01660 LET D=0
01670 LET T=T/N
01680 FOR Q=2 TO N
01690 FOR P=1 TO Q-1
01700 IF ABS(R(P,Q))< T THEN 2010
01710 LET D=1
01720 LET V=R(P,P)
01730 LET Z=R(P,Q)
01740 LET E=R(Q,Q)
01750 LET F=.5*(V-E)
01760 IF F=0 THEN 1790
01770 LET G=-(SGN(F))
01780 GO TO 1800
01790 LET G=-1
01800 LET G=G*Z/(SQR(Z^2+F^2))
01810 LET H=G/(SQR(2*(1+SQR(1-G^2))))
01820 LET K=SQR(1-H^2)
01830 FOR I=1 TO N
01840 IF I=P THEN 1920
01850 IF I=Q THEN 1920
01860 LET C=R(I,P)
01870 LET F=R(I,Q)
01880 LET R(Q,I)=C*H+F*K
01890 LET R(I,Q)=R(Q,I)
01900 LET R(P,I)=C*K -F*H
01910 LET R(I,P)=R(P,I)
01920 LET C=B(I,P)
01930 LET F=B(I,Q)
01940 LET B(I,Q)=C*H+F*K
01950 LET B(I,P)=C*K-F*H
01960 NEXT I
01970 LET R(P,P)=V*K^2+E*H^2-2*Z*H*K
01980 LET R(Q,Q)=V*H^2+E*K^2+2*Z*H*K
01990 LET R(P,Q)=(V-E)*H*K+Z*(K^2-H^2)
02000 LET R(Q,P)=R(P,Q)
02010 NEXT P
02020 NEXT Q
02030 IF D<>1 THEN 2060
```

```
02040 LET D=0
02050 GOTO 1680
02060 IF T>0 THEN 1670
02070 FOR I=1 TO N
02080 LET Q(I)=I
02090 NEXT I
02100 LET J=0
02110 LET V1=0
02120 LET J=J+1
02130 FOR I=1 TO N-J
02140 IF R(I,I)>=R(I+1,I+1) THEN 2220
02150 LET V1=1.0
02160 LET V2=R(I,I)
02170 LET R(I,I)=R(I+1,I+1)
02180 LET R(I+1,I+1)=V2
02190 LET P=Q(I)
02200 LET Q(I)=Q(I+1)
02210 LET Q(I+1)=P
02220 NEXT I
02230 IF V1<>0 THEN 2110
02240 FOR J=1 TO N
02250 PRINT
02260 LET K=Q(J)
02270 PRINT "ROOT"; J; "="; R(J,J)
02300 NEXT J
02310 LET K=K1
02320 LET P=N+1
02330 LET N=N1
02340 PRINT "TEST FOR EQUALITY OF GROUP MEAN VECTORS"
02350 PRINT "S=";(K-1);"OR";(P-1);"WHICHEVER IS SMALLEST"
02360 PRINT "M=";(ABS(K-P)-1)/2
02370 PRINT "N=";(N-K-P)/2
02380 PRINT "THETA=";R(1,1)/(1+R(1,1))
02390 END


READY
OLD
OLD FILE NAME--RAWD3

READY
LIST
```

```
01000    7.5
01010    20.1
```

```
01020    42
01030    10.9
01040    20.4
01050    43.2
01060    10.8
01070    17.9
01080    40.4
01090    12.2
01100    18
01110    84.3
01120    5.1
01130    15.4
01140    69.5
01150    6.2
01160    12.1
01170    99.8
01180    3
01190    21
01200    110.4
01210    0.6
01220    16.1
01230    101.4
01240    12.9
01250    13.8
01260    87.7
01270    4
01280    18
01290    115.2
01300    15.2
01310    11
01320    94.7
01330    11.7
01340    13.5
01350    70.8
01360    9.1
01370    7.8
01380    87.5
01390    7
01400    10.9
01410    125.6
01420    8.9
01430    15.1
01440    71
01450    11.7
01460    15.3
01470    133.5
01480    10.1
01490    13.8
01500    77.7
```

```
01510    6.2
01520    16
01530    70.3
01540    20.6
01550    9.6
01560    121.9
01570    20.8
01580    4.1
01590    101
01600    17.1
01610    5.8
01620    83.3
01630    15.1
01640    12.1
01650    121.4
01660    16.3
01670    8.9
01680    105.4
01690    14.9
01700    11.9
01710    128.8
01720    17.3
01730    5.8
01740    103.6
01750    13.7
01760    8.7
01770    163.3
01780    15.1
01790    10
01800    126.5
01810
```

READY
OLD
OLD FILE NAME--EMV

READY
RUN

EMV   14:55   9-MAY-74

PROGRAM NAME -- EMV
==

TOTAL NUMBER OF INDIVIDUALS ?27
NUMBER OF VARIATES ?3

```
NUMBER OF GROUPS K= ?3
K-VALUED VECTOR OF GROUP SIZES ?10,8,9
SET ZI AT I IF ARCSIN TRANSFORMATION REQUIRED ?0
IF ZI = I THEN SPECIFY NUMBER OF RANDOM TRIALS ELSE
TYPE ANY NUMBER ?0

PROFILE DATA

MEAN VECTOR OF GROUP I
 7.92  17.28  79.39

MEAN VECTOR OF GROUP 2
 9.9875  12.925  91.3875

MEAN VECTOR OF GROUP 3
 16.7667  8.54444  117.244

SAMPLE MEAN VECTOR
 11.4815  13.0778  95.563

SAMPLE MEAN  120.122

H-MATRIX

 396.096 -363.471  1657.22

-363.471  361.733 -1559.13

1657.22 -1559.13  6985.9

E-MATRIX

 221.005 -49.5202 -661.277

-49.5202  193.913 -50.8975

-661.277 -50.8975  16127.3

INV(E)

 5.55111E-3  1.4857E-3   2.32282E-4

 1.47857E-3  5.55505E-3  7.81584E-5

 2.32282E-4  7.81584E-5  7.17777E-5
```

H*INV(E)

 2.0463 -1.30392 0.182549

-1.84497 1.35017 -0.168066

 8.51681 -5.6647 0.764514

ROOT 1 = 12.1929

ROOT 2 = 0.361267

ROOT 3 =-8.39324

TEST FOR EQUALITY OF GROUP MEAN VECTORS
S= 2 OR 3 WHICHEVER IS SMALLEST
M= 0
N= 10
THETA= 0.924202

TIME: 2.51 SECS.

READY
OLD
OLD FILE NAME--TSTCOV

READY
LIST

TSTCOV   14:57   9-MAY-74

00010 PRINT "PROGRAM NAME --- TSTCOV"
00020 REM---   THIS PROGRAM COMPUTES THE ELEMENTS OF A TEST FOR THE
00030 REM   EQUALITY OF K COVARIANCE MATRICES. THE DATA ARE INPUT
00040 REM   FROM DISK FILE RAWD3 ARRANGED AS N1 SETS OF P NUMBERS.
00050 REM   HERE N1 INDICATES THE TOTAL NUMBER OF INDIVIDUALS IN
00060 REM   ALL K GROUPS AND P SIGNIFIES THE NUMBER OF VARIATES.
00070 PRINT "=== ===================== =================== ====================="
00080 FILES RAWD3
00090 DIM X(10,3),U(10,3),M(3),N(3),R(3,3),B(3,3),E(3,3)
00100 DIM A(3,3),Y(3,3),Q(3),T(3,10)
00110 REM
00120 REM---EXPLANATIONS TO MATRIX SYMBOLS:
00130 REM
00140 REM   X, U -MAX(N)*P ARRAYS WHERE MAX(N) INDICATES THE

```
00150 REM          NUMBER OF INDIVIDUALS IN THE LARGEST GROUP
00160 REM     N - A K-VALUED VECTOR OF GROUP SIZES
00170 REM     R, B, E, A, Y - P*P ARRAYS
00180 REM     M, Q - P-VALUED VECTORS
00190 REM     T - TRANSPOSE OF X
00200 REM
00210 REM
00220 REM---READ DATA
00230 PRINT
00240 PRINT "TOTAL NUMBER OF INDIVIDUALS N1="¡
00250 INPUT N1
00260 PRINT "NUMBER OF VARIATES P="¡
00270 INPUT P
00280 LET N=P
00290 PRINT "NUMBER OF GROUPS K="¡
00300 INPUT K
00310 LET G=K
00320 PRINT "K-VALUED VECTOR OF GROUP SIZES"¡
00330 MAT INPUT N
00340 LET O=0
00350 LET S1=0
00360 LET Z1=0
00370 MAT A=ZER
00380 LET F4=N1-G
00390 LET F5=1/F4
00400 LET O=O+1
00410 MAT M=ZER
00420 FOR H=1 TO N(O)
00430 FOR I=1 TO N
00440 READ #1, A
00450 LET X(H,I)=A
00460 LET M(I)=M(I)+X(H,I)
00470 NEXT I
00480 NEXT H
00490 FOR H=1 TO N(O)
00500 FOR I =1 TO N
00510 LET X(H,I)=X(H,I)-M(I)/N(O)
00520 NEXT I
00530 NEXT H
00540 MAT T=TRN(X)
00550 MAT R=ZER
00560 REM
00570 REM
00580 REM---COMPUTE WITHIN GROUP SUMS OF
00590 REM    SQUARES AND CROSS PRODUCTS
00600 FOR H=1 TO N
00610 FOR I=H TO N
00620 FOR J=1 TO N(O)
00630 LET R(H,I)=R(H,I)+X(J,H)*X(J,I)
```

```
00640 NEXT J
00650 LET R(I,H)=R(H,I)
00660 NEXT I
00670 NEXT H
00680 MAT A=A+R
00690 PRINT
00700 PRINT
00710 PRINT "ANALYSIS OF GROUP";O
00720 PRINT
00730 PRINT "COVARIANCE MATRIX"
00740 LET Z3=N(O)-1
00750 LET Z=1/Z3
00760 REM
00770 REM
00780 REM---COMPUTE WITHIN GROUP COVARIANCE
00790 REM   MATRIX AND ITS INVERSE
00800 MAT R=(Z)*R
00810 MAT PRINT R;
00820 MAT Y=INV(R)
00830 PRINT "INV OF COV MAT"
00840 MAT PRINT Y;
00850 PRINT
00860 LET D1=DET
00870 PRINT "DETERMINANT =";D1
00880 PRINT
00890 LET S1=S1+(Z3*LOG(D1))
00900 LET Z1=Z1+Z
00910 GOSUB 1190
00920 IF 0<G THEN 400
00930 LET Z=F5
00940 MAT R=(Z)*A
00950 MAT Y=INV(R)
00960 PRINT
00970 PRINT
00980 PRINT "POOLED COV MAT"
00990 MAT PRINT R;
01000 PRINT
01010 PRINT "INV OF POOLED COV MAT"
01020 MAT PRINT Y;
01030 LET D2=DET
01040 PRINT
01050 PRINT "DETERMINANT OF POOLED COV MAT =";D2
01060 GOSUB 1190
01070 REM
01080 REM
01090 REM---COMPUTE STATISTIC M AND C^(-1)
01100 LET M=F4*LOG(D2)-S1
01110 LET C1=1-(((2*N^2+3*N-1)/(6*(N+1)*(G-1)))*(Z1-F5))
01120 LET C=M*C1
```

249

```
01130 PRINT "M=";M
01140 PRINT "C^(-1) =";C1
01150 PRINT "CHI SQUARE =";C
01160 LET D7 =.5*(G-1)*N*(N+1)
01170 PRINT "THIS IS APPROX DIST AS CHI SQUARE AT";D7;"DF"
01180 STOP
01190 LET Z3=SQR(Z)
01200 LET O1=0
01210 G9=G
01220 REM -- EIGENVECTORS PROCEDURE
01230 MAT B=IDN
01240 LET A=0.00000001
01250 LET C=0
01260 FOR I=2 TO N
01270 FOR J=1 TO I-1
01280 LET C=C+2*(R(I,J)^2)
01290 NEXT J
01300 NEXT I
01310 LET Y=SQR(C)
01320 LET O=(A/N)*Y
01330 LET T=Y
01340 LET D=0
01350 LET T=T/N
01360 FOR Q=2 TO N
01370 FOR P=1 TO Q-1
01380 IF ABS(R(P,Q))< T THEN 1690
01390 LET D=1
01400 LET V=R(P,P)
01410 LET Z=R(P,Q)
01420 LET E=R(Q,Q)
01430 LET F=.5*(V-E)
01440 IF F=0 THEN 1480
01450 LET G=-(SGN(F))
01460 LET G=G*Z/(SQR(Z^2+F^2))
01470 GO TO 1490
01480 LET G=-1
01490 LET H=G/(SQR(2*(1+SQR(1-G^2))))
01500 LET K=SQR(1-H^2)
01510 FOR I=1 TO N
01520 IF I=P THEN 1600
01530 IF I=Q THEN 1600
01540 LET C=R(I,P)
01550 LET F=R(I,Q)
01560 LET R(Q,I)=C*H+F*K
01570 LET R(I,Q)=R(Q,I)
01580 LET R(P,I)=C*K -F*H
01590 LET R(I,P)=R(P,I)
01600 LET C=B(I,P)
01610 LET F=B(I,Q)
```

250

```
01620 LET B(I,Q)=C*H+F*K
01630 LET B(I,P)=C*K-F*H
01640 NEXT I
01650 LET R(P,P)=V*K^2+E*H^2-2*Z*H*K
01660 LET R(Q,Q)=V*H^2+E*K^2+2*Z*H*K
01670 LET R(P,Q)=(V-E)*H*K+Z*(K^2-H^2)
01680 LET R(Q,P)=R(P,Q)
01690 NEXT P
01700 NEXT Q
01710 IF D<>1 THEN 1740
01720 LET D=0
01730 GOTO 1360
01740 IF T>0 THEN 1350
01750 FOR I=1 TO N
01760 LET Q(I)=I
01770 NEXT I
01780 LET J=0
01790 LET V1=0
01800 LET J=J+1
01810 FOR I=1 TO N-J
01820 IF R(I,I)>=R(I+1,I+1) THEN 1900
01830 LET V1=1.0
01840 LET V2=R(I,I)
01850 LET R(I,I)=R(I+1,I+1)
01860 LET R(I+1,I+1)=V2
01870 LET P=Q(I)
01880 LET Q(I)=Q(I+1)
01890 LET Q(I+1)=P
01900 NEXT I
01910 IF V1<>0 THEN 1790
01920 LET O=O1
01930 LET G=G9
01940 RETURN
01950 END
```

READY
OLD
OLD FILE NAME--RAWD3

READY
LIST

```
01000     7.5
01010     20.1
```

01020	42
01030	10.9
01040	20.4
01050	43.2
01060	10.8
01070	17.9
01080	40.4
01090	12.2
01100	18
01110	84.3
01120	5.1
01130	15.4
01140	69.5
01150	6.2
01160	12.1
0.1170	99.8
01180	3
01190	21
01200	110.4
01210	6.6
01220	16.1
01230	101.4
01240	12.9
01250	13.8
01260	87.7
01270	4
01280	18
01290	115.2
01300	15.2
01310	11
01320	94.7
01330	11.7
01340	13.5
01350	70.8
01360	9.1
01370	7.8
01380	87.5
01390	7
01400	10.9
01410	125.6
01420	8.9
01430	15.1
01440	71
01450	11.7
01460	15.3
01470	133.5
01480	10.1
01490	13.8
01500	77.7

```
01510     6.2
01520     16
01530     70.3
01540     20.6
01550     9.6
01560     121.9
01570     20.8
01580     4.1
01590     101
01600     17.1
01610     5.8
01620     83.3
01630     15.1
01640     12.1
01650     121.4
01660     16.3
01670     8.9
01680     105.4
01690     14.9
01700     11.9
01710     128.8
01720     17.3
01730     5.8
01740     103.6
01750     13.7
01760     8.7
01770     163.3
01780     15.1
01790     10
01800     126.5
01810
```

READY
OLD
OLD FILE NAME--TSTCOV

READY
RUN

TSTCOV   14:53   9-MAY-74

PROGRAM NAME --- TSTCOV
==== =========== ================= =========== ==============

TOTAL NUMBER OF INDIVIDUALS NI= ?27

NUMBER OF VARIATES P= ?3
NUMBER OF GROUPS K= ?3
K-VALUED VECTOR OF GROUP SIZES ?10,8,9

ANALYSIS OF GROUP 1

COVARIANCE MATRIX

```
 12.5218 -1.07844 -52.3609

-1.07844  8.53511 -26.6524

-52.3609 -26.6524  840.434
```

INV OF COV MAT

```
 0.120714   4.29954E-2  8.88425E-3

 4.29954E-2 0.145355    7.82880E-3

 8.88425E-3 7.28830E-3  1.97450E-3
```

DETERMINANT = 53538.4

ANALYSIS OF GROUP 2

COVARIANCE MATRIX

```
 8.32696 -1.18536   7.98125

-1.18536  7.85643 -12.6739

 7.98125 -12.6739  634.51
```

INV OF COV MAT

```
 0.123638    1.66829E-2  -1.22196E-3

 1.66829E-2  0.133773     2.46219E-3

-1.22196E-3  2.46219E-3   1.64057E-3
```

DETERMINANT = 39020.

ANALYSIS OF GROUP 3

COVARIANCE MATRIX

 6.2525 -3.93958 -30.7371

-3.93958 7.76278 34.7115

- 30.7371 34.7115 515.228

INV OF COV MAT

 0.264903 9.12663E-2 9.65469E-3

 9.12663E-2 0.215802 -9.09415E-3

 9.65469E-3 -9.09415E-3 3.12955E-3

DETERMINANT = 10549.9

POOLED COV MAT

 9.20853 -2.06334 -27.5532

-2.06334 8.07972 -2.12072

-27.5532 -2.12072 671.971

INV OF POOLED COV MAT

 0.133227 3.54857E-2 5.57475E-3

 3.54857E-2 0.133321 1.87579E-3

 5.57475E-3 1.87579E-3 1.72266E-3

DETERMINANT OF POOLED COV MAT = 40718.9
M= 8.63953
C^(-1) = 0.817295
CHI SQUARE = 7.06105
THIS IS APPROX DIST AS CHI SQUARE AT 12 DF

TIME: 4.23 SECS.

READY
OLD

READY
LIST

SSSIM2   15:10   9-MAY-74


```
00010 PRINT "PROGRAM NAME --- SSSIM2"
00020 REM---    THIS PROGRAM COMPUTES DENDROGRAMS FOR P ENTITIES,
00030 REM    DETERMINES THEIR TOPOLOGY MATRICES, AND WRITES THESE
00040 REM    MATRICES IN DISC FILE TOPL.  THE DATA ARE GENERATED
00050 REM    INTERNALLY IN THE PROGRAM BY A RANDOM NUMBER GENERATOR
00060 REM    ACCORDING TO THE FOLLOWING PARAMETERS:
00070 REM       1.  NUMBER OF SPECIES
00080 REM       2.  NUMBER OF QUADRATS
00090 REM       3.  TOTAL NUMBER OF INDIVIDUALS PER SPECIES
00100 REM    THE EMPIRICAL DISTRIBUTION OF I(M:0) IS COMPUTED IN
00110 REM    PROGRAM SSSIM3 WHICH RECEIVES INPUT FROM SSSIM2.
00120 PRINT "==================================================="
00130 RANDOMIZE
00140 FILES TOPOL
00150 SCRATCH #1
00160 DIM X(25,7), V(7), R(7), L(7), T(7,2), D(7,7)
00170 DIM Y(7,7), F(7,7), N(7,2), Q(7,7), S(7)
00180 REM
00190 REM---EXPLANATIONS TO ARRAY SYMBOLS:
00200 REM
00210 REM       X - AN N*P ARRAY
00220 REM       D, Y, F, Q - P*P ARRAYS
00230 REM       T, N - P:2 ARRAYS
00240 REM       V, R, L, S - P-VALUED VECTORS
00250 REM    V,R,L,S - P-VALUED VECTORS
00260 REM
00270 PRINT "NUMBER OF QUADRATS";
00280 INPUT N
00290 LET KO=N
00300 PRINT "NUMBER OF SPECIES";
00310 INPUT P
00320 LET N=P
00330 PRINT "SPECIES TOTALS (VECTOR S)"
00340 MAT INPUT S
00350 PRINT "NUMBER OF DENDROGRAMS REQUIRED";
00360 INPUT Y2
00370 PRINT "SPECIFY SAMPLING RATIO";
00380 INPUT F3
```

```
00390 PRINT "TYPE 1 IF NORMALIZATION OF QUADRAT VECTORS "
00400 PRINT "REQUIRED ELSE TYPE ANY NUMBER OTHER THAN 1";
00410 INPUT Y8
00420 MAT R=CON
00430 MAT D=ZER
00440 MAT L=CON
00450 MAT Y=ZER
00460 MAT X=ZER
00470 FOR L=1 TO N
00480 LET Y(L,1)=L
00490 NEXT L
00500 MAT F=ZER
00510 LET M=KO
00520 GO SUB  2270
00530 REM
00540 REM---COMPUTE DISTANCE
00550 IF Y8=0 THEN 650
00560 FOR K=1 TO N
00570 LET S=0
00580 FOR Z=1 TO M
00590 LET S=S+X(Z,K)^2
00600  NEXT Z
00610 FOR Z=1 TO M
00620 LET X(Z,K)=X(Z,K)/SQR(S)
00630 NEXT Z
00640 NEXT K
00650 FOR K=1 TO N-1
00660 FOR L=K+1 TO N
00670 LET S=0
00680 FOR Z=1 TO M
00690 LET S =S+(X(Z,K)-X(Z,L))^2
00700 NEXT Z
00710 LET D(K,L)=S
00720 LET D(L,K)=S
00730 NEXT L
00740 NEXT K
00750 GO SUB 810
00760 GO SUB 1900
00770 LET C3=C3+1
00780 PRINT "FNSH PART"C3
```

257

```
00790 IF C3<Y2 THEN 420
00800 STOP
00810 LET A=0
00820 LET K=N
00830 LET N9=0
00840 REM
00850 REM
00860 REM---CLUSTERING ROUTINE
00870 FOR M=1 TO K
00880 LET Y=10000000
00890 LET U=10000000
00900 FOR L=1 TO K
00910 IF M<K THEN 930
00920 IF L=K THEN 1020
00930 IF M<>L THEN 950
00940 LET L=L+1
00950 LET F=R(M)+R(L)
00960 LET Z=(D(M,L)+D(M,M)+D(L,L))/F
00970 LET Z=Z-D(M,M)/R(M)-D(L,L)/R(L)
00980 IF Z>=U THEN 1010
00990 LET U=Z
01000 LET H=L
01010 NEXT L
01020 FOR L=1 TO K
01030 IF H<K THEN 1050
01040 IF L=K THEN 1140
01050 IF L<>H THEN 1070
01060 LET L=L+1
01070 LET F=R(H)+R(L)
01080 LET Z=(D(H,L)+D(H,H)+D(L,L))/F
01090 LET Z=Z-D(H,H)/R(H)-D(L,L)/R(L)
01100 IF Z>=Y THEN 1130
01110 LET Y=Z
01120 LET B=L
01130 NEXT L
01140 IF B<>M THEN 1360
01150 LET T(M,1)=M
01160 LET T(M,2)=H
01170 LET V(M)=R(M)+R(H)
01180 LET A1=R(M)
01190 LET A2=R(H)
01200 FOR L=1 TO R(M)
01210 LET A2=A2+1
01220 LET Y(H,A2)=Y(M,L)
01230 NEXT L
01240 FOR L=1 TO R(H)
01250 LET A1=A1+1
01260 LET Y(M,A1)=Y(H,L)
01270 NEXT L
01280 IF M>H THEN 1350
01290 LET N9=N9+1
01300 FOR L=1 TO V(M)
01310 LET F(N9,L)=Y(M,L)
01320 NEXT L
01330 LET N(N9,1)=V(M)
01340 LET N(N9,2)=(D(M,M)+D(H,H)+D(M,H))/V(M)
```

258

```
01350 GO TO 1390
01360 LET T(M,1)=M
01370 LET T(M,2)=0
01380 LET V(M)=R(M)
01390 NEXT M
01400 LET W=0
01410 FOR M=1 TO K
01420 IF T(M,2)>=T(M,1) THEN 1440
01430 IF T(M,2)>0 THEN 1520
01440 LET W=W+1
01450 LET T(W,1)=T(M,1)
01460 LET T(W,2)=T(M,2)
01470 LET R(W)=V(M)
01480 FOR L=1 TO K
01490 IF Y(M,L)=0 THEN 1510
01500 LET Y(W,L)=Y(M,L)
01510 NEXT L
01520 NEXT M
01530 LET K=W
01540 LET A=A+1
01550 FOR M=1 TO K
01560 LET J=T(M,1)
01570 LET E=T(M,2)
01580 IF E=0 THEN 1610
01590 LET D(M,M)=D(J,J)+D(E,E)+D(J,E)
01600 GO TO 1620
01610 LET D(M,M)=D(J,J)
01620 LET Y=D(M,M)/R(M)
01630 LET Z=Y/R(M)
01640 NEXT M
01650 FOR M=1 TO K-1
01660 LET J=T(M,1)
01670 LET E=T(M,2)
01680 FOR L=M+1 TO K
01690 LET G=T(L,1)
01700 LET C=T(L,2)
01710 IF E+C=0 THEN 1750
01720 IF E+C =C THEN 1770
01730 IF E+C=E THEN 1790
01740 GO TO 1810
01750 LET Z=D(J,G)
01760 GO TO 1820
01770 LET Z=D(J,G)+D(J,C)
01780 GO TO 1820
01790 LET Z=D(J,G)+D(E,G)
01800 GO TO 1820
01810 LET Z=D(J,G)+D(J,C)+D(E,G)+D(E,C)
01820 LET D(M,L)=Z
01830 LET D(L,M)=Z
01840 NEXT L
01850 NEXT M
01860 IF K>1 THEN 840
01870 RETURN
01880 REM
01890 REM
01900 REM---COMPUTE TOPOLOGY MATRIX
01910 PRINT "TOPOLOGY MATRIX"
```

259

```
01920 FOR H=1 TO N-1
01930 FOR L=H+1 TO N
01940 LET A1=0
01950 LET K1=0
01960 LET A2=0
01970 LET K2=0
01980 FOR E=1 TO N
01990 LET K4=0
02000 LET K5=0
02010 FOR J=1 TO N
02020 IF F(E,J)=0 THEN 2120
02030 IF  F(E,J)<>H THEN 2070
02040 LET A1=A1+1
02050 LET K1=1
02060 LET K4=1
02070 IF F(E,J)<>L THEN 2110
02080 LET A2=A2+1
02090 LET K2=1
02100 LET K5=1
02110 NEXT J
02120 IF K1+K2<2 THEN 2150
02130 LET Q(H,L)=A1+A2-1
02140 GO TO 2160
02150 NEXT E
02160 NEXT L
02170 NEXT H
02180 MAT PRINT Q:
02190 FOR H=1 TO N-1
02200 FOR J=H+1 TO N
02210 WRITE #1,Q(H,J)
02220 NEXT J
02230 NEXT H
02240 RETURN
02250 REM
02260 REM
02270 REM---RANDOM DATA GENERATOR
02280 LET F=F3
02290 LET P=N
02300 LET Q=M
02310 FOR H=1 TO P
02320 LET N7=0
02330 LET R7=INT(RND*100)+1
02340 IF R7>Q THEN 2330
02350 LET N7=N7+1
02360 IF N7>F*S(H) THEN 2390
02370 LET X(R7,H)=X(R7,H)+1
02380 GOTO 2330
02390 NEXT H
02400 RETURN
02410 END
```

READY

RUN

PROGRAM NAME --- SSSIM2
===

NUMBER OF QUADRATS ?25
NUMBER OF SPECIES ?7
SPECIES TOTALS (VECTOR S)
 ?1994,473,48,37,21,12,8
NUMBER OF DENDROGRAMS REQUIRED ?5
SPECIFY SAMPLING RATIO ?1
TYPE 1 IF NORMALIZATION OF QUADRAT VECTORS
REQUIRED ELSE TYPE ANY NUMBER OTHER THAN 1 ?1
TOPOLOGY MATRIX

```
0   1   4   2   5   3   6

0   0   4   2   5   3   6

0   0   0   3   2   2   3

0   0   0   0   4   2   5

0   0   0   0   0   3   2

0   0   0   0   0   0   4

0   0   0   0   0   0   0
```

FNSH PART 1
TOPOLOGY MATRIX

```
0   1   3   2   3   3   3

0   0   3   2   3   3   3

0   0   0   2   1   1   1

0   0   0   0   2   2   2

0   0   0   0   0   2   1

0   0   0   0   0   0   2

0   0   0   0   0   0   0
```

FNSH PART 2

261

TOPOLOGY MATRIX

```
0  1  3  2  4  3  3
0  0  3  2  4  3  3
0  0  0  2  2  1  1
0  0  0  0  3  2  2
0  0  0  0  0  1  1
0  0  0  0  0  0  1
0  0  0  0  0  0  0
```

FNSH PART 3
TOPOLOGY MATRIX

```
0  1  3  2  4  5  6
0  0  3  2  4  5  6
0  0  0  2  2  3  4
0  0  0  0  3  4  5
0  0  0  0  0  2  3
0  0  0  0  0  0  2
0  0  0  0  0  0  0
```

FNSH PART 4
TOPOLOGY MATRIX

```
0  1  2  3  3  3  3
0  0  2  3  3  3  3
0  0  0  2  2  2  2
0  0  0  0  1  1  1
0  0  0  0  0  1  2
0  0  0  0  0  0  2
```

```
0 0 0 0 0 0 0

FNSH PART 5

TIME: 39.45 SECS.

READY
OLD
OLD FILE NAME--SSSIM3

READY
LIST


SSSIM3          15:20          9-MAY-74



00010 PRINT "PROGRAM NAME --- SSSIM3"
00020 PRINT "FOR I(M,O).  RUN THIS PROGRAM AFTER SSSIM2."
00030 REM    I(M,O) IF RUN AFTER PROGRAM SSSIM2.
00040 PRINT "===== ============= ============= ============= ======"
00050 FILES TOPOL
00060 DIM T(5,21), I(10), O(10)
00070 REM
00080 REM---EXPLANATIONS TO ARRAY SYMBOLS:
00090 REM
00100 REM      T - A K*N ARRAY WHERE N=Q*(Q-1)/2 AND
00110 REM          Q IS THE ORDER OF A TOPOLOGY MATRIX
00120 REM      I, O - K*(K-1)/2 VALUED ARRAYS
00130 REM
00140 REM
00150 REM---READ DATA
00160 PRINT "ORDER OF A TOPOLOGY MATRIX";
00170 INPUT Q
00180 PRINT "NUMBER OF TOPOLOGY MATRICES";
00190 INPUT K
00200 LET N=Q*(Q-1)/2
00210 FOR H=1 TO K
00220 FOR J= 1 TO N
00230 READ #1,T(H,J)
00240 NEXT J
00250 NEXT H
00260 LET C=0
00270 FOR H= 1 TO K-1
00280 FOR J=H+1 TO K
00290 LET I=0
00300 FOR E=1 TO N
```

263

```
00310 LET M=(T(H,E)+T(J,E))/2
00320 LET I=I+T(H,E)*LOG(T(H,E)/M)
00330 LET I=I+T(J,E)*LOG(T(J,E)/M)
00340 NEXT E
00350 LET C=C+1
00360 LET I(C)=I
00370 NEXT J
00380 NEXT H
00390 LET C=K*(K-1)/2
00400 LET R=C+1
00410 FOR H= 1TO C
00420 LET M=0
00430 FOR J= 1TO C
00440 IF M>I(J) THEN 470
00450 LET M=I(J)
00460 LET Q=(J)
00470 NEXT J
00480 LET R=R-1
00490 LET O(R)=M
00500 LET I(Q)=-I(Q)
00510 NEXT H
00520 PRINT "ORDERED I(M,O) VALUES"
00530 MAT PRINT O;
00540 END
```

READY
RUN

PROGRAM NAME --- SSSIM3
FOR I(M,O). RUN THIS PROGRAM AFTER SSSIM2.
==

ORDER OF A TOPOLOGY MATRIX ?7
NUMBER OF TOPOLOGY MATRICES ?5
ORDERED I(M,O) VALUES

 0.753722 1.7619 1.98568 2.0887 4.24612 4.46059 4.8787 4.9528
 5.72433 6.05923

TIME: 1.11 SECS.

READY

GLOSSARY

Absolute value function: A metric with functional form described in Chapter II. See **Metric.**

Additivity: A property of commensurable variables. See **Commensurability.**

Agglomerative: A classification which combines individuals into groups.

a posteriori: Based on observation.

a priori: Deduced from basic principles or derived from external sources prior to the survey or experiment.

Association: The tendency toward common occurrence *(positive association)* or mutual exclusion *(negative association).*

Attribute: In this book a character. See **Character.**

Average linkage: A classification in which average similarity represents the clustering criterion.

Binomial: A probability distribution completely described by the expansion of $(p + q)^n$ where $p + q = 1$ and n indicates the number of random trials. Often assumed when the data represent frequencies. See **Distribution.**

BRAY & CURTIS distance: A potential semimetric with changing scale of measure, derived from the absolute value function by scrambling. Its functional form is given in Chapter II.

Categorical: Data consisting of zeros or positive integer numbers.

Centroid: The tip of a population or sample mean vector. See **Mean vector.**

Centroid clustering: A classification which combines groups based on the nearness of centroids.

Character: In this book a distinctive feature which may take on different values or states, or may be constant.

Chord distance: The length of the chord connecting two points on the circle or some sphere. Its functional form is given in Chapter II.

Classification: The process which partitions a sample into groups.

Clumping: Formation of overlapping groups.

Cluster: Any arbitrary group of points.

Coherence coefficient: The square root of the one complement of the square of RAJSKI's metric. Its values are between zero and one. Its functional form is given in Chapter II.

Complete enumeration: A survey in which all elements of a population are located and measured. See **Population.**

Component analysis: The method of summarizing linear continuous data structures on orthogonal axes. See **Orthogonal.**

Commensurability: A property of qualitatively comparable variables whose unit of measure is the same.

Consistent procedure: A logical sequence of statements indicating operations.

Continuity: A property of data structures which can be represented by a single point cluster of even density.

Continuity analysis: A method for summarizing non-linear continuous data structures. See **Continuity, Data structure.**

Continuous variable: One which can assume any value on the real number axis within natural limits. See **Variable.**

Correlation: (a) Any expression of relatedness. (b) A scalar (inner) product of normalized vectors with origin in the centroid. See **Scalar product, Normalization, Centroid.**

Covariance: The scalar (inner) product of two vectors with origin in the centroid. The vectors are not normalized. See **Scalar product, Centroid, Normalization.**

***D*-technique:** The D-algorithm of component analysis described in Chapter III.

Data structure: The manner in which sample points are spatially arranged, *e.g.* linear, curved, continuous, disjoint, etc.

Dendrogram: A classification tree indicating hierarchical relationships.

Density: Number of individuals per unit area or data points per unit volume.

Density function: Co-ordinate function of the normal distribution. See **Normal.**

Dependence: A property of variables responding to the influence of others.

Deterministic: (a) A mathematical model without random components. (b) The approach concerned with an exact determination of population parameters.

Direct gradient analysis: A method for displaying ecological information by arranging species or vegetation stands within an environmentally defined reference system. See **Ordination.**

Discrete variable: Whose values are positive integer numbers or zero.

Discriminant analysis: A family of statistical methods which use the generalized distance or other measures of affinity to distinguish between groups, or to find the most likely parent population for an individual or a group. See **Identification.**

Dissection: Partition of a continuous sample into groups. See **Continuity.**

Distortion: Scrambling in the data structure due to transformations or other adjustments in the resemblance function or method of analysis.

Distribution: A statistical concept for describing the frequencies with which different values or states occur in a variable.

Distribution function: The area function (integral) of a distribution. See **Normal.**

Divergence: A functional expression of difference between distributions. See **Distribution.**

Efficiency: In this book the extent to which an ordination or classification can account for variation in the data.

Equivocation: An information quantity representing the difference between joint and mutual information. Its functional form is given in Chapter II. See **Joint information, Mutual information.**

Empirical distribution: Frequency distribution derived on the basis of an experiment.

Entropy: The average information per observation. Its functional form is given in Chapter II.

Estimate: A sample value which replaces the unknown population value in statistical analysis.

Euclidean: The geometry or space in which vector scalar (inner) products, such as the covariance, represent a meaningful concept. See **Euclidean distance, Covariance.**

Euclidean distance: The common notion of distance as we know it from every day experience. Functional forms are given in Chapter II.

Euclidean space: See **Euclidean.**

Formal: Objective methods relying on mathematics and probability.

Function: (a) The changing structure. (b) An algebraic formulation. See **Structure.**

Gaussian: See **Normal.**

Generalized distance: A distance in standard units. Functional forms are given in Chapters II and V.

GENGERELLI's distance: Euclidean distance computed from oblique co-ordinates. Its functional form is given in Chapter II.

Geodesic metric: The length of the shorter arc between two points. The functional form is given in Chapter II.

Hierarchy: A nested clustering in which increasingly larger (or smaller) groups are formed by combining (or breaking up) groups in successive steps.

Identification: The process of finding the most likely parent population for an individual.

***I*-divergence:** A one-way information divergence such as $F^0 \rightarrow F$ where F is an observed distribution and F^0 is a specified standard. See Chapter II for functional forms.

Importance value: In this book the amount of sum of squares specifically accounted for by a species in the sample.

Independence: Lack of correlation, often meaning a zero covariance.

Indirect gradient analysis: Ordinations which use vegetation data to infer about trends in environmental variation. See **Ordination.**

Individual: The basic unit subjected to analysis.

Informal: In this book methods not based on mathematical formulations.

Information: Physical property of data; surprisal value; a multiple of entropy; or a divergence. See **Divergence, Entropy.**

Information clustering: Grouping together objects based on information content. See **Information.**

Inverse: A matrix derived from another matrix by certain algebraic manipulations. See Chapter IV for example.

J-divergecne: A two-way information divergence such as $F_1 \rightleftharpoons F_2$ where F_1 and F_2 are two observed distributions. Functional form is given in Chapter II. See **Information, Distribution.**

Joint frequency: A property of joint observations.

Joint information: A multiple of the entropy in joint frequencies. Functional form is given in Chapter II. See **Information, Joint frequency.**

Latent structure analysis: See Chapter IV for reference.

Linear: In this book (a) a data structure characterized by points falling within an ellipse or some ellipsoid, (b) a relationship between variables.

MAHALANOBIS' distance: See **Generalized distance.**

Matching coefficient: The one complement of the squared Euclidean distance computed from presence data expressed as proportions. See Chapter II for functional form.

Matrix: A two-dimensional array of numbers.

Mean vector: Whose elements represent the mean values of variates.

Metric: Which satisfies the metric space axioms; a distance. See Chapter II for functional forms.

Metric space: A set of points and a metric which defines relative spatial placement.

Metric space axioms: Described in Chapter II.

Minimum discrimination information statistic: An I-divergence with functional forms given in Chapter II.

Model: A set of statements in a formal algebraic language.

Monothetic: A clustering method in which groups are recognized on the basis of the presence of one or several common characters. See **Character.**

Multidimensional scaling: A method of ordination which derive co-ordinates from a matrix of similarity (dissimilarity) values. See **Ordination.**

Multivariate: Incorporating several correlated variables.

Mutual information: Shared information, common between two distributions. Functional forms given in Chapter II. See **Information.**

Normal: A probability distribution characterized by a bell-shaped curve. Often assumed when the data represent measurements. Functional forms are given in Chapter I. See **Distribution.**

Normalization: Adjustment of elements in a vector in such a way that their sum of squares is unity.

Object: See **Individual.**

OCHIAI coefficient: The scalar (inner) product of normalized vectors of binary elements. Functional form is given in Chapter II. See **Normalization, Scalar Product.**

Ordination: Ordering points on axes to achieve different objectives such as summarization of variation, multidimensional scaling, trend seeking, or reciprocal ordering. Descriptions are given in Chapter III.

Ordination efficiency: See **Efficiency.**

Orthogonal: In this book a relationship of variables characterized by zero covariance.

Poisson: A probability distribution assumed for counts under specific circumstances. Functional form is given in Chapter I. See **Distribution.**

Poisson-logarithmic: A probability distribution for counts in certain aggregated populations. See Chapter I for reference, and **Distribution.**

Poisson-Poisson: A probability distribution for counts in certain aggregated populations. See Chapter I for reference, and **Distribution.**

Polythetic: A classification based on the degree of resemblance between objects. See **Monothetic.**

Population: (a) The totality of individuals sufficiently alike to be classified as members of the same group. (b) All possible states or values of a variable characterized by some probability distribution. See **Variable.**

Population unit: The basic unit distinguished in sampling. See **Individual.**

Position vector: A directed line from the origin of the co-ordinate system to a given point in space.

267

Position vectors ordination: An ordination which manipulates vectors. See Chapter II for description, and **Ordination.**

Prediction: A statistical statement about an unknown state or value of a variable.

Preferential sampling: Subjective selection of units for description. Not a statistical method.

Probability: The likelihood of a value or state.

Probabilistic: (a) A mathematical model with random components. (b) Methods of analysis concerned with estimation and statistical inference.

Probability theory: All notions about probability.

Q-**technique:** In this book the Q-**algorithm** of component analysis described in Chapter IV.

RAJSKI's metric: A distance based on the equivocation information. Functional form is given in Chapter II. See **Equivocation information.**

Random: According to chance.

Random point: Determined by random co-ordinates.

Random sampling: In which every individual is given an equal chance to get into the sample. See **Sample.**

Randomly sited systematic sample: A systematic sample in which the pivot point is randomly sited.

Ranking: In this book ordering species in terms of their specific share of the total sum of squares. See Chapter I for descriptions.

Reciprocal ordering: Ordering quadrats based on species scores, or species based on quadrat scores. See descriptions in Chapter III.

Regression analysis: Fitting a line or a surface to points in space.

Resemblance: The likeness or unlikeness of objects measured in terms of the characters which they possess. See **Resemblance function.**

Resemblance function: A mathematical formulation to measure the similarity of objects. See descriptions in Chapter II.

Resemblance structure: A matrix of similarity or dissimilarity values.

Restricted random: Random sampling within compartments. See Chapter I for reference.

RQ-**technique:** See **Reciprocal ordering.**

Sample: A subset of the population.

Sample space: A set of points and a resemblance function which defines their relative spatial placement. See **Resemblance function.**

Sampling unit: See population unit.

Scalar product of vectors: An inner product of vectors, *i.e.* the product of their lengths and the cosine of the enclosed angle.

SHANNON's entropy: See **Entropy.**

Stochastic: Which accord with some probability law.

Stress: The departure of resemblance structure from a standard.

Structure: See resemblance structure.

Subdivisive: Clustering by subdivisions.

Successive clustering: Clustering in which a group is completely formed before the formation of another begins. See Chapter IV for references.

Sum of squares: Sum of squared deviations.

Symbols:

a	An element in a 2×2 table.
$a_i.$	Total of a_{ij} in species i.
$a_{..}$	Group total of all a_{ij}.
$a_{.j}$	Total of a_{ij} in stand j.
a_{ij}	Abundance of species i in stand j.
$a(j, k)$	Absolute value function.
$\mathbf{A}$	Centered, or centered and standardized data matrix.
$\mathbf{A}'$	Transpose of $\mathbf{A}$.
A_{hj}	The h, j element of matrix A.
A_{Xm}	Affinity of external individual $\mathbf{X}$ and group m.
α_{jk}	The subtending angle of two intersecting lines.

b	An element in a 2 × 2 table.
b_i	A column vector of $\mathbf{B}$.
b'_i	Transpose of b_i.
b_{hi}	A component coefficient.
$b(j, k)$	BRAY & CURTIS distance
B	A scale factor; lable for a group; a point; or abbreviation for a character name.
$\mathbf{B}$	Matrix of component coefficients.
c	An element in a 2 × 2 table.
$c(j, k)$	Chord distance.
$\chi^2_{\alpha;\,DF}$	The α probability point of the χ^2 distribution with DF degrees of freedom.
d	An element in a 2 × 2 table.
$\overline{d^2}$	Mean of squared elements in $\mathbf{D}$.
$\overline{d^2_j}$	Mean of squared elements in the jth row (column) of $\mathbf{D}$.
$d(A, B)$	Distance of points A and B.
$d(\mathbf{F}_h;\mathbf{F}_i)$	RAJSKI's metric.
$d(j, k;\,m)$	Distance of quadrats j, k in group m.
$\mathbf{D}_p$	Distance matrix of quadrats computed from p species.
$\mathbf{D}_P$	Distance matrix of quadrats computed from P species.
Δ	A matrix with a characteristic element $\delta(j, k)$.
Δ_j	A correction term for oblique co-ordinates.
$\Delta(1;\,2)$	The difference of two I-divergences.
δ_{jkh}	The dissimilarity of quadrats j, k with respect to species h.
$\delta(j, k)$	The observed dissimilarity of quadrats j, k.
$|S_h|$	Determinant of S_h.
$e(j, k)$	Absulate Euclidean distance.
$\mathbf{E}$	Within groups component of the covariance matrix.
$\mathbf{E}^{-1}$	Inverse of $\mathbf{E}$.
E_{hi}	An element of $\mathbf{E}$.
$E(S_h)$	Expectation for the hth sample covariance matrix.
$E(\bar{X}_h)$	Expectation for the hth sample mean.
$E(\mathbf{F}_h;\mathbf{F}_j)$	Equivocation information.
exp	Exponent.
f_{hj}	An element in $\mathbf{F}_h$.
f^0_{hj}	An element in $\mathbf{F}^0_h$.
$f_h.$ or $f^0_h.$	hth distribution total.
$f._j$	jth column total.
$f_{..}$	Grand total.
$f(j, k)$	A pair-function.
$f(X)$	Function of X.
F	The variance ratio.
$\mathbf{F}_h$	hth frequency distribution.
$\mathbf{F}^0_h$	hth standard frequency distribution.
$F_{\alpha;\,DF}$	The α probability point of the F distribution with degrees of freedom DF.
$g(j, k)$	Geodesic metric.
h	Label for species or row.
$\mathbf{H}$	Between groups component of the covariance matrix.
H_{hi}	The h,i element of $\mathbf{H}$.
$H(\mathbf{P}_h)$	Entropy of order one.
$H(\mathbf{P}_h)^k$	Entropy of order k.
$H(\mathbf{P}_h;\mathbf{P}^0_h)$	Information of order one.
i	A label for species, row, or initial size of population.
I_A	Information in group A.
I_{A+B}	Information in the fusion group.
$I(\mathbf{F}_h)$	The $f_h.$ multiple of entropy of order one.
$I(\mathbf{F}_h;\mathbf{F}^0_h)$	The $f_h.$ multiple of information of order one; an I-divergence.

$I(A; B)$	I-divergence of the marginal distributions in two subtables.
$I(species; quadrats)$	Mutual information of species and quadrats.
∞	Infinity.
j	Label for quadrat, or column.
$J(F_h; F_j)$	A J-divergence.
k	Label for quadrat, or column.
κ	Inverse of continuity.
λ	An eigenvalue, or mean number of individuals per unit area.
m	Label for species, or group.
$m(j, k)$	Generalized distance.
M_{Xi}	The mean of non-zero elements in the $i$the data vector.
max	Maximum value.
min	Minimum value.
μ	Population mean, or birth rate.
N	Population size.
N_t	Population size at time t.
ν	Death rate of a population.
$o(j, k)$	Euclidean distance based on oblique axes.
p	Number of species in the sample; proportion, or probability.
P	Number of species in the population.
$\mathbf{P}_h$ or $\mathbf{P}_h^0$	Distributions with elements expressed as proportions.
$p(k)$	Probability of k successes.
P_{hj}	jth element of $\mathbf{P}_h$.
P_{hi}^0	jth element of $\mathbf{P}_h^0$.
$Pjkh$	$= P(\delta \leqslant \delta_{jkh})$.
π	3.1416
π_{jk}	A product of independent probabilities.
q	The one-complement of the probability p.
q_{jj}	Sum of squared values in the jth quadrat vector; jj element in $\mathbf{Q}$.
q_{jk}	Cross product of elements in quadrats j, k; j, k element in $\mathbf{Q}$.
$\mathbf{Q}$	A cross product matrix for quadrat vectors.
Q_h	The hth factor of standardization or adjustment.
Q_j	Sum of elements in the jth column vector.
Q_{jk}	Total of elements in quadrat vectors j and k.
Q_A	Sum of squares in group A.
Q_{A+B}	Sum of squares in the fusion group.
r_{hi}	Product moment correlation of variates h and i.
$r(F_h; F_i)$	Coherence coefficient.
R	Correlation of species and stand scores.
$\rho^2(\mathbf{D}_p; \mathbf{D}_p)$	Squared product moment correlation of $\mathbf{D}_p$ and $\mathbf{D}_p$ regarded as two strings of $N \times N$ numbers.
s	Number of frequency classes, or number of stand scores.
s_h	Number of elements in the hth freguency distribution.
$\mathbf{S}$	Sample covariance matrix.
$\mathbf{S}^{-1}$	Inverse of $\mathbf{S}$.
SS	Sum of squares.
S_i	A measure of dispersion for species i in the sample.
S_{hi}	The h, i element in $\mathbf{S}$, the covariance of species h, i.
$S(j, k)$	A similarity index.
σ	Population standard deviation.
σ^2	Population variance.
σ_{ii}^2	i, i element in Σ; the variance of the ith variable.
$\sigma(p; N; P)$	Stress in $\mathbf{D}_p$ relative to $\mathbf{D}_p$ at fixed N, P and varying p.
Σ	Population covariance matrix.
Σ	Summation sign.
T^2	HOTELLING's T^2 statistic.

270

θ	A test criterion with known sampling distribution.
$\theta_{\alpha;s,m,n}$	The α probability point of the θ distribution with parameters s, m, n.
$u(j, k)$	A relative form of Euclidean distance.
$v(j, k)$	BEALS' variant of $b(j, k)$.
w_{hi}	The subtending angle of two intersecting lines.
$w(j, k)$	Relative form of the absolute value function.
$\mathbf{X}$	Data matrix.
X_i	ith generic variable; axis, species score.
$\mathbf{X}_i$	ith row (species) vector.
$\bar{X}_i$	Mean of row (species) i.
X_{ij}	An element in $\mathbf{X}$; the quantity of species i in quadrat j.
$\mathbf{X}_j$	jth column (quadrat) vector.
$\bar{\mathbf{X}}_m$	mth group mean vector.
Y_i	ith component (axis).
$\mathbf{Y}_i$	An eigenvector.
$\mathbf{Y}'_i$	Transpose of $\mathbf{Y}_i$
Y_{ij}	A component score, ordination co-ordinate.
Y_{hj}	Co-ordinate of point j on axis h, or a component score.
$|\ |$	Absolute value.
$\rightarrow$ or $\leftarrow$	One-way divergence.
$\rightleftharpoons$	Two-way divergence.
$!$	Factorial sign.
$:=$	Becomes.

Systematic: Sampling in which individuals are taken at regular intervals. See Chapter I for descriptions.

Topology: In this book the pattern of fusions in a dendrogram. See **Dendrogram.**

Topology matrix: In this book a matrix of fusion counts. See example in Chapter IV, and **Topology.**

Transpose: A matrix derived by interchanging the rows and columns of another matrix.

Type: An abstraction; equivalent to population. See **Population** (a).

Univariate: Incorporating a single variable.

Variable: A property, character, that varies. See **Character.**

Variate: In this book a variable. See **Variable.**

Vegetation type: See **Type.**

Author Index

Agnew, A.D.Q. 124, 143
Anderson, A.J.B. 164, 165
Anderson, D.J. 94, 101, 164
Anderson, T.W. 164, 165
Armstrong, J.S. 164, 165
Austin, M.P. 99, 101, 164, 165
Ball, G.H. 165
Bartlett, M.S. 164, 165
Basharin, G.P. 40, 62
Baum, B.R. 125, 143
Beals, E.W. 35, 46, 62, 81, 83, 98, 101, 271
Becking, R.W. 6, 23
Benzécri, J.P. 94, 101
Braun-Blanquet, J. 103, 143
Bray, J.R. 45, 47, 62, 80, 81, 82, 85, 90, 91, 92, 97, 98, 99, 100, 101, 161, 265, 269
Cajander, A.K. 103, 143
Carlson, K.A. 122, 123, 124, 143
Carmone, F. 85, 86, 161
Carroll, J.D. 87, 88, 92, 100, 101, 161, 164, 168
Cattell, R.B. 123, 143
Cavalli-Sforza, L.L. 114, 119, 127, 143
Češka, A. 60, 62, 164, 165
Clements, F.E. 103, 143
Cole, A.J. 164, 165
Cooley, W.W. 164, 165
Cormack, R.M. 105, 108, 143, 164, 165
Cottam, G. 164, 165
Crovello, T.J. 3, 23, 163, 164, 165
Curtis, J.T. 45, 47, 62, 80, 81, 82, 85, 90, 91, 92, 97, 98, 99, 100, 101, 161, 265, 269
Dagnelie, P. 123, 143, 163, 165
Dale, M.B. 3, 22, 23, 94, 101, 105, 107, 108, 144, 163, 164, 165, 167

Dempster, A.P. 164, 165
Dix, R.L. 81, 101
Dokuchaev, V.V. 103, 143
Ducker, S.C. 118, 143
Edwards, A.W.F. 114, 119, 127, 143
Emden, van M.H. 165
Escofier-Cordier, B. 94, 101
Estabrook, G.F. 124, 144, 164, 166
Fraser, D.A.S. 164, 166
Frechet, M. 164, 166
Gauch, H.G. 80, 90, 99, 101, 164, 166
Gengerelli, J.A. 30, 53, 62
Gibson, W.A. 123, 143
Gittins, R. 123, 143, 164, 166
Goff, F.G. 165
Goldstein, R.A. 164, 166
Goodall, D.W. 48, 49, 60, 62, 122, 123, 125, 127, 143, 151, 157, 163, 164, 166, 170
Goodman, L.A. 164, 166
Gower, J.C. 34, 62, 75, 101, 108, 109, 143, 164, 166
Greig-Smith, P. 11, 13, 23, 96, 101, 106, 144, 163, 164, 166
Grench, R.E. 164, 166
Grigal, D.F. 164, 165
Groenewoud, van H. 164, 166
Hatheway, W.H. 94, 101, 161, 166
Heck, D.L. 131, 144
Hill. M.O. 94, 101, 161, 164, 166
Holgate, P. 164, 166
Hook, M.E. 114
Hotelling, H. 65, 101, 270
Jackson, D.M. 165, 166
Jancey, R.C. 119, 120, 121, 124, 126, 144, 170
Jardine, N. 107, 144, 165, 166, 167
Juhász-Nagy, P. 163, 164, 166
Kemeny, J.G. 169

Subject Index

Absolute value function, see Distance
Additivity 7
ALC 112, 170, 224
BASIC 169
Choice of method 158
Classification
  agglomerative 107
  classical approaches 103
  clumping 107
  difficulties 104
  disection 107
  efficiency 126
  hierarchical 107
  medium 103
  monothetic 107
  objectives 105
  or ordination 106
  overlapping 107
  polythetic 107
  predictive 134
  subdivisive 107
Classification techniques, see
  Clustering techniques
Clustering techniques
  affinity analysis 125
  average linkage 108, 112, 119, 156
  Baum & Lefkovitch 125
  Carlson 124
  centroid clustering 118
  clustering by ordination 123
  clustering by positive association
    124
  Edward & Cavalli-Sforza 119
  graph theory 124
  information 121, 122
  Jancey 119, 121, 124, 126
  latent structure 123
  Macnaughton-Smith 125
  probability 123
  specified number of groups 124

  successive cluster formation 122
  sum of squares 113, 119, 156
  Williams & Lambert 125
Coefficients, measures, indices
  affinity 152, 154, 156
  coherence 44, 122, 136, 138
  correlation 35, 58, 70, 71
  Goodall 48
  Gower 34, 109
  Ochiai 34, 35
  Sokal's matching 34
  probabilistic 48, 49, 60
Commensurability 7
Complete enumeration 13
Continuity analysis, see Ordination
Correlation, see Coefficients
  influence on distance 29, 30
CORRS 36, 37, 169, 170, 184
Covariance 15, 35
Data structures 64, 65, 87
Data components 22
Dendrograms, comparison of 139,
  143
Distances
  absolute value function 36, 38,
    45, 46, 47, 99
  Beals 47, 59, 61
  Bray & Curtis 45, 46, 59, 61
  chord 28, 29, 34, 38, 61, 77, 81,
    99
  Euclidean 27, 36, 47, 56, 58, 61
  generalized 30, 31, 33, 58, 61,
    145, 150, 157
  Gengerelli 30, 31, 58
  geodesic 38, 58
  Rajski 38, 44, 45, 60, 61, 136,
    139
  unnamed 58, 81, 99
EMV 132, 170, 238
Entropy 40